GRASSLANDS
OF THE GREAT PLAINS

Their Nature and Use

GRASSLANDS OF THE GREAT PLAINS

Their Nature and Use

by

J. E. Weaver

Professor Emeritus of Plant Ecology, Department of Botany, University of Nebraska

and

F. W. Albertson

Chairman of Biological Sciences, Fort Hays Kansas State College, Hays, Kansas

with
special chapters by

B. W. Allred and Arnold Heerwagen

Soil Conservation Service

JOHNSEN PUBLISHING COMPANY

Lincoln, Nebraska

LIBRARY OF CONGRESS CATALOG CARD NUMBER 56-9095

PRINTED AND BOUND AT THE LAKESIDE PRESS
R. R. DONNELLEY & SONS COMPANY
CHICAGO, ILLINOIS
AND CRAWFORDSVILLE, INDIANA

Preface

THIS book is the result of a long-felt need by the authors and their students for a comprehensive survey of the numerous studies that have been made on plains grasslands. From southern Texas far into Saskatchewan the mid and short grasses form a magnificent prairie nearly 2,500 miles in length and approximately 400 miles wide. Kinds of communities, their composition, nature, significance and uses are fully described. Such information is of value not only to students, range technicians, and other professional conservationists, but also to ranchers and other land owners—in fact, to anyone interested in the economy of our midwestern grasslands. The damaging effects of drought on forage production in this unstable climate and the restoration of the plant cover are of such great importance that they have been given special attention. Climate, soils, and the proper use of the forage for its sustained production are described.

A third of a century of study and experimentation in plains grassland by the authors permits accurate description and interpretation. Important studies that have been made on the vegetation since the coming of the white man to the present day are reviewed. Early investigations have been recorded in papers, bulletins and books, many of which are now out of print or difficult of access. Therefore permission was asked and promptly given by the Carnegie Institution of Washington, Duke University Press, *Ecological Monographs*, *Ecology*, and several other journals to re-use materials originally furnished by the authors. Such sources are carefully cited in the text. Only by such cooperation has this book been made possible.

This great prairie land has been thoroughly examined as to its way of life both above ground and deep into the soil, which it has helped to build and so efficiently protects. Extensive, long-time investigations have elucidated many problems. The scope of the work has been broadened and deepened by the aid of a large number of advanced students who have sought graduate study in this field. To them, many of whom are today leaders in conservation of range management or in teaching a new generation of students the values of ecology in our economy, we are deeply grateful for their interest and cooperation. Two of them are so familiar with the grasslands of Texas and New Mexico, respectively, that each has contributed a chapter to this book.

Both common and scientific names of grasses are according to Hitchcock and Chase (1950) revised Manual of the Grasses of the United States. Other scientific names follow Gleason's New Britton and Brown Illustrated Flora (1952) or Harrington's Manual of the Plants of Colorado (1954). Common names are nearly all according to the second edition (1913) of Britton and Brown or the second edition of Standardized Plant Names (1942).

GRASSLANDS OF THE GREAT PLAINS

A COMPANION VOLUME

by

J. E. Weaver

☼ ☼ ☼

NORTH AMERICAN PRAIRIE

348 pages, 6x9, 87 figures

GRASSLANDS OF THE GREAT PLAINS

Their Nature and Use

CHAPTER 1

The Great Plains and the Mixed Prairie

THE GREATEST expanse of North American grassland occupies the dry interior of the continent. It extends eastward from the Rocky Mountains in Canada through New Mexico to the Central Lowlands. These lowlands begin at the foot of the Great Plains. Their drier western part was occupied by the wonderfully developed sod-forming grasses which composed the True Prairie, recently described (Weaver, 1954). The grasslands of the Great Plains will now be considered. This is the home of the Mixed Prairie, the most extensive grazing area in North America (Fig. 1). Indeed, the Mixed Prairie, except its western extension into northern New Mexico and Arizona, lies almost entirely in the Great Plains.

ORIGIN AND EXTENT OF THE GREAT PLAINS

This plains area became dry land at the close of the Mesozoic Era many million years ago. It was uplifted without much disturbance (deformation) of the rock strata as the great Cretaceous Sea, which extended from the Arctic Ocean to the Gulf of Mexico, gradually withdrew. About 50 million years ago, the great Rocky Mountain Ranges were uplifted on its western border. The plain itself was built up by rivers and streams carrying fluviatile gravels, sands and clays from the Rocky Mountains and their outliers. These were deposited over the whole area by heavily loaded streams which spread out fanlike, overflowing and depositing the materials widely. It is an alluvial or stream-built plain. The deposition extended across the entire area, streams building up myriads of bars and shoals, old shallow channels being filled as the braided streams shifted their courses again and again over many miles in width. Nowhere else has such a vast alluvial plain been built at the base of mountain ranges.

The grand spectacle has been described by Johnson (1899–1900) as follows: "The Great Plains are of such vast dimensions it is only in

FIG. 1. (Upper) Mixed Prairie on rolling upland of western North Dakota; (lower) prairie of mid and short grasses on the High Plains of western Kansas; and (center) a typical view of livestock that harvest the forage crop.

imagination that they can be regarded as a foot slope to the Rocky Mountains. However, in the sense that, superficially, ranging down to several hundred feet in depth, they have been built to a smooth surface by mountain waste, stream-spread to great distances, they have this character. At the base of the mountains the plains mass has a thickness, to sea level, of several thousand feet. It is made up in the main of marine-rock sheets with a general inclination eastward, due to broad regional tilting, in which the plains and mountains have shared together.

"But the present surface grade of the Plains is not that of the original tilting. The surface has undergone a series of transformations. These have all been accomplished by the eastward-flowing streams from the mountains. In a first stage the mountain streams, traversing the Plains, cut into their smooth structural slope and produced a topography of parallel broad valleys and ridges. In a second stage they ceased to cut, depositing instead, and refilling the valleys they had excavated, even burying the intervening ridges, to a smooth upper surface. The original surface was a product of deformation, the second of a destructive process of stream erosion, the third a product of stream deposit and construction, involving the spreading of a waste sheet to great distances and a uniform level, and to a depth over the greater valleys often of several hundred feet. In the final and present stage, virtually the same streams have returned to the earlier destructive habit, and erosion has in large part carried away the high-level plain of stream construction. About midway of the long slope, in a north-south irregular belt, large uneroded fragments of the smooth constructional plain remain. . . . These fragments constitute the High Plains."

The Great Plains occupy the vast area between the Rocky Mountains and the Central Lowlands. From the Rio Grande River the plains extend northward, according to physiographers, to the delta of the Mackenzie River, which flows northward into the Arctic Ocean. The eastern edge is topographically indistinct; there is no continuous and distinct physiographic boundary. The line of 20-inch rainfall has been a much used eastern boundary and also the 97th meridian, which corresponds in general with an altitude of 1,500 feet. The western boundary, which is about 400 miles distant, has an altitude which varies considerably but averages close to 5,500 feet. Here the mountains rise abruptly several thousand feet above the plain. The general eastward slope of the plains is about

10 feet per mile. Thus, the Great Plains extend through a subtropical belt and a temperate zone into the subarctic region.

The large central part of the Great Plains constitutes a natural topographic division. It extends from the high Pine Ridge Escarpment, near the Nebraska-South Dakota boundary, southward through the staked plains (Llano Estacado) of Texas almost to the Rio Grande and is known as the High Plains. These are crossed by eastward flowing parallel rivers which, until recently, preserved untouched an original smooth surface characteristic of the Great Plains as a whole.

Johnson (1900–1901) states: "The High Plains are conspicuously uplands of survival. Yet their mass, to depths often of several hundred feet, is of unconsolidated silt, sand, and gravel. They are plateaus by virtue of their resistance to erosion; yet they are soft plateaus. Their survival has been due to the protective influence of a universal close-knit sod, to which a subhumid precipitation especially has given origin, and yet against which it is unequal, on a grade of 10 feet to a mile, to accomplish the first faint beginnings of erosion and the initiation of drainage. There is no run-off. Even heavy local downpours, which in the arid belt, by rapid concentration, would result in local floods and sharp channeling, are here rendered practically inert by the grass mat until disposed of through ground absorption and evaporation. The High Plains, in short, are held by their sod." But 55 years have now passed. The plow and fenced-in grazing herds have done untold damage to the native vegetation. The soil is blowing and washing away.

North of the High Plains lies the Missouri Plateau, which extends into Canada. This area is geologically older and more complex than the adjoining region southward. In many places, erosion has practically destroyed the original plains surface. Badlands in portions of Wyoming and the Dakotas, especially, are fantastic forms of erosion which have resulted from the removal of the vegetation. Upon these earlier deposits were spread during post-glacial time the alluvial deposits along drainage ways, the eolian sand derived chiefly from these deposits, and occasional layers of volcanic ash.

Some of the features of the Great Plains are sand hills, loess plains, hilly lands, buttes and isolated mountains, mesas and canyons, badlands, stream terraces, wind-blown depressions, buffalo wallows and sink holes, scoria resulting from burning beds of lignite, and glacial features in North-

FIG. 2. (Upper) Loess hills of central Nebraska, and (lower) hilly land in western North Dakota. Both furnish a wide variety of forage consisting of numerous short and mid grasses and legumes.

ern Montana and North Dakota. A great diversity of topography and soils has afforded and still presents many habitats for grassland vegetation, which has been at home on the Great Plains for millions of years (Fig. 2).

ORIGIN OF MIXED PRAIRIE

The work of students of the earth's structure and of plant and animal fossils of past geological periods, together with the study of past climates and climax vegetations, has given us the history of the earth's surface, its animal life, and its vegetation. The origin of Mixed Prairie probably dates back 25 million years to Tertiary times. In the Eocene period a warm temperate forest occupied the Great Plains. At this time the climate was warm and moist. But as the Rocky Mountains rose, they intercepted the moisture-laden winds from the Pacific Ocean. Since water was precipitated mostly to the west of the mountains, only dry winds, which produced very little rainfall, reached the eastern side. Low summer precipitation was accompanied by dry winters.

Era	Period	Epoch	Years since beginning of epoch (approximate)
Cenozoic		"Recent"	8,000
		Pleistocene	1,000,000
	Tertiary	Pliocene	
		Miocene	20,000,000
		Oligocene	
		Eocene	
		Paleocene	60,000,000
Mesozoic	Cretaceous		

Clements (1936) in his study of Mixed Prairie states: "It is probable that the evolution of grassland proceeded more rapidly in the period of mountain-making in the upper Oligocene to produce the forerunner of the modern prairie in the Miocene, where the typical genus *Stipa* [needlegrass] is recorded, along with horses of the grazing type, *Merychippus* and *Protohippus*." During the Miocene "to the east of the Rocky Mountains, increasing aridity reduced the forest vegetation and its opportunities for preservation to such an extent that the fossil record there is limited. A wide extent of grasslands is indicated by the abundance and diversity of grazing mammals." Indeed, grazing animals have roamed the Great Plains throughout geological ages. Geologists have found the remains of such ancient animals as the four-toed horse in deposits which they believe to be at least 45 million years old. In fact, the evolution of horses from very small animals approximately to their present size has been traced from their preserved skeletal parts in fossil beds scattered over the plains. Many other mammals long since extinct, as camels, elephants, rhinoceros and primitive types of buffalo, roamed the plains and fed upon the grass and other vegetation. The evidence indicates a great multiplication of species of grasses between early Tertiary periods and the Pleistocene.

"Until recently there was almost no direct evidence of the sedges and grasses which now cover the prairies and form such an essential food for the grazing mammals. Since the teeth of the plains-dwelling mammals showed marked specialization for such food during the Miocene, it had been inferred that the prairies became widespread at that time. Prairie grass is harsh food and tends to wear down the grinding teeth. To make up for this, modern grazing animals, like horses and cattle, have high-crowned teeth that grow out to replace the loss. All the early Cenozoic mammals possessed low-crowned teeth; but during the Miocene the horses, camels, rhinoceroses, and other groups dwelling on the plains began to show rapid changes to the high-crowned grazing teeth. Within the last decade wonderfully preserved grass seeds have been found to occur abundantly in the sands of middle and late Miocene and Pliocene deposits of the High Plains, and now about 30 species are known. Since none have yet been found in lower beds of the same region, the fossil record now seems to confirm the inference drawn years ago from the adaptation seen in mammalian teeth, namely, that the grasses first spread over the plains in Miocene times" (Schuchert and Dunbar, 1941).[1] This discovery in western Kansas and eastern Colorado by Elias (1932, 1935, 1942) included several forms of needlegrass (*Stipa*), a panic grass (*Panicum*) and a bristlegrass (*Setaria*), and several forbs of the borage family.

In Pleistocene time the ice at the period of greatest expansion in the United States covered only a relatively small part of the Mixed-Prairie area in northern Montana and North Dakota but it extended eastward from the Missouri River in the Dakotas. The Great Plains from central Montana and southwestern North Dakota southward to Texas were free of ice. The period of glaciation had nevertheless a profound effect upon

[1] Reprinted by permission from Schuchert and Dunbar "Historical Geology" 1941, John Wiley and Sons, Inc.

the cover of vegetation. It seems certain that the Boreal Forest was pushed far southward and later retreated northward during warm, dry periods. Evidence of this is found in the persistence of white spruce to this day at higher altitudes in the Black Hills and the survival of paper birch and aspen, all cold climate species, in the deep canyons and elevated plateaus. Indeed, many types of vegetation retreated and advanced across the Great Plains during the pulsations of cool, moist and warm, dry periods in Pleistocene time. These mass movements of grassland dominants were apparently associated with a period of intensive evolution.

The eastern edge of the Black Hills has numerous relics of eastern Deciduous Forest trees, such as bur oak, ash, elm and others, which here found refuge and remained behind the eastwardly retreating woodland which once covered the plains. A relic, in an ecological sense, is a community or a fragment of one that has survived some important change, often to become a part of the existing vegetation. Other evidence is the presence of hard maple and other remnants of Ohio forests in the deep Caddo Canyon in west-central Oklahoma. It is also believed that tall grasses occupied the Great Plains for a period following the retreat of the deciduous forest.

According to Clements, an outstanding authority on vegetation, needlegrasses (*Stipa*), Junegrass (*Koeleria*), wheat grasses (*Agropyron*) and wild-rye grasses (*Elymus*) are of northern derivation as are also various bluegrasses (*Poa*) and Idaho fescue (*Festuca idahoensis*), as well as thread-leaf sedge and needle-leaf sedge (species of *Carex*). All are cool-season plants.

Concerning the short grasses, "their homeland was the mountain plateaus of Mexico and Central America. Such far-ranging species as [blue grama] *Bouteloua gracilis* and [side-oats grama] *B. racemosa* [*curtipendula*] and [buffalo grass] *Buchloe dactyloides* have pushed north to the Canadian border or beyond, but the majority are confined to the region west and south of Texas. [Three-awn] *Aristida,* although of somewhat different form, is a regular associate of *Bouteloua* and of similar southern origin and xeric nature" (Clements, 1936). These are distinctly warm-season grasses. Curly mesquite (*Hilaria belangeri*), a dominant short grass of the Texas plains, and galleta (*H. jamesii*) are other grasses of southwestern origin.

The warm-season tall grasses, big bluestem (*Andropogon gerardi*), switchgrass (*Panicum virgatum*) and Indian grass (*Sorghastrum nutans*) together with the mid grass, little bluestem (*Andropogon scoparius*), are of semitropical origin and are believed to have come from the east and southeast.

With the slow southward movement of the glaciers and increasing cold, wheatgrasses, needlegrasses and others of northern origin were slowly spread into the southern Great Plains and the Southwest. Upon the retreat of the glaciers to the polar cap during a long, warm, dry period these grasses (though some remained) migrated far northward. Moreover, the short grasses and their associated warm-season species moved northward from their place of origin on the Mexican Plateau. During one of the glacial epochs (Nebraskan or Kansan) it is believed that certain tall grasses, such as big bluestem, migrated westward ahead of the westerly moving deciduous forest. Thus, great and repeated migrations and a vast mingling of species over the Great Plains have resulted from the various pulsations of climate during glacial times.

The dry climatic cycle of 1933 to 1940 has recapitulated in miniature the much larger cycles of long duration of postglacial times. During these seven years of extreme drought, Mixed Prairie replaced True Prairie over an area of 100 miles in width from South Dakota to central Kansas. This included the destruction of species populations and local mass migrations. Composition of the vegetation was greatly changed and the form of the plants modified by dwarfing. The drought cycle had a marked effect on both vegetation and soil throughout the plains. As usual, the effects were more pronounced along the ecotones or transitional areas from one plant association to another (Weaver, 1943).

Deep canyons, steep protected slopes, cool north exposures, sunny dry ridges, and soil with increased moisture, from whatever cause, have been the refuges of numerous species which were able to exist in the changing climates. Such havens, as will be shown, were especially numerous in rough country and along the mountain borders.

SOILS AND CLIMATE

Soils from near the Kansas-Oklahoma boundary northward lie in the Chernozem (Black Earth) zonal soil area in the eastern edge of Mixed Prairie. A large central portion is in the northern Dark Brown belt, and much of eastern Colorado, Wyoming and Montana is in the Brown soil zone. Southward the soils are mostly Reddish Chestnut although areas of sand and rough breaks occur in the central area and along the edge of the caprock in the Canadian River Valley. The Shinnery Oak Savannah lies almost entirely upon Rendzina soils. The low rainfall and high evaporation rates, together with vigorous absorption of water by the vegetation, result in a concentration of lime at relatively shallow depths. This is often 3 to 4 feet in the eastern part but only 8 to 18 inches under the low rainfall westward. The deeper soil is not generally moist and the water table is far beyond the reach of plant roots. Since these soils have not been leached of their nutrients, they are quite fertile. The soils vary from blowing sand to tight, hard adobe. The greater percentage consists of clay loams, silt loams, and sandy loams, often referred to in the literature as "hard lands", which, of course, they are not, in contrast to the sandy soils ("soft lands") which have little or no cohesive properties. Kinds of soil vary so widely locally that they will be described with the vegetation they support.

Climatic conditions over the Mixed Prairie are difficult to describe. The climate is one of extremes. It is commonly called semiarid but in some years it is humid and in others desert-like. It is not a permanently established climate but a dynamic one with large scale fluctuations and wet and dry trends (Borchert, 1950). Located in the interior of a continent, the climate is subject to pronounced changes in temperature. Hot summers, usually with cool nights, occur throughout. In northern North Dakota and Montana the frost-free season is about 120 days, but in Texas it is 200 days or more. Frozen ground and snow prevail northward through a long winter; in the southern portion of the prairie both are rare.

The western boundary of mixed prairie has a rainfall of about 15 inches along the Colorado Mountain front, but it is near the 10-inch line in general. The eastern boundary has 13 inches on the Canadian border, 23 inches in Kansas, but 27 inches in the South. However, the efficiency of the rainfall is about the same in North Dakota as in Texas. This is due to the marked increase in evaporation southward. In west-central Texas it is about 60 inches (from a free water surface during the six summer months) but in North Dakota, less than 30 inches. To compensate for this greater evaporation, 10 inches of efficient rainfall are required.

The impress of the climate even during rather normal years is marked. In connection with studies on experimental vegetation, crops of spring wheat, oats, and barley were grown at Burlington, Colorado, and Phillipsburg, Kansas, both in Mixed Prairie, and at Lincoln, Nebraska, in True Prairie climate (Weaver, 1924). Each kind of crop was planted from the same lot of seed at the same time and grown under conditions of farm practice common to the several localities, respectively. This was in 1920 and 1921. Both height-growth and dry weight of the three cereals correlated directly with available water content of soil, which was least at Burlington and greatest at Lincoln. The structure of the plants was pro-

FIG. 3. Blazing star (*Liatris punctata*) showing normal stature of this perennial on good years (left) and dwarfed condition during severe drought. The taproot is usually 8 or more feet in depth.

foundly modified (Bruner and Weaver, 1923). Native species respond to the drier climate in a similar manner. Species which grow both in True Prairie and on the plains are invariably smaller westward. Their growth during years of normal rainfall and in severe drought is illustrated, but not exaggerated, in (Fig. 3).

Seasonal distribution and variation in amount of precipitation are extremely important features. East of the mountains 70 to 80 per cent of the moisture falls during the growing season. May and June are usually the months of greatest rainfall northward, elsewhere, except in New Mexico, May, June and July are about equal (Kincer, 1923). Some rain falls in heavy showers and much of the water is lost to the soil. Much rainfall is also lost in light showers followed by bright sunshine and wind. Slow, steady rains are far less frequent. Fortunately, much of the precipitation falls at night when temperatures and evaporation are lowest. Hail storms are common. Sometimes the native vegetation is beaten down and the tops of plants destroyed, and the soil is pitted and pock-marked to a depth of a half-inch. Precipitation is frequently poorly distributed and drought is always imminent—drought that strikes at unpredictable intervals. Wind velocities are higher in Mixed Prairie than in any other part of the country, except certain seashores. Hot, dry southerly winds frequently parch the soil in summer. Great blizzards, with temperatures far below zero and strong northwest winds, often sweep the powdery snow from the uplands of the northwest prairies into ravines and depressions. However, the Chinook winds, which have lost their moisture to the northern mountains, descend toward the plain where the air is compressed, heated and dried. The warm air takes up the snow and may keep the winter ranges open to grazing.

Vegetation frequently suffers from recurrent periods of drought. Severe drought is an ever-present threat to livestock operations. Only occasionally is the precipitation in sufficient amount and so evenly distributed as to moisten the soil during the entire summer. Often the range grasses cease growth in late July or early August, and not infrequently spring drought delays early development of the plant cover. At Miles City, Montana, from 1878 to 1939, drought occurred on the average of once every 5 years. This is a typical example of Northern Great Plains weather and is substantiated by a 60-year record, ending in 1939, at Havre, Montana, 250 miles northwest near the Canadian border (Hurt, 1951). The terrible droughts in the West and Southwest are well known. They are of frequent but irregular occurrence throughout the great expanse of Mixed Prairie, where only a wonderfully adjusted vegetation, to be described, has successfully met all these hazards throughout thousands of years (Campbell, 1936).

As pointed out by Shantz (1950), "It is doubtful if man has ever equalled nature in making such productive and sustained use of a limited supply of rainfall as nature has exemplified on the High Plains. . . . Nature uses three most important methods: (1) catch water in the soil when it falls, (2) use it as soon as possible for forage production and (3) maintain a plant cover on the soil to prevent soil blowing."

CHAPTER 2

Vegetation of Mixed Prairie

THE MIXED PRAIRIE is by far the largest of the several grassland associations of North America. It extends from southern Alberta and Saskatchewan through the Staked Plains (Llano Estacado) of Texas and onward over the Edwards Plateau. Its eastern boundary is True Prairie. Mixed Prairie extends from the east of central North Dakota to central Montana on the west and at low elevations contacts the Palouse Prairie of the Northwest at its southeastern limits in western Montana, eastern Idaho and northern Utah. From central Oklahoma it ranges beyond the general mountain front and extends through northern New Mexico and Arizona to the Colorado Valley (Weaver and Clements, 1938). By provinces and states, it includes most of the grassland of Saskatchewan and Alberta and the western two-thirds of North and South Dakota and Nebraska. It occupies the western half of Kansas and approximately the western third of Oklahoma and extends over western Texas, eastern and northern New Mexico, and northern Arizona. From the eastern third of Colorado it extends northward through Wyoming to cover more than half of eastern and northern Montana.

GRASSES AND FORBS [1]

This great central grassland owes its name to the fact that its climax or original plant cover, undisturbed by civilized man, was composed of both mid grasses and short grasses intermixed and occurring on more or less equal terms. Mid grasses formed the upper layer of vegetation and short grasses and sedges the lower one (Fig. 4). It will be shown that the roots of both mid and short grasses extend to about the same level. They have equal opportunity to absorb soil moisture. The short grasses are shaded more or less by the taller ones but they are less handicapped by grazing. Although the vegetation is not uniform over its vast expanse, many of the more abundant and important grasses occur throughout. This

[1] Forbs are non-grasslike herbaceous plants.

FIG. 4. (Upper) Mixed Prairie of little bluestem (*Andropogon scoparius*) and blue grama (*Bouteloua gracilis*). The short grass forms a layer beneath the bunches of bluestem. Photo in eastern Colorado Sept., 1917. (Lower) Mixed Prairie of blue grama and buffalo grass (short grasses) alternating or intermixing with open stands of sand dropseed (*Sporobolus cryptandrus*) (foreground) and other taller grasses. Alma, Nebraska.

leaves no doubt about its unity. The almost constant association of mid and short grass was thoroughly examined by Clements (1920) during and following 1914. He traversed the Great Plains region from east to west. In 1914 the climax grassland was studied in 88 localities east of the Rocky Mountains and mid grasses and short grasses were associated as dominants in 83 of these. During six years, he found at least one mid grass and one short grass together as dominants in all but 15 of the 393 localities examined. Three mid-grass dominants, needlegrass (*Stipa comata*), western wheatgrass (*Agropyron smithii*) and Junegrass (*Koeleria cristata*) did not yield to the short grasses but continued across the plains and into the foothills of the mountains of Montana, Wyoming and Colorado. As a result of his extended researches the old terminology of mid-continental grasslands of prairie and short-grass plains was replaced in 1920 by the proper ecological terminology of True Prairie and Mixed Prairie associations.

Over the area as a whole the medium water relations limit the growth of the mid grasses. Only in the most favorable places do they form continuous stands comparable to those of True Prairie. Mixed Prairie is limited on the east by increased soil moisture sufficient to support a continuous growth of mid grasses under which a short-grass understory is kept out by the dense shade.

The transition from True to Mixed Prairie is a gradual one and occurs in an ecotone (transitional area) approximately 50 miles in width, at least in the central portion (Weaver and Bruner, 1954). In this westward transition certain taller and more mesic species are replaced by those of lower stature and greater ability to endure drought. For example, needlegrass (*Stipa spartea*) gives way to needle-and-thread (*S. comata*), and tall dropseed (*Sporobolus asper*) and prairie dropseed (*S. heterolepis*) yield to sand dropseed (*S. cryptandrus*).

Both little bluestem (*Andropogon scoparius*) and big bluestem (*A. gerardi*) largely disappear, except as postclimax relics in the best watered (usually sandy) soil. Junegrass (*Koeleria cristata*) and side-oats grama (*Bouteloua curtipendula*) continue throughout, and western wheatgrass (*Agropyron smithii*), despite reduction in size, becomes far more abundant than in True Prairie. Moreover, many grasses and sedges not found in True Prairie, or occurring there only sparingly, are widely spread in this drier climate.

Forbs of Mixed Prairie respond in a manner similar to that of the grasses. They are largely the same species as those of True Prairie, at least over the great central area. The societies or groups of forbs are smaller, fewer, and the individuals less densely aggregated than in True Prairie. Societies are here best developed under a rainfall of 15 or more inches (Fig. 5). Prairie clovers (*Petalostemum*), blazing star (*Liatris punctata*), few-flowered psoralea (*Psoralea tenuiflora*) and smooth goldenrod (*Solidago missouriensis*), like others from the eastern prairie, were formerly abundant over much of the area, especially on broken hills and in somewhat sandy soil where water was available at some depth throughout the growing season. The climate is unfavorable to many species of True Prairie, such as prairie phlox (*Phlox pilosa*), false indigo (*Baptisia* spp.) and Canada anemone (*Anemone canadensis*) and scores of other species which are typically eastern. Over the Great Plains as a whole the more xeric species are now most important. Examples are red false mallow (*Sphaeralcea coccinea*), crazyweed (*Oxytropis lambertii*), fringed sage (*Artemisia frigida*) and western species of *Astragalus* and cactus (*Opuntia*).

SHORT-GRASS DISCLIMAX

As stated by McArdle and Costello (1936) "it was virgin country in 1540 when the Spanish captain, Coronado, led the Conquistadores up from Mexico through what is now Texas and on northward over the lush grass of the never-ending plains. It was the free and unchallenged home of the buffalo and antelope in 1805 when Lewis and Clark made their intrepid march to the mouth of the Columbia. And it was still virgin territory in 1835 when Colonel Dodge and his party of Government explorers spent the entire summer following the Platte River toward its source, traveling across the Great Plains, along the frontal wall of the Rockies, and returning eastward by way of the Arkansas River. As late as 1858, buffalo roamed over the land where Denver now stands. Those who set forth three-quarters of a century ago to cross this vast, uncharted, little-known wilderness saw the land as Coronado saw it three centuries before." Unfortunately the botanists who first saw the primeval mixed prairie along with the early explorers were plant collectors and not ecologists. They had little regard for the importance of species as expressed in dominance; modern concepts of plant ecology were not yet

FIG. 5. A small part of societies (from top downward) of Carolina anemone (*Anemone caroliniana*); a legume, lead plant (*Amorpha canescens*); blazing star (*Liatris punctata*); and another legume, silver-leaf psoralea (*Psoralea argophylla*).

developed. The two men who traveled most widely and understood this vegetation best in their generation were F. E. Clements and H. L. Shantz. Their studies began after 1895.

It is believed, as stated by Stewart (1936), that "the buffalo, deer, elk, mountain sheep, antelope and other forms of wildlife, large and small, that were the first users of the range had little or no discernible effect upon it in terms of depletion. Heavy use by vast roaming or migrating herds of buffalo was common, and around strategic watering places, salt licks, and on favorite breeding grounds range forage would be so fully grazed that little or no feed remained. Yet in every instance seasonal migrations of the herds permitted recovery of the vegetation between grazing periods."

Since the coming of the herds of the cattlemen and the settlement of the land, the story of the Great Plains is one of prodigal exploitation of a vast natural resource on a scale never witnessed before. This began in 1880–85 and was aggravated from time to time by severe droughts, while settlement continuously decreased the amount of range land (*cf.* Stewart, 1936).

During the period when the cattle industry on the Great Plains was in a thriving condition, the free range was considered as an inexhaustible supply of forage for cattle, sheep and horses. When vegetation became short in one place, it was only necessary to move to a new area. Then came the dryland farmers and barbed wire fences and grazing became more restricted and increased in intensity. The taller and more accessible mid grasses have been grazed out to the extent that they are often little in evidence and short-grass communities thus produced appear to be climax in nature. That overgrazing results in definite modification of grasslands has been clearly recognized. The bluestem prairies of Illinois, for example, were changed to bluegrass pastures by overgrazing. Sampson (1921) states: "Intensive grazing accompanied by the introduction of blue grass and red top destroyed practically all of the native prairie plants of the farms not cultivated. The bluestem prairie became blue grass pastures." This change occurred throughout the extent of True Prairie, and all stages in its degeneration both on lowland and upland have been fully studied (Weaver, 1954). Smith (1899) stated that before the red prairies of Texas were overgrazed the grasses were largely bluestems (*Andropogon*), often as high as a horse's back. After pasturing and subsequent to the trampling and hardening of the soil, the three-awn grasses spread over the whole country. After further overstocking and trampling, these grasses were driven out by mesquite grass (*Hilaria*) and buffalo grass (*Buchloe*), which then became the most prominent species. The occurrence of any one of these as the dominant or most conspicuous grass is, to some extent, an index of the state of the land and of the stage of overstocking and deterioration that has been reached. The writers have observed the change of Mixed Prairie to short-grass range in western Kansas and Nebraska, but surrounding prairie, mowed annually for hay, did not undergo this change.

"The first intimation that the short-grass plains were not a climax in the climatic sense was obtained during the summer of 1915; this was a season of excessive rainfall coinciding with the lowest sunspot minimum known for a century. The mid-grasses appeared abundantly in the cover of short-grass and in many places obscured the latter more or less completely. Since these were all perennials, it was obvious that they could not be regarded as recent invaders but must have been present in the community in less conspicuous form" (Clements, 1934). Wet seasons on the Great Plains, by increasing water content and decreasing competition, have regularly reproduced the Mixed Prairie in a convincing manner, during the first quarter of the present century, over wide areas that were apparently short-grass climax during dry years.

Before this relationship was understood, the wide expanses of short-grass cover led to the assumption that this represented the climax vegetation of the Great Plains. It is now generally recognized that the short grass is a disclimax (disturbance climax). Thus, a permanent sod of short grass indicates overgrazing alone, the intensity of which varies with the degree to which mid grasses and prairie forbs have vanished and the understory itself has been modified and invaded by weeds.

After long continued study of North American grasslands, there has been accumulated from various sources evidence which makes it clear that the dominance of the short grasses in the Great Plains has resulted from overgrazing Mixed Prairie. Weaver and Clements (1938) state: [1] "Overgrazing greatly handicaps the taller grasses and correspondingly favors the short grasses; it has been so widespread and serious as to justify

---

[1] Reprinted by permission from "Plant Ecology" by Weaver and Clements, 1938. McGraw Hill Book Company, Inc.

the impression that the short-grass plains are the most xerophytic of the grassland formation. Three sources of evidence have, however, combined to prove that it is a modification of the mixed prairie. In all protected places as well as those where sandy soil or broken topography are available, the mid grasses still persist. Even more convincing evidence has been secured from exclosures fenced against cattle, in which the mid grasses return in a few years. Further, when the pressure of grazing is offset by normal or excess rainfall, the taller grasses are able to compete with the short ones on equal terms or even to dominate them more or less completely. Finally, photographs taken by the Hayden Expedition in 1870 prove beyond any question that the undisturbed cover of the Great Plains was dominated by mid grasses." Under overgrazing, forbs may suffer as much as mid grasses, and the short-grass plains are today often an almost unbroken sod of blue grama and buffalo grass (*cf.* McArdle *et al.*, 1936).

Grazing disclimaxes occur in many places and some extend over vast areas. Excessive grazing has kept them in this condition for so long a time that many stockmen do not realize that their ranges once supported a quite different and more productive type of vegetation and under scientific range management could do so again.

The pioneers in the plains had little conception of the nature or value of grass. Their viewpoint of a crop was that of the farmer, the producer of corn, wheat and clover. The crops were totally harvested annually. Thus, why not harvest all the grass crop by continuous grazing? Anyway, grass was plentiful, enough for everyone. At first their chief concern was to get enough livestock to harvest all of this wonderful grass. They knew little or nothing of the physiology of plants. In their use of the range, they failed to realize that part of the foliage of every growing plant must be left intact in order that it may grow and make food to store as reserves in the parts underground for next year's plant development. They failed to understand that grass required protection from continued close grazing throughout the growing season and especially in spring. Indeed, it has taken years of experience and experimentation to discover that approximately half of the forage must be left on the soil if continued maximum production of high quality forage is maintained. A range plant that has lost its vigor by repeated overuse not only produces less foliage in subsequent years but also is less able to withstand the invasion of weeds, which produce small amounts of low-quality forage.

Little was then understood of the importance of vegetation in forming the soil that supports it or the importance of a cover of vegetation in promoting water penetration and lessening runoff. A good cover of vegetation, living or dead, must be kept on the soil to prevent raindrops from striking the bare earth and loosening the soil particles. These then enter and clog the soil pores and decrease water infiltration while promoting runoff and erosion (Ellison, 1944). Thus, about half of the annual forage may safely be harvested for food. The other half manufactures plant food that is stored in crowns and roots, while shielding the soil against rain and wind. Later this half furnishes residues which decay and become mixed with the soil and thus aid in maintaining its tilth and fertility.

Pioneer cattlemen and ranchers were busily engaged in grazing the crop of forage or in plowing up the grass. Only in relatively recent years has much concerted effort been given to scientific study of native grasslands and methods of maintaining and improving them (Edwards, 1948).

LAND OF PERENNIAL GRASSES

The characteristic life form of mixed prairie is perennial grass, including grasslike, dryland sedges. Where annual grasses occur in abundance it is a distinct sign of some sort of disturbance. Interspersed among the grasses, thickly in places but more thinly in others, is a large variety of forbs. These too are mostly of long life span and, like the grasses, once established maintain their place in the prairie year after year. Vast areas of Mixed Prairie from Canada to Texas are generally green in summer and brown or gray in winter or in severe drought.

On level land the vast prairie in summer is a sea of waving grasses dotted with flowers of many forbs. Where mid grasses and taller forbs have been reduced by grazing and trampling, the short grasses, in early summer, form a continuous carpet of green stretching away as far as the eye can see. The appearance is that of great uniformity and almost of monotony, at least to all but the plainsmen (Fig. 6). More generally, however, the land is gently rolling and some areas are rough and broken. Slopes, ravines and valleys are plentiful and sand hills frequently occur. Lake beds, river terraces, plateaus and buttes have resulted from erosion. Heavily eroded places along the Little Missouri River and in the Badlands of several northern states are common. Mesas and ridges occur as well as small isolated mountainous areas. Strong contrast and sharp delimitation of valley, mesa and plain are among the characteristic features.

FIG. 6. (Upper) Undisturbed Mixed Prairie near Medora, southwestern North Dakota. The upper layer, about 2 feet high, is composed of needle-and-thread (*Stipa comata*), green needlegrass (*Stipa viridula*) and western wheatgrass (*Agropyron smithii*). Blue grama (*Bouteloua gracilis*) and thread-leaf sedge (*Carex filifolia*) form a lower layer of vegetation about 8 inches tall. (Lower) Mixed Prairie near Burlington, Colorado, reduced by overgrazing to a short-grass disclimax. Short grasses and cactus are the chief species. Photo in July, 1917.

Over all these topographic variations a rather similar vegetation occurs. This wide distribution of grasses in these various habitats indicates great adaptability to a wide range in climate and soils. Although certain species, such as blue grama, needle-and-thread and western wheatgrass, occur almost throughout, the adaptability of the vegetation results in part from a difference in the kinds of grasses rather than from variations of a single species.

The native grasses are nearly all palatable to livestock and furnish excellent grazing during both summer and winter. Ranges for winter grazing, of course, are usually not used in summer. Even in Canada the setting aside of areas for winter grazing (about 15 acres per steer) is a common practice. "The forage plants growing on our western ranges are the results of thousands of years of elimination and adaptation, having been grazed by animal life for long periods, and are not easily improved upon or destroyed by man within a few years time" (Vass and Pearson, 1933). Plants of mixed prairie have the hardiness to withstand extremes of cold and heat, floods and drought; they are not depleted by plant disease or the general rigors of the habitat, even recovering from great damage by hail. They live successfully in a plant cover where competition is severe.

Mixed Prairie is of vital economic importance not only for grazing, production of hay, and control of wind and water erosion but also for watershed protection and food and shelter for wildlife. Mixtures of numerous grasses and grass-like plants usually clothe the better grazing grounds. A wide variety of palatable forbs is often present, and on many ranges browse plants occur as well. Some begin growth and mature very early, others furnish much forage later in spring and throughout the summer. Many grasses, if uneaten, cure on the ground and like browse are valuable food in winter. The field ecologist and range man, as will be shown, learn by experience that each species of plant has its own distinctive habits of growth, particular value and time as food for animals, and as protection of the soil. Consequently, as pointed out by Allred (1945), "sound management of the native forage crop, which consists of many species, is thus rendered more difficult than that of a single farm crop." The teeming populations of the many species of herbivores which inhabited the plains and the thriving herds of cattle and flocks of sheep which replaced them all testify to the high forage value of the vegetation.

Certain grasses and sedges are so vigorous and abundant that they may compose the bulk of the vegetation. Their influence upon the habitat and effect on other species are so profound that they determine in a large measure the conditions under which the remaining species must develop. These most important or controlling plants are termed dominants. They possess many or all of the following characteristics: they are well adapted to the environment; they have a long life span which insures permanent occupation; they attain large size (height and volume) compared with other competitors in the upper or lower layer, respectively, where they spread their foliage. Close adaptation to the soil and climate enables them to compete successfully with other vegetation over a wide area. An interesting and most valuable feature of grassland is its ability to re-establish itself after it has been modified by close grazing or disturbed by cultivation. It seems to possess an irresistable impulse to reproduce and maintain the climatic climax. The dominant grasses of mixed prairie are the ones best adapted to the plains climate. Dominants markedly reflect the impress of the climate; they react strongly to the forces of the habitat and are usually the best indicators of range conditions and trends. Consequently they deserve particular attention.

Important variations in vegetation of Mixed Prairie are due to the distribution of the rather numerous dominants, especially from north to south. Four major mid-grass dominants range almost throughout. These are needle-and-thread (*Stipa comata*), sand dropseed (*Sporobolus cryptandrus*), western wheatgrass (*Agropyron smithii*) and Junegrass (*Koeleria cristata*) (Fig. 7). Red three-awn (*Aristida longiseta*) and a short grass, blue grama (*Bouteloua gracilis*), enjoy an equally wide range. The importance of the preceding widespread dominants varies greatly. They intermix with several regional dominants and form various communities within this extremely large association. Species largely restricted to the northern prairie are thread-leaf sedge (*Carex filifolia*) and needle-leaf sedge (*C. eleocharis,* formerly *C. stenophylla*). Three-awn (*Aristida* spp.) and buffalo grass are most abundant in the central plains. Side-oats grama (*Bouteloua curtipendula*) is mostly central and southern. Dominants found wholly or largely in the southern Mixed Prairie are galleta (*Hilaria jamesii*), curly mesquite (*H. belangeri*), squirreltail (*Sitanion hystrix*), ringgrass (*Muhlenbergia torreyi*) and New Mexicao feathergrass (*Stipa neomexicana*).

Another group of about a dozen species is somewhat less important in

the general area of Mixed Prairie. Each will be described when communities in which it occurs are discussed. In addition, little bluestem (*Andropogon scoparius*) and even the tall grass, big bluestem (*A. gerardi*), with certain other species form distinct types of postclimax vegetation where topography and soils are such that the plants can benefit from an unusually large water supply.

According to Clements, the mid grasses are circumpolar in origin. The short grasses and side-oats grama came in from the southwest, and the bluestems and other tall grasses are, as a rule, southern or subtropical. Conversely, the several species of grass-like sedges are of northern derivation. The intermixing of these species derived from so many sources is another reason for the name, Mixed Prairie. Each of the major dominants will be rather fully described.

NEEDLE-AND-THREAD

Stipa comata is a cool-season, perennial bunch grass best adapted to uplands. It resumes growth in late March or early in April. It develops rapidly and reaches a height of 1 to about 3 feet when in flower early in June (Fig. 7). It reaches maturity in July when the ripe seeds are shed. This grass is very palatable and nutritious in spring and early summer. Its use is later decreased since the sharp-pointed seeds often injure grazing animals, especially sheep, by working into the mouth parts and the hide. The plant becomes more or less dormant during the hot summer, but if moisture is available it later renews growth and furnishes green feed in fall and even in winter. Although it is highly drought resistant, its appearance at a time when other green forage is not abundant, together with its high palatability, often results in its being grazed out. The bunches are small, usually only 1 to 3 inches in diameter, and not closely spaced. The plant does not tiller abundantly and propagation is mostly by seed. The very narrow leaves, which seldom exceed a foot in length, are ridged and rough on the upper surface but smooth and shiny beneath. Typically the tips of the leaves die back an inch or more even in good seasons for growth. The membranous, sharp-pointed ligule at the base of the leaf blade is about one-fourth inch long.

FIG. 7. (Upper) Needle-and-thread (*Stipa comata*) and Junegrass (*Koeleria cristata*); heights are about 2.5 feet and 1 foot, respectively. (Lower) Sand dropseed (*Sporobolus cryptandrus*), about 1.5 feet high, and western wheatgrass (*Agropyron smithii*) 2.5 feet tall.

The panicle is 5 to 10 inches long; although the base is usually enclosed by the uppermost leaf sheath, it is often open and loosely spreading. The common name is derived from the long-awned seed which resembles a threaded sewing needle. The seeds (or fruits), which are born singly, are about half an inch in length but the awns on the upper ends are usually 4 to 6 inches long. At first the yellowish awns are flexible and straight and extend upward and outward, but upon drying they become hard, bent and much twisted. It is then that they have the threaded needle appearance. On the lower end of the seed there is a sharp-pointed, bearded base or callus. When the brownish seeds fall to the ground, the hygroscopic awn becomes nearly straight when wet but twists tightly again upon drying. Since it is held in place more or less by the bases of plants, the seed is bored into the soil to a depth, usually, of 1 to 3 inches. Thus, this grass literally plants the seeds in a soil environment favorable to germination. In June, an upland prairie may seem to be a sea of waving needle-and-thread, although actually this species may furnish only 20 per cent or less of the ground cover. During favorable years this grass produces hay of good quality, which must be cut either before the seeds mature or after they have fallen.

Needle-and-thread is very widely distributed over the Mixed Prairie, a name which, for convenience, will hereafter be used as a common noun. This grass ranges from Texas to the valley of the Yukon River. It presently occurs in considerable amounts from northern Colorado and north of central Nebraska far into Canada.

SAND DROPSEED

Sporobolus cryptandrus is a widely distributed, drought-resistant species found especially in sandy areas and on dry, coarse soils of plains, valleys and foot hills throughout the mixed prairie. In sandy habitats or following great drought it is often the most abundant species. The plant forms tufts or open bunches; the stems, which often spread somewhat at the base, reach a height of 1 to 3 feet when mature (Fig. 7). The short, wide, sharply pointed leaves, which are rough on the upper surface, are mostly confined to the lower half of mature plants. Conspicuous long, white tufts of hair appear where the leaf blade joins the sheath. Flowering occurs in August or thereafter. The panicle is usually partially and often entirely enclosed by the upper leaf sheath; its exposed parts are often purplish in color. The small seeds are produced in great numbers; several thousand have been obtained from a single enclosed panicle. The tiny seeds shatter readily (drop seed) when mature. This prolific production of wind-blown seeds together with drought resistance may account largely for the rapid return of this grass in overgrazed and drought-injured ranges, where seedlings develop rapidly.

Sand dropseed produces a fairly large amount of forage of good palatability, especially early in summer. Its preference by livestock is not as great as that for many native wheatgrasses and bluegrasses. Sometimes it is eaten as readily as blue grama and buffalo grass. Even if grazed closely, some nearly horizontal stems may produce seed. In winter it furnishes some grazing. The upper, wind-whipped leaves fray out in a characteristic manner.

WESTERN WHEATGRASS

Agropyron smithii is a hardy, perennial, sod-forming grass with abundant long, branched rhizomes, by means of which the plant spreads rapidly and widely. It is usually intermixed with blue grama, buffalo grass and other grasses but often grows in dense, nearly pure stands. It is widely distributed especially in the western United States and is most abundant in the northern and central parts of the Great Plains. This cool-season grass is 2 to 3 feet tall in good years but is much dwarfed by drought (Fig. 7). In the short-grass disclimax it is greatly suppressed and may flower only rarely.

Growth begins in March and proceeds rapidly. The abundant leaves are 6 to 12 inches in length but less than one-fourth inch in width. The blades are stiff and more or less erect and do not droop as do those of most grasses. The upper surface is deeply ridged and rough but the lower one is smooth. The leaves of this drought-resistant plant roll tightly inward when the soil becomes dry and thus greatly reduce the surface for transpiration. The foliage and flower stalks usually appear bluish-green because of a grayish, waxy bloom. This grass may readily be recognized even at a distance by its bluish-green color. The auricles of the leaves, which clasp the stem, are nearly always distinctly darker in color than the leaf sheath. The prominent spikes, 2 to 6 inches long, are held well above the foliage, usually at a height of 2 to 4 feet. Blossoming occurs in June and the seeds ripen in August or September.

Wheatgrass is adapted to a wide range of soils. It thrives in loams to heavy clay, often with a claypan or somewhat alkaline. In low level lands that receive excess drainage water, it often forms pure stands. It also grows in considerable abundance on dry uplands, intermixed with thread-leaf sedge, blue grama and needle-and-thread.

Western wheatgrass furnishes excellent forage for cattle and horses the year around. It has highly nutritive qualities and its palatability rating is high. It is particularly valuable for winter grazing since it remains palatable on drying and retains much of its nutrient quality. Moreover, it is taller than the short grasses, stands up well, and may be available to livestock when other forage is covered with snow. When cut for hay in the early heading stage it produces forage of high feeding value. Because of its rhizomes, it may persist in land broken for cultivation. If such land is abandoned, this aggressive plant frequently spreads so rapidly as to more or less completely re-occupy the soil in a few years. It is a good soil binder.

JUNEGRASS

Koeleria cristata is a major dominant of wide distribution. It ranges throughout the grasslands of southern Ontario to British Columbia and southward to Texas. It is a small, cool-season, bunch grass which also occurs throughout the true prairie, especially on uplands, but rarely composes more than 3 to 10 per cent of the cover. In mixed prairie it rarely forms pure heavy stands but is one of the most common and widely distributed of the western grasses. The rather dense foliage, which is mostly basal, attains a height of only 5 to 10 inches (Fig. 7). The rather short leaves are soft, irregularly corrugated on the upper surface and conspicuously dark green. The tufts are usually only 2 or 3 inches in diameter and the yield of forage per plant is small. Growth is renewed in spring 2 or 3 weeks before that of blue grama, and livestock seek this highly palatable, tender forage. Abundant flower stalks 10 to 20 inches tall are developed late in May. Their densely flowered, contracted, spike-like panicles somewhat resemble those of timothy. Flowering usually occurs in June and seed matures a month or two thereafter. The plants mature early; they are somewhat dormant during the dry summer but green up again with cooler, moist weather in autumn.

Junegrass furnishes fairly good forage which is relished especially early in the season by all classes of livestock. This plant increases its area by tillering and reseeding. It is neither long-lived nor very drought resistant. It maintains its stand by rapid reseeding.

BLUE GRAMA

Bouteloua gracilis is a warm-season short grass that is abundantly distributed throughout the mixed prairie from Texas and Arizona to Alberta and Saskatchewan (Fig. 8). It is well adapted to very fine sandy silt loam soils (hard lands) and to sandy soil as well. It is also found on ridges and dry uplands where few other grasses can thrive. It is a bunch grass of far greater drought resistance than most plains grasses, not excepting buffalo grass. The foliage is usually 3 to 5 inches tall when mature in midsummer, but the numerous slender flower stalks, erect and distinctly jointed, reach heights varying from 6 to 20 inches. Unlike buffalo grass the leaves are usually smooth and almost free from hairs except at the ligule and on the collar. They range from about 2 to 6 inches in length; they are slender and often curled, bluish-green in color, and largely confined to the base of the plant. In its southern range the plants are leafier, taller and more vigorous and assume a bunch habit which results in a more open cover. Northward the plants are less leafy and shorter, and the smaller bunches form a rough sod. A somewhat similar decrease in height occurs at higher elevations where the plants have shorter leaves and flower stalks and form a low turf.

The very efficient root system of this hardy grass is minutely branched and extends deeply. Blue grama is a good soil binder; it is resistant to grazing and trampling and adapted to extremes of environmental conditions. Like buffalo grass, its leaves are so close to the soil that even under close grazing much green food-making tissue remains. Moreover, it thrives best when not shaded by taller plants. It tends to increase in heavily grazed areas at the expense of higher yielding mid grasses. Consequently, along with buffalo grass, it has remained the most important species in the short-grass disclimax.

This late spring grass usually does not produce new forage in the central plains until May or (northward) in early June. But it develops rapidly and may produce flowers and seed within 60 days. A second period of flowering may occur in autumn. In drought it becomes dormant but renews its activities quickly when soil moisture again becomes available.

FIG. 8. (Upper) Side-oats grama (*Bouteloua curtipendula*) and blue grama (*B. gracilis*). (Lower) Staminate plants of buffalo grass (*Buchloe dactyloides*) (right) and pistillate or seed bearing plants (left). Stolons are often 24 or more inches long.

The plant depends on tillering and seed for propagation. Each of the very numerous flower stalks produces 2 to 5 spikes, the smaller number northward, 1 to 2 inches long. These extend at a sharp angle from the stem. On drying they may curve backward and become a golden yellow color.

The forage, although very palatable to all classes of stock, is produced in relatively small amounts. It is also palatable and nutritious when mature and furnishes excellent grazing even after the plants are dried. This makes it especially valuable during periods of drought and for winter grazing. Because of its low stature and low total production it is not an important grass for hay.

Variations in the growth of blue grama from seed produced in various sections of the Great Plains are described by Riegel (1940). He found that plants from seed harvested in the vicinity where the plants were grown (at Hays, Kansas) were more satisfactory than those from seed obtained farther north, as the northern plants were inferior as forage producers. Plants from seed obtained farther south exceeded in forage production if they were able to withstand the environmental conditions imposed by the more northerly climate.

CHAPTER 3

The Vegetation (continued)

PRAIRIE IS composed of groups of various species of many grasses and forbs, intermixed in places with a few shrubs or half-shrubs. A study of the grassland should begin with the acquisition of some knowledge of the most important plants. This is essential to an understanding of their ecological relations to other species with which they live and must compete for light, water, and nutrients. Moreover, knowledge of their responses to grazing and drought is essential to the proper use of the forage crop which they produce each year.

BUFFALO GRASS

Buchloe dactyloides is a warm-season short grass which becomes green late in spring and dries early in fall. It may be recognized by the grayish-green color of the turf it forms and the hairy, curly leaf blades. It belongs to the same tribe (*Chlorideae*) as blue grama, which is a chief associate, but can be distinguished from it by the presence of stolons or runners, which are sometimes 2 to 2.5 feet long (Fig. 8). These root freely at the nodes and produce additional plants. Under favorable conditions stolons elongate 0.5 to 2 inches per day and form a close, even mat which may become several inches thick. Thus, patches a few feet to a rod wide may be formed or, indeed, a continuous sod. In poor dry sites, only small tufts may occur.

The height attained by the foliage of this low-growing perennial is usually only 4 to 5 inches and flower stalks are 4 to 8 inches high. Thus, it is not as tall as blue grama and is more easily shaded out or buried by snow or wind-blown dust. The narrow leaves occur mostly near the soil surface and thus all of the leaf can not be grazed. They are variable in length, but usually 1 to 4 inches long, slender, and hairy on both sides. In drought they become the color of straw. Pollen-bearing and seed-bearing flowers are usually born on separate plants, but a small percentage of plants have flowers of both sexes. Pistillate flowers are partially hidden among the leaves and are usually not observed since here the foliage is mostly higher than the stems. Staminate plants produce one-sided spikes on stems higher than the leaves. These resemble those of blue grama, but they are much smaller. After the pollen ripens, these spikes wither and disappear. The spikes or burs of the pistillate flowers each produce 2 to several rather large, disk-shaped seeds. The burs shatter readily from the short stalks and become entangled in the grass on the ground. The seed crop is light except in wet years and difficult to harvest with ordinary farm machinery. Seeds remain viable for several years; old seeds germinate more readily than new ones.

Buffalo grass extends in a broad belt over the southern and central mixed prairie but is less abundant northward. In North Dakota it is found sparingly in the western part and rarely eastward. "In Montana it is most abundant in the southeastern plains section south of the Yellowstone and east of the Bighorn Rivers" (Woolfolk, 1949). In Wyoming it occurs, but not continuously, extending westward less than 150 miles from the eastern border.

This grass is generally found on hard lands since it can not withstand the effects of shifting sand. It grows well except on sandy soil but thrives best in swales, depressions and on stiff clay soils, even if somewhat saline. It occurs on well drained upland soils, intermixed with many other grasses. It is less drought resistant than blue grama, but, like blue grama, it has the ability repeatedly to become dormant and recover rapidly even after long periods of drought. The whole plant cures on the ground. Buffalo grass produces much palatable and highly nutritious forage, for a short grass, which can be utilized by all classes of stock for either summer or winter grazing.

In Kansas cattle graze buffalo grass more closely than blue grama. In Wyoming and North Dakota its palatability is very much less than that of blue grama. It withstands close grazing and trampling in a remarkable manner and over thousands of square miles has increased under overuse at the expense of other species, especially taller grasses. Yields are increased by its proper utilization. Although too short to be harvested for hay, it ranks first among the native grasses in the southern and central Great Plains for control of wind erosion. The sod houses of the early settlers were made mostly from the tough sod of buffalo grass. (*cf.* Webb, 1941; Beetle, 1950.)

SIDE-OATS GRAMA

Bouteloua curtipendula is the largest and most widely distributed of our grama grasses. Although it has spread from its home in the Southwest to Montana and North Dakota, it is most abundant and important in the central and southern mixed prairie. This grass is a perennial, warm-season plant with short rhizomes. It forms small tufts to wide bunches and only infrequently a sod. It is most abundant on rough soil of breaks and on lighter soils, but it also frequently accompanies the bluestems on lowlands. In spring it develops rapidly; it reaches a height of 1.5 to more than 2 feet in summer and remains green late in the season (Fig. 8). The flat to slightly rolled, broad leaves vary in length from 2 to 7 inches. They are somewhat hairy, especially on their margins, where the hairs have a conspicuously swollen base. Flower stalks appear about the first week in July and blooming continues into September. The inflorescence consists of 35 or more pendulous spikes on a slender flower stalk. The zigzag appearance of the rachis is very characteristic. When in bloom, bright reddish stamens protrude conspicuously. The lower leaf sheaths are also often reddish in color. This grass reseeds readily and, although less drought resistant than the smaller gramas, it frequently becomes very abundant following drought.

Side-oats grama furnishes excellent forage of high palatability in summer and is fairly good winter grazing, even in North Dakota. Mature stems are relatively unpalatable and are not grazed. When mowed it provides a good quality of hay.

Variations in the growth of side-oats grama at Hays, Kansas, from seed produced in various parts of the Great Plains are described by Hopkins (1941). Results were similar to those obtained with blue grama by Riegel. (*cf.* Cornelius, 1947.)

GREEN NEEDLEGRASS

Stipa viridula is an important species on the mixed prairie. It has a wide distribution in western North America but is most abundant on the upland prairies and ranges of the Northern Great Plains. Usually it is not a major constituent of the grassland except in swales or on flat land subject to flooding. It grows thickly in abandoned cultivated fields in the early stages of the subsere and in disturbed places in prairie. Like needle-and-thread, although found on many soil types, it grows better on sandier soils, if water is sufficient, than on heavier soils. Green needlegrass is a perennial bunch former, which varies in height from 1.5 to 3 feet. The leaves, which are mainly basal, vary from 6 to more than 12 inches in length and from an eighth to a fourth of an inch in width. They are usually partially rolled. Growth begins early in spring and, except during drought, continues well into the fall. The greenish, rather compact, panicles produce flowers early in June and seeds mature late in June or early in July. An inch-long, bent awn on each seed (fruit) is covered with short hairs. The awns are conspicuous but not nearly so troublesome to livestock as those of needle-and-thread. This grass furnishes good pasture for all classes of livestock, even in winter. It can be grazed at any time without injury to the animals. In some areas it furnishes a considerable portion of native hay of good quality.

THREAD-LEAF AND NEEDLE-LEAF SEDGE

Carex filifolia and *C. eleocharis* are representatives of short sedges which have accompanied the boreal grasses in their migration from circumpolar regions. They are found in the Palouse Prairie as well as in the mixed prairie of the northern Great Plains.

Thread-leaf sedge is grass-like in appearance and habit. It is a very long-lived perennial which grows in dense bunches and forms a tough sod. Each tuft or bunch produces light green, thread-like, tufted leaves usually from 2 to 5 inches long, except in wet years when they may reach 10 inches (Fig. 9). The basal sheaths are brown and papery. Slender flower stalks, often exceeding the leaves in length, produce a brown, chaffy spike or flower head about half an inch in length. This plant resumes growth very early in spring (middle to late March in Montana and North Dakota), along with certain native bluegrasses. This is somewhat earlier than western wheatgrass and a month earlier than blue grama. It is especially valuable for grazing at this period. Although it completes its growth late in May, it maintains high palatability for all classes of stock until about the end of June, when it becomes dry and tough.

This sedge has a very wide range from Yukon and Saskatchewan to Texas. Its chief importance in mixed prairie occurs in the five plains states north of Colorado. Here it often ranks among the four or five most im-

FIG. 9. (Upper) Bunches of thread-leaf sedge (*Carex filifolia*) growing with needle-and-thread in South Dakota. (Lower) Tumblegrass (*Schedonnardus paniculatus*), about 10 inches high and in seed, and hairy grama (*Bouteloua hirsuta*).

portant grass-like species. It is highly drought resistant and makes its best growth on dry, sandy soils where it sometimes forms nearly pure stands. Usually, however, it grows with blue grama, needle-and-thread, and a variety of other grasses, but it also occurs and even thrives on dry ridges and in places where not much other vegetation can survive. It is thus of great value in control of erosion. Its habit of low growth and the resistance of its tough wiry roots enables it to withstand heavy grazing and heavy trampling very successfully.

Needle-leaf sedge (*Carex eleocharis*) is another sedge of such abundance that it also ranks high among the species of mixed prairie. The stiff, smooth, pale green stems form small tufts, springing from creeping rootstocks, and the plants often occur in dense patches which furnish very early grazing.

RED AND PURPLE THREE-AWN

Aristida longiseta, formerly called wire grass, is a perennial bunch grass. The bunches vary from 3 to 6 inches in width and from 7 to 12 inches in height, the outer stems spreading somewhat from the base (Fig. 10). Stems are fine and unbranched. Leaves, which are mostly basal, are usually 4 to 6 inches long, very narrow, with harsh upper surface, inrolled and sharp-pointed and contain much fibrous tissue. The few-flowered, narrow panicles at the ends of the flower stalks are erect and held high above the foliage. The spikelets have a reddish color. The whole plant is conspicuous because of its silvery-gray color. The sharp-pointed, three-awned seeds (fruits) are produced in abundance. The awns are 3 inches or more in length. This plant is a vigorous seeder, the awned seeds being scattered far and wide by the wind as well as by animals.

Purple three-awn (*Aristida purpurea*) is a very closely related and important grass. It forms taller (12 to 20 inches), more upright bunches consisting of coarser stems not so densely aggregated (Fig. 10). Moreover, the awns are shorter (1 to 2 inches) and the panicles usually purplish. In Kansas this species is less drought resistant than red three-awn. Both species grow best on somewhat sandy soils of plains, mesas and foothills but are widely distributed over the Great Plains, except in low, wet places. They rapidly populate bared or disturbed soil. The ranges of the two species overlap widely but red three-awn occurs farther northward, to Montana and North Dakota. Both are common southward to Texas

FIG. 10. (Upper) Purple three-awn (*Aristida purpurea*) on left and red three-awn (*A. longiseta*) on right. These are widely distributed grasses that become especially abundant in an open cover. (Lower) Squirreltail (*Sitanion hystrix*), about 14 inches tall, is widely distributed.

and extend westward through northern New Mexico to Arizona. In the Southwest these grasses are eaten to some extent by livestock until flowers are produced. But elsewhere they are usually considered worthless for forage. Indeed, the ripe fruits are troublesome to grazing animals of the plains because of the hard, sharp points of the seed which may injure eyes, nose, or mouth or damage the hide of sheep.

GALLETA

Hilaria jamesii is a very drought resistant, erect perennial plant but with base often decumbent and foliage usually about 4 to 6 inches high. Flower stalks are often 12 to 20 inches long. It is distributed over mesas and plains from Wyoming and Nevada to New Mexico and Texas. North of the Arkansas River it occurs in scattered stands with blue grama in the sage-brush zone. Southward and westward, under a rainfall of 10 to 18 inches, it occurs abundantly over extensive areas in northern New Mexico and Arizona and in Utah on the upper plains and lower mountain slopes, and in the Great Basin. It is a common constituent of the plant cover on shale outcrops and soils derived from shale, attaining its major development on soils of heavy texture with calcareous surface or slightly saline. Wooton and Standley (1915) stated that in areas in northwestern New Mexico it forms pure stands many miles in extent.

A chief characteristic is the system of large, tough, woody rhizomes which may attain a length of 4 to 6 feet. These soil-binding stems resist heavy grazing and trampling in a remarkable manner and are also the chief means of propagation. Under long abuse, new rhizomes are only a few inches long and the root system, which may spread 12 to 18 inches laterally and reach a depth of 4 feet, becomes greatly shortened and lateral spread of roots much restricted (Flory and Trussell, 1938). Despite the presence of rhizomes this grass usually grows in bunches or large mats and only when the bunches spread to occupy intervening areas (a condition rarely attained under grazing) is a sod produced.

The numerous, rather short leaves are narrow and mostly basal. They are rigid and harsh and bluish in color. The spike has a chaffy appearance; it is at first purplish but fades to nearly white. It is covered with fine hairs. Galleta has a high palatability during the summer, rainy growing season but when it becomes dry it is of little value. It produces much forage on many southwestern ranges where it is grazed heavily.

FORBS AND OTHER NON-GRASSES

Prairie is not merely land covered with grass. It is a complex and definite entity with interrelated parts developed and adjusted throughout very long periods of time. It is the handiwork of climate and soil. Vegetation not only is closely adjusted to these agencies but also is an expression of them. It is quite as proper to speak of prairie soil and prairie climate as of prairie vegetation. Prairie may be considered from many points of view; a most important one is that of the species of which it is composed. Although the kind of prairie is distinguished by its dominant species, subdominant and secondary species are also important.

Forbs are always present and often abundant in prairie. They are an integral part of it. Often they are more conspicuous, although nearly always less important, than the grasses and are therefore designated as subdominants. Some are rare, others occur abundantly. By far the greatest number of species are composites and legumes, other plant families each furnishing only a small percentage. Most of the legumes are especially valuable as forage, although a few are poisonous. The list of mixed prairie forbs that are regularly eaten by livestock and hence decrease under close grazing is a long one; the list of those that are grazed but little and increase in pastures and ranges is much shorter. Forbs provide a valuable variety in the diet of livestock, they are especially rich in calcium and phosphorus, and cattle do better on mixed herbage than on grasses alone (Costello, 1942).

Native forbs, in conjunction with various kinds of grasses, have long been employed as indicators of the degree of severity of grazing. When supplemented by a knowledge of the presence of invading species and condition of the surface soil, they afford a reliable index of the degree of degeneration from climax prairie and of the productivity of range land.

Species of forbs greatly outnumber those of grasses. In the western third of true prairie, where as many as 250 species of plants have been found in a single square mile, 142 forbs occurred in at least 10 per cent of the nearly 200 prairies examined. The number of perennial forbs in mixed prairie is also large but smaller than in true prairie. Moreover, the abundance of the individuals is reduced because of decreased precipitation and drier soil.

That forbs are largely under the control of the grasses is shown in several ways. Most forbs are more deeply rooted than the grasses and many subsist mostly on water that has penetrated beyond the depth of the grass roots. Even in upland true prairie the rainfall furnishes enough water for both grasses and forbs. In mixed prairie westward the water content of soil becomes a limiting factor and forbs decrease gradually in number, size of individuals, and the extent of their groupings or societies.

A society is a community characterized by one or more subdominants (usually forbs in prairie), that is, species of a different life form from those of the regional dominants. The species of a society are very abundant over portions of an area already characterized by the dominants. In mixed prairie, as in grasslands generally, a society is usually conspicuous for only a part of the season. In mixed prairie, societies are smaller, less luxuriant, and less mixed than in the eastern grassland. They are more abundant in the eastern part of mixed prairie than under decreased rainfall westward. There they are better developed on lower slopes and in the valleys and decrease markedly on uplands. Societies of plants blooming in spring, summer, or autumn have much to do with the general appearance or aspect of the grassland at those times. Each seasonal aspect varies considerably over this extensive prairie land. The species concerned will enter into the description of the various plant communities and their utilization in grazing. Descriptions of representative, important, and widely distributed nongrasses of the mixed prairie follow.

RED FALSE MALLOW

Sphaeralcea coccinea (*Malvastrum coccineum*), also called scarlet globemallow, is a perennial plant with a woody base occurring singly or in societies. The much branched stems are 4 to 10 inches long (Fig. 11). They may stand erect but are usually decumbent. The plant is densely clothed with star-shaped silvery hairs. Leaves are dissected and the flowers salmon-colored to red. The strong taproot penetrates deeply before branching and thus competes little with the grasses for water. This mallow begins growth early and loses most of its leaves with the advent of drought, and the few that remain curl during the dry period. It is the most drought-resistant forb and actually increased considerably during the extended drought of the 1930's. The plant is readily eaten by livestock. It occurs throughout the Great Plains from southern Texas and New Mexico to the prairie provinces in Canada.

FIG. 11. (Upper) Red false mallow or scarlet globemallow (*Sphaeralcea coccinea*) and few-flowered psoralea or scurfpea (*Psoralea tenuiflora*) with heath aster beneath. (Lower) White prairie clover (*Petalostemum candidum*) (left) and purple prairie clover (*P. purpureum*).

PSORALEAS

Few-flowered psoralea (*Psoralea tenuiflora*), a tall legume, arises in spring from the crown of a thick, very deep taproot. The stem elongates several inches before the leafy, branched top is expanded. This legume, with a slender stem and trifoliate leaves, overtops the grasses and reaches a height of 2 to 3 feet (Fig. 11). The small purple flowers are grouped at the ends of the branches. It ranges from North Dakota and Montana to Texas and Arizona. Great abundance of these plants indicates deep soil moisture. In late summer the plant breaks off near the soil surface and becomes a tumbleweed. It has little grazing value but enriches the soil with nitrogen.

Silver-leaf psoralea (*Psoralea argophylla*) and prairie turnip (*P. esculenta*) are closely related species. The first often occurs in such abundance that it forms societies especially on lower slopes where water content of soil is greater than on higher land. On the drier level lands of the Dakotas the plants often occur as scattered individuals rather than in groups. The plants are of a bright leaden or silvery color. They are usually 12 or more inches in height when mature. They develop branched, open crowns several inches wide; beneath this crown the stem is bare. The small, blue flowers, produced in early summer, are not conspicuous. This plant is also a tumbleweed.

Prairie turnip, a less abundant legume of somewhat similar size, has a deep taproot with an enlarged portion a few inches below the soil surface. In mature plants this part is often nearly spherical in shape and 1 to 2 inches in diameter. It was a native food plant of greatest importance to the Indians, who dug it in quantity for the winter food supply.

Whether or not these species of *Psoralea* are eaten by livestock depends considerably upon earliness of grazing. The plants put forth rather thick stems which elongate to 3 to 5 inches before branching occurs. Later, as the stems become woody the leaves and tender branches may be grazed. These legumes do not occur, ordinarily, in ranges that have been long overgrazed.

PRAIRIE CLOVERS

White prairie clover (*Petalostemum candidum*) and purple prairie clover (*P. purpureum*) are both widely distributed and often abundant species of mixed prairie. These perennial legumes begin growth in spring with the grasses. The usual 1 to 3 stems per plant (but often many more) soon exceed the grasses in height. They are often about 2 feet high in July when blossoming begins (Fig. 11). The small flowers are densely clustered in conspicuous heads, which are 0.5 to more than 2 inches in length. They are held high above the level of the grasses on the ends of the branched tops. Both species have leaves composed of many leaflets. Leaves of white clover are larger but clothe the stem less thickly than the smaller leaves of plants with purple flowers. Both species are readily grazed in their earlier development before the stems become woody. The forage is very nutritious.

CUT-LEAVED GOLDENWEED

Haplopappus (Sideranthus) spinulosus is a composite with a wide distribution from Canada to Northern New Mexico (Fig. 12). It frequently forms extensive societies. Numerous erect or ascending stems of this forb arise from the crown of a strong woody taproot, which branches profusely, spreads widely, and absorbs at about the same soil levels (1 to 5 feet) as many grass roots. A height of 8 to 24 inches is attained. The plant is usually glandular. Tips of the abundant pinnately lobed leaves are slightly prickly. The abundant flowers, which occur in heads, are yellow. It has little or no forage value for cattle but is sometimes eaten by sheep.

HAIRY GOLDEN ASTER

Chrysopsis villosa is a common and conspicuous composite of plains and sand hills ranging widely throughout but seldom or never occurring in pure stands. It varies in height from 6 to 20 inches and usually has 8 to 14 erect or widely spreading unbranched stems (Fig. 12). It is a very long-lived perennial with a woody taproot many feet in depth. The alternately arranged leaves are 0.5 to 2 inches long but less than a fourth as wide and the whole plant feels rough. The flower heads are about an inch in width and are few or several near the ends of the branches. The golden-tinted ray flowers give this plant its name. This species, like most golden asters, is usually considered worthless for any type of livestock, but it is sometimes eaten by sheep.

FIG. 12. (Upper) Cut-leaved goldenweed (*Haplopappus spinulosus*) and smooth or Missouri goldenrod (*Solidago missouriensis*). (Lower) Hairy golden aster (*Chrysopsis villosa*) and blazing star (*Liatris punctata*) in fruit.

SMOOTH OR MISSOURI GOLDENROD

Solidago missouriensis is the most widely distributed and most abundant of the numerous goldenrods of true prairie. It also extends far over the Great Plains. It is a coarse perennial that spreads by means of stout rhizomes but in the plains climate reaches a height of only 8 to 16 inches (Fig. 12). The smooth stems are usually not clustered but form an open growth. Societies are rather definitely limited. The surface as well as the deeper soil is well occupied by roots and it competes strongly with the grasses for water and may detrimentally shade them as well. The golden-colored, flat or round-topped panicles present myriads of tiny yellow flowers after midsummer. The plant is grazed moderately in spring and early summer but often increases under grazing.

BLAZING STAR

Liatris punctata is a coarse, purple-flowered, perennial composite, well adapted by its long life, extensive root system, and harsh, narrow leaves to grow in dry soil. Few to numerous stems, rather densely clothed with long, narrow leaves, reach a height varying from 6 inches to more than 2 feet (Fig. 12). The flower heads are crowded into dense spikes at the ends of the stems, each separated from the one above by a small leaf or bract. Blossoming occurs in late summer or fall. This is one of the most drought resistant of the blazing stars. It ranges from Saskatchewan to Texas and New Mexico. It tends to disappear in overgrazed places, since it is regularly eaten when young.

FALSE BONESET

Kuhnia eupatorioides is widely scattered but seldom abundant. Sometimes it is several-stemmed and bush-like, but often stems are few. Growth begins in May, the new shoots arising from the enlarged crown on the strong, very deep and woody taproot. The leaves are long and narrow and a bush-like plant produces considerable shade. Flower heads are rather small but numerous and clustered at the ends of the much branched stems. Blooming of the very small yellowish-white flowers occurs in autumn. Then the plant becomes conspicuous as the hair-like structures (pappus) which float the wind-blown seeds expand to form a white head. The plant is readily grazed in spring and early summer.

BROOM SNAKEWEED

Gutierrezia sarothrae is a half-shrub with woody crown and stem bases. The numerous, green stems are herbaceous, erect, and mostly unbranched except at the top (Fig. 13). With their long narrow leaves, they form a bushy plant usually 6 to 18 inches but sometimes more than 2 feet high. It grows in a wide range of soils, except saline areas. Although widely distributed it is usually most abundant in localities with poorly disintegrated soil and in overgrazed ranges. Myriads of small, yellow flowerheads of this composite are crowded into clusters on the branched ends of the stems and rather completely cover this bushy perennial in late fall. The stems may remain green a long time, but upon drying they turn brown and remain standing throughout the winter. The woody taproot is deep and extremely well branched, especially in the surface soil. This plant is usually considered worthless or almost of no value for forage. When cattle are forced to eat broom snakeweed, the palatable grasses, according to Costello (1944b), are liable to serious damage.

WAVY-LEAVED THISTLE

Cirsium undulatum is conspicuous in mixed prairie and its short-grass disclimax (Fig. 13). Rosettes of large, spreading leaves cover the soil surface. The leaves are tipped with spines several millimeters in length and they are distinctly wavy margined. Because of the dense hairy covering they appear grayish green. The stem, also hairy, is 1 to 2.5 feet high but clothed with smaller leaves. The heads occur singly or 2 or 3 per plant at the end of the stem or its branches. This plant, while common, is rarely abundant; it has no value as forage.

SMALL SOAPWEED

Yucca glauca is a wide-spread and characteristic species of mixed prairie (Fig. 13). It grows on dry ridges and in coarse gravelly or sandy soil but is found widely spread in porous loam soil as well and is often most abundant in sand hills. The leaves of this large, coarse, evergreen plant arise from thick, woody, mostly underground stems, which vary in position from erect to horizontal. Since these stems produce numerous plants, soapweed usually occurs in groups. The leaves are one-fourth to one-half inch wide and 1 to 3 feet in length. They are pale in color, rigid, and

FIG. 13. (Upper) Wavy-leaved thistle (*Cirsium undulatum*) and fringed sage (*Artemisia frigida*). (Lower) Small soapweed (*Yucca glauca*) and broom snakeweed (*Gutierrezia sarothrae*).

sharp-pointed. They form a dense basal tuft from which they spread in all directions from vertical to horizontal.

In June several flower stalks extend well above the leaves and bear the abundant greenish-white flowers. It is then that the plants are most conspicuous, since the flower clusters are 1 to several feet long and the lily-like flowers are 1.5 to 3 inches broad. These develop upright, oblong, green, six-sided fruits, 2 to 3 inches long and about an inch thick. Later they dry, turn brown and split open, releasing the shiny black seeds. Young plants may be eaten to some extent and the flower clusters are palatable to cattle and sheep. Yucca, like cactus, is a range weed.

FRINGED SAGE

Artemisia frigida is a perennial half-shrub usually from 4 inches to nearly 2 feet tall (Fig. 13). It has a strong, deep, woody root with branches which absorb in the surface soil. A spreading woody base gives rise to additional roots and numerous annual stems. The lower portions of the stems are often woody. The small leaves are divided two or three times (pinnatifid) into several linear parts. They are ¼ to ½ inch long, silvery-hairy (as are also the young stems), and often densely crowded at the base. They have the odor of camphor or sage, though no *Artemisia* is a true sage. The flower heads are nearly spherical, small, but very numerous, with or without short stalks, and occur in nodding clusters along the ends of the stems.

Fringed sage not only occurs from Mexico and Arizona to Canada and Alaska but also in northern Asia and Europe as well. It is found abundantly on the high plains east of the Rocky Mountains. Extensive local areas occur from northern Arizona to southern Colorado, but it is well distributed over the mixed prairie from northern Nebraska and Colorado far into Canada and is often an outstanding species. This plant has many habitats but is perhaps most typically found on lighter, dry, porous soils.

Fringed sage is seldom grazed by cattle in spring or summer on the central and northern plains but furnishes good forage, especially for sheep, in late fall, winter, and early spring. It often increases rapidly where too heavy grazing occurs and is thus both an indicator of range condition and an excellent safeguard against soil erosion. It spread widely during the recent great cycle of drought.

CACTUS

Cacti constitute a definite and conspicuous portion of the vegetation of mixed prairie. There are 20 species in Colorado alone, ranging in size from the relatively small pincushion or ball cactus (*Neomammillaria*), which extends from the southwest to North Dakota, Montana and Canada, to the shrubby *Opuntia arborescens*, found northward to southern Colorado, with trunk up to 2.5 inches in diameter and a height of 6 to 7 feet. Cacti are represented principally by species of the pricklypear (*Opuntia*). Their sharp spines prevent their utilization by livestock and they occupy space where grasses could grow. During years favorable for their growth, they also compete successfully with grasses for more space.

Opuntia humifusa and *O. macrorhiza* are the dominant species in prairies of western Kansas; *O. polyacantha* is very abundant on the plains of eastern Colorado. The transition from abundance of one species to the other, of course, is gradual. All but the last depend almost entirely upon seed for propagation. Seed is often carried by rabbits and rodents. When green foliage is scarce, rabbits feed upon the succulent fruits containing the mature seed. These pass unharmed through the digestive tract and are frequently deposited at considerable distances from the parent plant. Sometimes rodents bury large quantities of cactus seed, some of which may never be eaten but may germinate under favorable conditions of moisture and temperature (Timmons and Wenger, 1940). Moreover, it is not uncommon for branches of cactus to be broken from the plant and carried for a distance on the hoofs of cattle. The pieces readily produce roots when in close contact with moist soil. In this way new plants are produced vegetatively.

Opuntia polyacantha propagates widely by rootsprouts (Harvey, 1936). Numerous plants were often found originating in this manner (Fig. 14). These small plants develop rapidly and in only a few years produce a large clump 1 or more feet in diameter. Sometimes several plants coalesce to form an enormous clump 8 to 12 feet in width. Some have been found which formed a continuous mat of branches for a distance of 30 feet.

FIG. 14. (From top downward) Pasture near Ellis, Kansas, in 1939, showing abundance of cactus in overgrazed short grass. Same view in 1943. Insects had killed nearly all of the cactus; only small fragments remained. Stages in development of cactus from seed. Plant on right is 1 year old. Roots of a pricklypear cactus (*Opuntia polyacantha*) showing numerous young plants.

Opuntia was generally most abundant on level or rolling land with clay loams or other heavy types of soil. Cactus increased greatly in abundance during the long cycle of drought, but decreased in a remarkable degree during the four years with more than normal precipitation (Fig. 14) (Costello, 1941). Increase in number and size of plants continued from 1933 until 1940. The plants were often so dense that not only were some ranges entirely worthless for grazing, but even jack rabbits avoided them. It sometimes grew so thickly that it was impossible for livestock to lie down on the range without coming in contact with this spiny plant (Costello, 1941, Turner and Costello, 1942). Its increase during drought was attributed primarily to little or no competition with a greatly depleted plant cover but also to the aridity of the atmosphere which was unfavorable to the development of insects which tend to destroy it. Especially damaging were the larvae of a moth (*Melitara dentata*) which consumed the pulp inside the stems (Cook, 1942).

Increased precipitation following drought not only was conducive to a dense growth of vegetation but also furnished a favorable environment for insects injurious to the cactus (Bugbee and Riegel, 1945). Vast numbers of cacti died and others were greatly injured. Their place was soon taken by the grass. Usually, however, some cacti remained, but the general population was greatly reduced, somewhat to the proportion in which it occurred before the dry cycle. Clumps of cacti did protect the native grasses growing in or near them, many of which produced seed when soil moisture was sufficient. Thus, there were local sources of seed supply on many ranges almost devoid of vegetation.

CHAPTER 4

Plant Communities in Western Kansas

THE GROUPING of the plains species as they occur in the different communities of the mixed prairie will now be described. Since the vegetation varies considerably in the different portions of the plains region, it will be expedient to consider various grassland types separately before discussing the general distribution of the vegetation of the entire area.

A large, centrally located, representative area of the High Plains occupies the western half of Kansas. Here the vegetation is much like that of eastern Colorado and western Nebraska. Moreover, similar vegetation, soils, and climatic conditions occur in western Oklahoma and northwestern Texas. The Kansas area has been studied continuously over a very long period of time. The vegetation was described before the great drought began in 1933; ecological studies were continued year after year throughout the drought; and the recovery and changes in vegetation have been followed to the present time. An acquaintance with the nature and behavior of the principal grasses and forbs of this region, uncomplicated with widespread differences in soil types, forms an excellent background for a survey of other portions of the Great Plains.[1]

CONDITIONS FOR DEVELOPMENT

The topography of western Kansas is generally level or only slightly rolling. Hilly land occurs especially in the breaks bordering streams and where the underlying rock outcrops. Exposures of the Fort Hays limestone, Smoky Hill chalk, and Ogallala deposits are examples. Thus, all of western Kansas is not a flat featureless plain. Parts of the High Plains here have an altitude of approximately 4,000 feet. The slope is eastward and an elevation of only about 1,500 feet occurs along its eastern edge in

[1] This chapter is largely an extension of the work of Albertson, Ecological Monographs 7:481–547, 1937.

central Kansas, where the wide smooth plain is replaced by prominent hills and valleys. The change from Chernozem or Black Earth soils to a narrow belt of Northern Dark Brown soils westward and then, in the extreme west, to Northern Brown soils is not demarked by the mixed-prairie vegetation, except as it gradually becomes somewhat shorter and more xeric with the change in precipitation from about 23 inches on its eastern border to 17 inches in the west.

This semiarid region has a frost-free growing season extending from about May 1 to mid-October. Occasional rains, high temperatures, low relative humidity, and a relatively high wind velocity are outstanding climatic features. In summer, hot drying winds often promote water loss from both vegetation and soil during continuous periods of several days. If sufficient rainfall in summer to supply the demands of growing vegetation is lacking, the air becomes dry and temperatures of both soil and air immediately increase. Often the daily maximum air temperature reaches 98° to 100° F., and relative humidity decreases to 20 or even 10 per cent. The prevailing southerly winds have a daily average of 5 to 13 miles per hour throughout the growing season and on certain days attain a velocity of 25 to 30 miles. Dust storms are not infrequent in spring and summer. Then the air may become so filled with dust that the sun is scarcely or not at all visible. Winters are mostly mild, but temperatures of −10° F. or lower sometimes prevail over several successive days. There is only light precipitation. Snowfall is ordinarily of slight value in replenishing soil moisture of uplands and exposed situations, since the wind sweeps most of the snow into ravines and other protected places. As is usual over the Great Plains, annual rainfall varies greatly from year to year as well as from place to place. Deficiencies of 7 to 10 inches below normal precipitation are not uncommon. These are the conditions under which the vegetation develops.

The vegetation is naturally grouped into three major communities or types, although there is some degree of intermixing. The relatively small areas of sandhills, originating mostly from materials blown from the valleys of the Arkansas and Cimarron Rivers, will be described elsewhere. By far the most extensive community is that of the nearly level uplands which receive their water supply directly from the rainfall. This is the home of the blue grama-buffalo grass community.

A second community, found widespread in valleys and ravines of hilly land and even on lower slopes where there is additional moisture from run-in water, is dominated by big bluestem (*Andropogon gerardi*) and certain other tall and mid grasses. Exceptions are places where strips or areas of shale occur. Here the soil derived from them may be so slowly permeable to water that short grass forms corresponding belts and patches of vegetation. The lower hillsides and ravines are usually covered with a thick mantle of eroded materials forming a deep soil.

The little bluestem (*Andropogon scoparius*) community is found throughout on rocky hillsides and steep protected slopes of rolling or rough lands and also in shallow ravines where the soil receives extra moisture from wind-blown snow and run-in water. Sometimes this type extends over the brows of hills, where the soil is porous, and even across the upper slopes to the level uplands. Although all three types of vegetation occur repeatedly where topography is sufficiently rolling to present the proper conditions of habitat, the short-grass type is by far the most extensive.

SHORT-GRASS COMMUNITY

A chief difference between the vegetation of mixed prairie and true prairie is the presence of a more or less continuous layer of short grass beneath the taller vegetation. This short-grass community derives its name from the almost continuous presence of such a layer of blue grama or buffalo grass or a mixture of the two grasses. Extensive quadratting in nearly all parts of the area before the great drought revealed that the short grasses rather regularly composed 70 to 90 per cent of the vegetation. The average percentage was about 80. Various other grasses, mostly mid grasses, and rather numerous forbs composed the remainder of the plant cover. These were typically scattered throughout. In the driest places they decreased to leave a nearly complete stand of low-growing grasses, but in more favorable habitats they thickened their stand until they formed the bulk of the vegetation or at least became locally the conspicuous feature of the landscape.

The foliage of the short grasses is 3 to 7 inches tall, but flower stalks may add several inches to their stature, especially that of blue grama. The color of the grass carpet is variable; it is dark green when moisture is plentiful, but various shades of yellowish green prevail in drought. During drought-dormancy the color becomes that of straw or a light gray, but when drought is broken the former green color is rapidly replaced by the new growth. Such changes occur almost every season. Indeed, the bleached light-gray color prevails during years of drought. The uniform, velvet-like plant cover conceals the whole of the soil surface in most places. This is known as the closed-mat type. In other places, especially slight depressions with "tight" soil, the open-mat type occurs where only 15 to 30 per cent of the soil surface is covered with vegetation even during years of normal rainfall.

Other low-growing grasses and sedges occur in the mats of short grasses. Examples are false buffalo grass (*Munroa squarrosa*), *Carex praegracilis* and penn sedge (*C. pennsylvanica*). Hairy grama (*Bouteloua hirsuta*) also occurs, especially on rough rocky ridges and on lighter types of soil.

False buffalo grass is a much branched annual which resembles buffalo grass only superficially. It forms mats 12 to 20 inches wide. The short, flat, stiff leaves occur in fascicles. It is common in recently disturbed places such as around hills of harvester ants, in prairie dog towns, and on drought-bared soil.

Sun sedge (*Carex heliophila*) is a grasslike, sod-forming perennial whose root system is almost confined to the surface foot. This low-growing sedge renews growth very early in spring, much before the short grasses. It flowers early and is thereafter inconspicuous despite its abundance.

Hairy grama is a perennial similar in stature and general appearance to blue grama, except that the leaves are very hairy, the rachis or stem of the spike is extended, and it grows in small bunches. It is common on thin, droughty soil and rocky hilltops and it is usually abundant in sandy soil (Fig. 9).

A more or less continuous upper story of taller grasses occurs almost everywhere. The mats and bunches of these are abundant in the most favorable sites and more scattered elsewhere. The taller grasses are conspicuous and give character to the landscape even where they are not abundant. The most common and abundant are side-oats grama (*Bouteloua curtipendula*), red three-awn (*Aristida longiseta*), purple three-awn (*A. purpurea*), little bluestem (*Andropogon scoparius*) and squirreltail (*Sitanion hystrix*) (Fig. 10).

Little bluestem is an erect, warm-season, perennial grass well adapted to thrive on uplands under a higher rainfall, such as occurs in true prairie. But in mixed prairie the bunches are not closely spaced except where soil moisture is plentiful. Growth in the compact bunches begins about mid-April. Stems are abundant and the slender leaves with prominent midveins are partially folded. A height of 6 to 15 inches is attained

FIG. 15. (Upper) Windmill grass (*Chloris verticillata*) common in disturbed places in the southern Great Plains. (Lower left) Little barley (*Hordeum pusillum*), an annual ranging from 3 to 15 inches in height and abundant in short-grass ranges. Foxtail barley (*Hordeum jubatum*) commonly found in moist depressions.

by mid-July and flower stalks which exceed the foliage in height are produced in late summer and fall.

Squirreltail is a small, perennial bunch grass, 6 to 18 inches tall and bright green in color. The flower head or spike is similar in appearance to that of wild-rye, with awns 2 to 3 inches long. The spike is 3 to 6 inches long and often partly enclosed in the upper leaf sheath. Unlike wild-rye, the main axis of the flower head is jointed; it breaks at the joints and shatters when ripe (Fig. 10).

Other important species are western wheatgrass (*Agropyron smithii*), which usually forms streaks or patches but may be scattered thinly in the short-grass sod. Sand dropseed (*Sporobolus cryptandrus*) may occur only sparingly but increases enormously during periods of drought. Bunches of Junegrass (*Koeleria cristata*) are much smaller. Even the tall, big bluestem (*Andropogon gerardi*) is found in the least xeric places. It has spread far more widely since the great drought. Desert saltgrass (*Distichlis stricta*) is found locally in and near saline soils often with alkali sacaton (*Sporobolus airoides*) and foxtail barley (*Hordeum jubatum*) (Fig. 15).

Tall dropseed is a perennial bunch grass. In mixed prairie it is usually only 1 to 2 feet tall on uplands. The stems are usually unbranched and the compact panicle, which is enclosed in the upper leaf sheath, varies from 3 to about 6 inches in length. Flowering occurs in autumn. The long fibrous leaves bleach white and, much frayed, may cling to the stem a second summer.

A notable difference in mixed prairie grasses, even the same species if it also occurs in true prairie, is the smaller or even dwarfed stature. Like other grasses that are found at home in the Great Plains, they bear the xeric impress of the drier climate.

Most of the forbs extend above the layer of short grasses. Cut-leaved goldenweed (*Haplopappus spinulosus*), broom snakeweed (*Gutierrezia sarothrae*), and velvety goldenrod (*Solidago mollis*) are characteristic western species which are 1.5 to 2 feet tall and illustrate the nature of the upper layer. False boneset (*Kuhnia eupatorioides*), blazing star (*Liatris punctata*), many-flowered aster (*Aster ericoides*) and smooth goldenrod (*Solidago missouriensis*) are in stature unlike the bushy plants of the same species 3 to 3.5 feet tall found in the true prairie. Yet they are of sufficient size to greatly overtop the short grasses. Gumweed (*Grindelia squarrosa*), wavy-leaved thistle (*Cirsium undulatum*) and few-flowered psoralea (*Psoralea tenuiflora*) are conspicuous even at a distance in the landscape (Fig. 16).

Other important plants are greenthread (*Thelesperma*) and scarlet gaura (*Gaura coccinea*). Prairie coneflower (*Ratibida columnifera*) is both conspicuous and abundant. Other species of first rank in mixed prairie are silky sophora (*Sophora sericea*), tooth-leaved primrose (*Oenothera serrulata*) and puccoon (*Lithospermum incisum*). Western ragweed (*Ambrosia psilostachya*) is a common plant and often occurs in large numbers. Likewise, Missouri milk vetch (*Astragalus missouriensis*) and woolly loco (*A. mollissimus*) are among the principal species of forbs. Many species of cacti also occur, frequently in considerable abundance.

An under layer of various annual plants is interspersed within and between the mats and bunches of short grasses. Although small of stature they are so abundant as to be both conspicuous and important. Chief among these are six-weeks fescue (*Festuca octoflora*), little barley (*Hordeum pusillum*), Pursh's plantain (*Plantago purshii*) and spinulose plantain (*P. spinulosa*). Of these the grasses are short-lived and while green in spring they soon ripen and are then conspicuous because of their yellowish color. Plantains, where abundant, produce patches of silvery gray. Numerous rosette and mat-forming plants are also common to abundant in the short-grass layer. The following are examples: prairie cat's-foot (*Antennaria neglecta*), yellow sheep sorrel (*Oxalis stricta*), heath aster (*Aster arenosus,* formerly *Leucelene ericoides*), rough penny-royal (*Hedeoma hispida*), Carolina anemone (*Anemone caroliniana*), Short's vetch (*Astragalus shortianus*) and ground plum (*Astragalus crassicarpus*). Red false mallow (*Sphaeralcea coccinea*) is a species of wide distribution and extreme drought resistance. Various species of small, low-growing cacti are not infrequent.

The vegetation of mixed prairie waxes and wanes and a single description at any one time can not tell the whole story.

DEVELOPMENT UNDERGROUND

In order to understand the ecological relations of one species to another and the general behavior of vegetation during good years and drought, a knowledge of the underground plant parts is necessary. The root extent of numerous grasses and forbs has been examined and will be described

FIG. 16. (Upper) Many-flowered aster (*Aster ericoides*) and stiff goldenrod (*Solidago rigida*). (Lower) Gumweed (*Grindelia squarrosa*) and lead plant (*Amorpha canescens*). These plants vary in height from 1.5 to 2.5 feet.

later. The usual depth of roots of blue grama and buffalo grass is about 4 feet. They are fine and extremely well branched. It is remarkable that grasses with such small stature are rooted so deeply; they are short only above ground. The roots of purple three-awn are also about 4 feet deep but somewhat coarser. The root system lacks the abundant, widely spreading laterals of the short grasses. Roots of both little bluestem and side-oats grama are quite similar in depth and lateral spread to those of purple three-awn; but little bluestem roots, especially, are much coarser. Many perennial forbs have strong, deep taproots which may absorb chiefly in the deeper soil. They sometimes extend downward 9 feet or more.

From the preceding data we must conclude that over western Kansas prairie plants, which are about 95 per cent long-lived species, are rooted rather deeply, a condition which, as will be shown, exists generally over the Great Plains.

BIG BLUESTEM COMMUNITY

The big bluestem community of true prairie extends westward far beyond its climatic limit in valleys and ravines and on lower slopes in the Great Plains. Here the increased soil moisture resulting from runoff water and wind-blown snow supplements the low precipitation, and the adjacent slopes decrease wind movement and water loss from both plants and soil. Thus, the deep soil of ravines and lowlands affords a habitat where the tall grasses can maintain complete possession. The short-grass layer can not develop here because of the deep shade. This community is most nearly like the true prairie, although the more arid climate dwarfs all of the plants. In the eastern plains this prairie community is common and well developed. It extends in a fragmentary manner throughout, being represented westward, except on rough terrain, as narrow bands and patches of vegetation in the valleys.

Big bluestem (*Andropogon gerardi*) is usually the most abundant species, frequently composing 50 to more than 90 per cent of the vegetation. Indian grass (*Sorghastrum nutans*) is a common associate, but, as in true prairie, it nearly always occurs sparingly. Two somewhat more mesic species are switchgrass (*Panicum virgatum*) and Canada wild-rye (*Elymus canadensis*). These, with Virginia wild-rye (*E. virginicus*) and a tall sedge (*Carex gravida*), are most abundant in the wetter places but they are often intermixed with the bluestem.

Big bluestem is one of the most widely spread and abundant species of true prairie. It is a warm-season grass with strong rhizomes which spread to form a sod. The roots are coarse but very deep. The dense, tall foliage casts so much shade that most other grasses can not thrive. This often results in nearly pure stands. Big bluestem grows throughout the summer and flower stalks are produced in late summer or autumn. In deep, moist, well aerated soil of true prairie, the foliage is often 4 to 6 feet high and the flowers stalks 7 to 10 feet. Here it furnishes very palatable forage or a yield of 2 to 4 tons per acre of excellent hay. In mixed-prairie big bluestem can withstand the dry climate only in areas receiving runoff water, except where it grows in sandy soil. Even here it attains only half or less of its stature eastward.

Indian grass is also a tall, coarse, warm-season grass. Its period of growth and its stature are very similar to those of big bluestem, with which it regularly associates eastward. The leaves have a somewhat more erect habit of growth. This grass is usually far less abundant than big bluestem and the large, golden panicles are very different from the forked finger-like racemes of big bluestem. Both grasses occur only as postclimax vegetation of mixed prairie.

Switchgrass and Canada wild-rye cover considerable areas of wet land in true prairie between communities of big bluestem on the drier side and sloughgrass or prairie cordgrass (*Spartina pectinata*) on the wetter one (Weaver, 1954). Switchgrass is a warm-season grass 4 to 7 feet tall (eastward) with coarse roots 6 to 10 feet deep. After a long period of uninterrupted growth, the large panicles appear in abundance (Weaver and Fitzpatrick, 1934).

Canada wild-rye is a relatively shallow-rooted, cool-season plant which increases in abundance northward. Established plants renew growth 2 to 3 weeks earlier than most warm-season grasses and thus furnish some early grazing. Foliage height varies (in true prairie) from 2 to 3 feet. The conspicuous heads (spikes) which appear in midsummer are held about a foot above the foliage level. Plants of Canada wild-rye and switchgrass are quite beyond their normal climate and consequently much dwarfed in mixed prairie, where neither grass is at all abundant. Unlike many grasses of the plains, these four tall grasses have little nutrient value after the plants have matured and dried.

Other associates of big bluestem in Kansas mixed prairie are western wheatgrass (*Agropyron smithii*) and side-oats grama (*Bouteloua curtipendula*). Tall dropseed (*Sporobolus asper*) is also abundant, especially the variety *hookeri*. Silver beardgrass (*Andropogon saccharoides*) and sand dropseed (*Sporobolus cryptandrus*) are common species usually of secondary importance.

Often the vegetation is mowed annually for hay, or the accumulated debris may be removed by fire. Then growth of the cool-season western wheatgrass, sedges, and wild-rye begins early. The tall grasses may develop so rapidly that early in June a foliage height of 8 to 10 inches is attained. During years with good rainfall the dense foliage of big bluestem may, by late July, reach a height of 2 feet; later the flower stalks may become 4 feet tall. Thus, throughout the growing season there is insufficient light for the development of an understory of short grass. Kentucky bluegrass (*Poa pratensis*), so characteristic eastward, is almost absent, but in its place plains bluegrass (*P. arida*) may be found. Where slight elevations occur and the usual cover is more open, blue grama and buffalo grass do appear. During a series of dry years the invasion of the short grasses is marked. The rate and degree of their forming an understory to the tall grasses vary almost directly with the dwarfing of the dominants, which determines the amount of light for growth of the smaller competitors.

Many coarse forbs common to true prairie occur in this type. Those usually found eastward are represented by Baldwin's ironweed (*Vernonia baldwini*), Maximilian's sunflower (*Helianthus maximiliani*), loosestrife (*Lythrum alatum*), licorice (*Glycyrrhiza lepidota*), dogbane (*Apocynum sibiricum*) and entire-leaved rosinweed (*Silphium integrifolium*). Other species more common to upland true prairie are also plentiful. Examples are many-flowered aster (*Aster ericoides*), lead plant (*Amorpha canescens*), Pitcher's sage (*Saliva pitcheri*), fleabane (*Erigeron strigosus*), false boneset (*Kuhnia eupatorioides*), stiff goldenrod (*Solidago rigida*), and few-flowered psoralea (*Psoralea tenuiflora*) (Fig. 16).

This lowland vegetation is characterized by tall sod-forming grasses with coarse stems intermixed with numerous forbs. Although the basal cover is not usually more than 8 to 13 per cent, yet the foliage is so dense that the light intensity in and beneath the vegetation is low, frequently only 2 to 5 per cent of full sunshine. Forbs of low stature, such as vetch (*Vicia americana*), purple poppymallow (*Callirrhoe involucrata*), and meadow violet (*Viola papilionacea*), develop rapidly and blossom and mature comparatively early. Conversely, plants of the mid and upper layers blossom in midsummer, and those which extend well above the shading grasses are often later in blooming. The preceding forbs, of course, may not all occur in any one area. Moreover, other species, not recorded here, may be found.

Roots of grasses of this community nearly all penetrate deeply. This is in accord with the usually deep soil and amounts of water sufficient to wet it deeply in sites where big bluestem dominates. Depths of the coarse roots of big bluestem of 5 to 6 feet are usual. The roots are much branched. Where the sod is dense, the root masses are continuous in the first 2 feet. Then they gradually become smaller and more finely branched. Roots of western wheatgrass are equally deep, and switchgrass sometimes attains depths of 7 or more feet. Although the roots of western wheatgrass are finer than those of big bluestem, those of switchgrass are much coarser. The roots of Canada wild-rye are much finer than those of any except wheatgrass; however, they are usually confined to the first 2.5 feet of soil. Forbs likewise extend their roots deeply, some to more than 10 feet.

LITTLE BLUESTEM COMMUNITY

This type occupies an intermediate position, as regards water relations, between the prairie of uplands and the tall grasses on low ground. It is characterized nearly everywhere in undisturbed habitats by little bluestem, which is also the highest ranking dominant of upland true prairie. It dominates steep hillsides characterized by bunch grasses and clothes porous thin soils of rocky slopes. Here, as on the eastern prairies, the landscape appears light green in spring and early summer but reddish brown as the grasses mature normally or are overtaken by drought. Thus, it is in the ravines of big bluestem and on the adjacent slopes of little bluestem that the brilliant autumnal colors are so pronounced. They contrast strikingly with the green, straw color or gray of most grasses prevalent on level uplands.

Little bluestem forms distinct bunches in drier places but, as in true prairie, a continuous sod-mat in wetter ones. Growth is renewed early in April. The mature bunches vary from 4 to 10 inches in width and occur usually 5 to 10 inches apart. Despite the openness of stand, this species is controlling. In the sod-mat type tufts are much smaller and so closely spaced that they form a nearly continuous sod. When fully developed, late in July, the foliage is 12 to 14 inches in height, a stature which is increased but little by the appearance of the flower stalks in late summer. During years of deficient moisture the height may be only one-third as great and neither flowering nor seed production occurs.

Chief grasses associated with the dominant are certain species common to the more mesic areas on the one side and those of the more xeric upland species on the other. On lower to mid-slopes especially, scattered plants to thick patches of big bluestem are often intermixed, as are also switchgrass and Indian grass. Even more common is side-oats grama, a much more xeric species than little bluestem. Tall dropseed of the hairy variety occurs, sometimes abundantly, in bunches 3 to 6 inches in diameter.

Squirreltail and a few other species may be intermixed, especially on the upper slopes. Buffalo grass finds this an uncongenial habitat; it is seldom present. Hairy grama, especially, and less often blue grama may form tufts or small bunches. No continuous layer of short grasses is developed.

A greater number of species of forbs occurs in this intermediate habitat than in either of the preceding. More favorable soil moisture prevails here than in the blue grama-buffalo grass type, and the shade is far less dense than under the tall grasses. Consequently societies are almost as well developed as in upland true prairie where three rather distinct layers occur. Skullcap (*Scutellaria resinosa*), rough pennyroyal (*Hedeoma hispida*) and whitlow-wort (*Paronychia jamesii*) are examples of forbs found with hairy grama and blue grama in the understory. The middle layer, composed largely of little bluestem, side-oats grama and tall dropseed, has relatively fewer forbs. But extending above the level of the mid grasses are few-flowered psoralea (*Psoralea tenuiflora*), purple coneflower (*Echinacea angustifolia*), lead plant (*Amorpha canescens*) and slender indigo bush (*Dalea enneandra*) (Fig. 17). Western ragweed (*Ambrosia psilostachya*), narrow-leaved stenosiphon (*Stenosiphon linifolius*), small soapweed (*Yucca glauca*) and small-flowered gaura (*Gaura parviflora*) are other characteristic species of the upper layer. To this list of prominent species should be added tooth-leaved primrose (*Oenothera serrulata*), Fremont's leather-flower (*Clematis fremontii*), western wallflower (*Erysimum asperum*) and blazing star (*Liatris punctata*).

The plant population is so dense that the normal foliage cover is often

80 to 100 per cent. By midsummer the general level of the vegetation is 12 to 16 inches high. On thin soils, as may occur on the brows of hills, it is much less. Basal cover ranges from 20 to 50 per cent, but, as will be shown, it varies greatly with the occurrence of drought.

Where the slopes change abruptly to level upland, the area of transition (ecotone) between the little bluestem and the short grass type is narrow. Where the upper slope is long and gentle, little bluestem during years of good rainfall may extend its community far into the area claimed by shortgrass when deficient rainfall occurs. Here then is an area repeatedly lost or regained by either community depending upon the climatic cycle. Little bluestem gains by shading, blue grama and buffalo grass by resistance to drought.

In accord with the location of the little bluestem community on soils where rainfall penetrates readily or where soil moisture is supplemented by run-in water or by hillside seepage, water content of soil is greater here than on the level land. Root penetration, while not so deep as that of the tall grasses, is often deeper than it is in the short-grass type. On hillsides with rock outcrops, roots of various plants may absorb water and nutrients deeply from sands and clay occurring in the crevices and cavities of the decaying rocks. Here the courses of the roots are often devious and tortuous. Conversely, small, early blooming plants, commonly limited to upper slopes and brows of hills, may extend only a foot in the shallow, rocky soil. Ragwort (*Senecio plattensis*) and tall ditaxis (*Ditaxis mercurialina*) are examples (Fig. 17). Albertson (1937) has made extensive studies near Hays, Kansas. Trenches 3 to 13 feet deep and aggregating nearly 400 feet in length were excavated, often through the limestone rock, to study the relations of underground plant parts.

Albertson (1937) studied the detailed structure of the several communities of mixed-prairie, the causes for their distribution, and the interrelations of the plants both above and below ground. He also measured the intensity of the edaphic and aerial environmental factors. This study was made near Hays during 1933–1936. A large winding ravine with numerous tributaries extended across a 750-acre prairie. Broad strips of nearly level tableland occurred between the ravines. The upland sloped gently to the brows of the hills; there the descent was commonly steep to the bottoms of the ravines and fairly level land below. The Chernozem soil overlying the Fort Hays limestone on the rounded hilltops and tablelands

FIG. 17. (Upper) Small plants of narrow-leaved four-o'clock (*Mirabilis linearis*), prairie rose (*Rosa suffulta*) and a legume, slender indigo bush (*Dalea enneandra*). (Lower) Prairie ragwort (*Senecio plattensis*) with yellow flowers and woolly loco (*Astragalus mollissimus*) with purple blossoms early in summer.

was usually several feet deep. The ravine bottoms and soils were likewise deep and fertile. Thin, rocky soils clothed the limestone outcrops and their upper slopes.

The dark, silty clay loam of the uplands is a fine-textured, deep, fertile, residual soil with a mature profile. A distinct lime layer occurred at 25 to 38 inches and indicated the usual depth of soil moisture penetration. These uplands were characterized by a fine stand of short grasses, buffalo grass and blue grama occurring in about equal abundance, which composed approximately 80 per cent of the vegetation. Bunches of little bluestem and three-awn were scattered thinly in places but abundantly where the water supply was more plentiful. Side-oats grama, western wheatgrass and squirreltail were of lesser abundance but common.

On the slopes, the immature, dark gray, granular, porous soil contained many limestone fragments. Depth varied from a few inches to 2 feet. Plants were not rooted in this soil only but also in the underlying limestone which contained myriads of large fissures and crevices filled with sandy clay. On these sites little bluestem was dominant. Its distribution was largely determined by the shallow depth of soil above the underlying limestone. On the upper slope with a gradually deepening soil it became less abundant and was almost replaced by the short grasses. From the lower slopes with deeper soil of greater water content, big bluestem, switchgrass, and side-oats grama extended as minor components of the little bluestem type some distance up the slopes. Their place was taken nearer the brows of the hills by the more xeric hairy tall dropseed, hairy grama and blue grama.

Soil of the lowland was many feet in depth. It was fertile, dark colored, granular and porous, and contained much silt and clay. Fragments of limestone were common and layers of finely broken limestone pebbles were present at a depth of about 4 feet. Such sites were characterized by several tall and mid grasses and numerous tall coarse herbs, most of which occur eastward in true prairie. The most abundant grass was big bluestem, but switchgrass, side-oats grama, tall dropseed and western wheatgrass were important species.

Precipitation was extremely variable. During six years preceding the study it averaged 5 inches above the mean of 22.8 inches, but during the following years (1933–1935) it was 7.5 inches below the average.

The mature, fine-textured, silty clay loam soils of the upland are a part of the western residual soil region of Kansas. The A horizon of granular, platy and columnar soil was 20 inches deep. The B horizon extended 18 inches deeper; and the massive or C horizon, much deeper to the underlying limestone.

Experiments showed that water percolated most rapidly in the hillside soils under little bluestem, less rapidly in the lowland soil, and slowest in the level soils of the upland. Amounts of water in inches entering the several soils during a period of 9 hours were, in the preceding order, 14.5, 8.3, and 6, respectively. The slow rate of percolation in soils covered with short grass resulted in high runoff. The soils on hillsides and especially on the lowland benefited from this water loss from the uplands.

Weekly soil sampling showed a close correlation between water content and precipitation. There was often no water available (that is water above the hygroscopic coefficient) in the surface foot of short-grass soil. During several extended periods each year this condition prevailed to a depth of 3 to 6 feet. The grasses underwent corresponding periods of dormancy. Periods of extreme water shortage also occurred in the shallow soils beneath little bluestem. Here the deeply rooted vegetation survived by absorbing from soil in the crevices and pockets of the rock. Water was nearly always available in the big bluestem habitat except one year when none was present at any depth to 5 feet, but this deficiency was of short duration.

Composition and structure of the vegetation corresponded closely with that already described for the general region. In fact the Hays area was selected as typically representative of the general Kansas territory only after careful consideration by both authors. Here representative areas of mixed prairie, ungrazed at least for 15 to 20 years, were examined. They presented repeatedly the three great types or communities. The thorough study of root systems in both soil and rock crevices is classic. It was here that the distribution of the three communities of mixed prairie in Kansas was first clearly correlated with topography and especially with the soil environment. Available water content of the soil was found to be the controlling factor in plant development.

The ecological classification of the preceding plant communities may be of interest to students. The grassland formation is made up of several associations including true prairie, mixed prairie, Palouse prairie and others. An association is composed of various areas controlled by a single dominant (as little bluestem in true prairie) or by a group of two or more dominants (as needle-and-thread and blue grama in mixed prairie). The first is termed a consociation, the second a faciation. These terms apply only to climax vegetation. Only one grouping (faciation) of climax dominants, blue grama and buffalo grass, has been described. The mid grasses have largely lost their dominance because of grazing. Hence, the chief climax unit remaining in this disturbed climax is the blue grama-buffalo grass faciation.

Postclimax vegetation is denoted as a facies if the dominants are two or more in number but a consocies if a single dominant composes most of the vegetation. Thus, the little bluestem community which occurs regularly on uplands in true prairie but forms only postclimax communities in mixed prairie is there designated as a little bluestem consocies. Likewise in mixed prairie big bluestem forms a postclimax consocies. A complete classification of North American vegetation is given in "Plant Ecology" (Weaver and Clements, 1938).

CHAPTER 5

Beginning of the Great Drought

A BRIEF statement of the breaking or grazing of vast areas of western Kansas grasslands will furnish a proper background for an understanding of the tragic story of the drought.[1] When the pioneers came from the East to make new homes on the Great Plains, they found a dense cover of native vegetation. It was disturbed only by buffaloes, prairie dogs, other plains animals, Indians, and prairie fires. The Federal Government required that a certain amount of land be broken and put under cultivation, whether the land was obtained as a homestead or as a timber claim.

BREAKING THE PRAIRIE

The practice of the settlers was to break up a small tract of the prairie on which they could grow enough winter feed to sustain their cattle, horses, and other animals. The remainder of the land was kept for pasture. Frequently the cultivated fields were cropped for a number of years and then abandoned to return to native prairie. Then the pioneers broke up and put under cultivation other similar areas.

As the number of settlers increased and the demand for small grains, corn and sorghum became greater, additional acres were put under the plow. Agriculture approached stability with the growing of grain and forage crops incidental to the production of livestock. With the introduction of labor-saving machinery, it became possible for more land to be cultivated with even less manpower. This stimulated more extensive crop production. Even with the increased demands for farm products the native grassland still remained of great importance to the farmer who kept livestock to increase his income.

---

[1] Materials in this and the following chapter are condensed from portions of studies by Weaver and Albertson, Ecology 17:567–639, 1936 and Ecological Monographs 12: 23–51, 1942. Seven of the 83 illustrations have been re-used.

The native grasslands of the Great Plains region are exceedingly important to the economic well-being of the people of the Midwest. In 1935 it was estimated that there were approximately 100,000,000 acres of land under cultivation, as compared with 175,000,000 that remained unbroken (Great Plains Committee, 1936).

The high prices of wheat during and following the first World War caused many farmers, as well as wheat-farming corporations, to break vast areas in western Kansas. In fact, immense areas that had previously been regarded as "too risky" for growing wheat were broken for crop production. It was estimated that 18,000,000 acres were under cultivation. In comparison, only 11,000,000 acres of grassland remained. Until about 1930, there was an unlimited market for wheat. Many farmers amassed considerable wealth through an extensive use of this one-crop system.

At the beginning of the 1930's, however, the wheat market reached the saturation point and the price was reduced to less than 30 cents per bushel. Even at this low price it was impossible to dispose of any great quantity. Another factor that changed the outlook of the farmers was the period of deficient rainfall that occurred early in the 1930's. As a consequence of this drought, it was impossible to produce adequate crops; hence, there was an increased need for more grassland. Since the amount of the range land could not be increased in proportion to the demand, overgrazing resulted. This, in turn, led to a breakdown of the prairies. As cultivation continued despite the decreased rainfall, the soil became more pulverized, less porous, and more susceptible to erosion by both wind and water. Runoff was increased manyfold, and the rate of erosion was accelerated enormously. One dashing shower sometimes removed as much as an inch of fertile soil, an amount which is probably produced naturally only over a period of more than a hundred years (McDonald, 1938; Bennett, 1939). Dust storms which have occurred on the Great Plains since 1934 have been of unprecedented extent and intensity (Brandon and Kezer, 1936).

Just when the raising of cultivated crops became less important and the need for good pastures much more so, the combined effects of drought, dust and overgrazing reduced the yield of vast areas of grasslands in the Great Plains region to almost nil.

The year 1933 marked the beginning of a period of great desiccation in the mid-continental grasslands. The most severe drought ever recorded swept over the Great Plains, the vegetation of western Kansas receiving its full impact. An intimate knowledge of this vegetation made it possible to follow the drought effects very closely.

Despite a series of the worst dust storms in the history of Kansas during late winter and spring of 1935, vegetation made an excellent early growth. But this was followed by severe wilting and frequently by death of plants. As will be shown, the vegetation was greatly modified throughout the area, but the exact changes in the environment and the degree of injury in a selected representative place will first be given.

ENVIRONMENT IN SOIL AND AIR

The mean annual precipitation at Hays (formerly Fort Hays), Kansas, was approximately 23 inches over a period of two-thirds of a century. Summer was the rainy season with 3 to 3.5 inches of rain falling each month from May to September. Six years preceding 1933 had a mean annual precipitation of nearly 5 inches above the average. The vegetation was, consequently, in a thriving condition. During the early years of drought there was a deficiency of precipitation of more than 7 inches below the mean.

A moist spring in 1933 was followed by drought in June and low rainfall throughout the hot summer. Spring in 1934 was extremely dry; a single heavy rain occurred in June, otherwise rainfall was dissipated in light showers. Even August had a single rainy period but then only the surface inch or two of the soil was moist. Late fall and winter were extremely dry. In fact, from mid-October to May 11 of 1935 there was no efficient precipitation. Then the drought was temporarily broken by good, well distributed showers during May and June. These were followed by seven weeks of severe drought and not until September was the soil again moistened. A clear picture of water relations was obtained from weekly samples of the soil to a depth of 5 feet.

The June drought (1933) resulted in complete exhaustion of water available for growth to a depth of 1 to 3 feet in the deep, silty clay loam soil which was covered with short-grass vegetation. Although the deeper subsoil retained 1 to 5 per cent available moisture, only intermittently was water available in the surface foot. By June, 1934, water was unavailable to plants at all depths except in the surface inches. Then the surface foot was supplied with a low water content for 3 weeks; a small percentage occurred in the second foot but for a shorter period. Moisture was fairly abundant in the surface foot from mid-May to late June in 1935. Otherwise none was available at any depth until September.

In the big bluestem habitat soil moisture was available to 6 feet in depth, although at some periods in small amounts during the growing season of 1933 and 1934. A slight exception occurred in the surface layer. But in the second week of July (1934) water became deficient in the surface 6 inches; later this depletion extended to a depth of a foot. Two weeks later no water was available to 3 feet in depth. Late in August and until September soil moisture became nonavailable at all depths, except that intermittently local showers moistened the surface soil.

The little bluestem type in this area occupied a rocky slope with only two feet of soil overlying much-decayed Fort Hays limestone. Here periods with dry soil were somewhat intermediate between conditions in the two preceding types. Examination showed that little bluestem drew upon soil moisture stored in the clay and sand filling the pockets and crevices of the rocks to a depth of 3 feet. Roots of many other plants extended to 4 feet.

Continuous records of air temperatures 4 inches above the soil surface and soil temperatures 3 inches below the surface revealed unusually adverse conditions for vegetation in the short-grass community. From late June to late August of 1934 the average day temperatures varied from 86° to 97° F. and average daily maximum temperatures by weeks ranged between 96° and 111°. Average daily soil temperatures were at first less but finally exceeded those of air temperature. The bare surface soil not infrequently attained temperatures of 140° to 150°. Hot, desiccating winds of high velocity were common during the summer.

Relative humidity regularly decreased to 25–15 per cent and it was often 10 per cent or less. The high temperatures and low humidity greatly accelerated water losses by transpiration as well as by evaporation from the surface soil. These losses from sods of various types of vegetation were ascertained. Typical blocks of sod, one square foot in area and 18 inches deep were placed in heavy, cylindrical, metal containers of 1.5 cubic feet capacity. This was done without disturbing the vegetation or the structure of the soil. The surface of the containers was placed even with the surface of the soil. The short grasses lost 8 to 12 pounds of water per week in their habitat; little bluestem, 10 to 14 pounds in its community; and big bluestem, 11 to 12 pounds on the lowland.

These were the conditions to which vegetation was subjected in early drought in the best watered (eastern) part of the Great Plains. Drought, as will be shown, was far more effective in damaging the vegetation under normally lower rainfall of 15 to 17 inches westward.

EFFECTS ON VEGETATION

Effects of drought upon the cover of vegetation were ascertained from 160 previously established, permanent quadrats and by continued observations and estimates over a large area. The pantograph-chart method was used in mapping the vegetation. Quadrats which record the amount of vegetation in a locality from year to year show exactly what changes take place. They are especially valuable when the results from a large number are averaged. Frequent and extensive studies over large areas, with a careful record of the conditions observed, are also imperative.

The best short-grass cover revealed losses of only 10 to 20 per cent, although certain native forbs disappeared entirely. In the open-mat type, characteristic of less favorable soil, losses were somewhat higher in 1934. Some of this loss was replaced the next year. Even where the early losses greatly depleted the stand, numerous small groups of living plants remained. Buffalo grass put forth stolons which rapidly and rather completely reclaimed the area in May and June of 1935. From 20 to 95 per cent of this new growth was destroyed by the ensuing drought; the percentage varied with the available water supply.

The development of new stolons of buffalo grass began almost immediately following the rains. When they became 6 to 8 inches long, they were observed to increase their length at the remarkable rate of .6 inch per day. This rapid growth was soon retarded by drying soil. Then the process of dying back began. The new roots were not only more numerous but also nearly twice as long on the nodes that had not died as on those on some distant parts of the stolons; these had succumbed to drought.

Blue grama made only small gains despite the seven-week period for growth in 1935, nor were its losses great during the following drought. This behavior indicated that buffalo grass is less drought resistant than blue grama. However, any remaining plants of buffalo grass spread rapidly to re-establish a new sod. Blue grama is far more stable and regains its losses only slowly. This, as we shall see, was one of the most fundamental lessons learned from the seven-year drought.

Compared with other vegetation, seasonal variations in basal cover were most extreme in the short-grass type. For example, reduction from 80 per cent to 15 per cent basal cover occurred during 1934, but cover increased to 80 per cent by the next summer. This was followed by a decrease to 25 per cent cover by autumn. Burial under 0.5 to 1.5 inches of dust often killed the short grasses (Fig. 18).

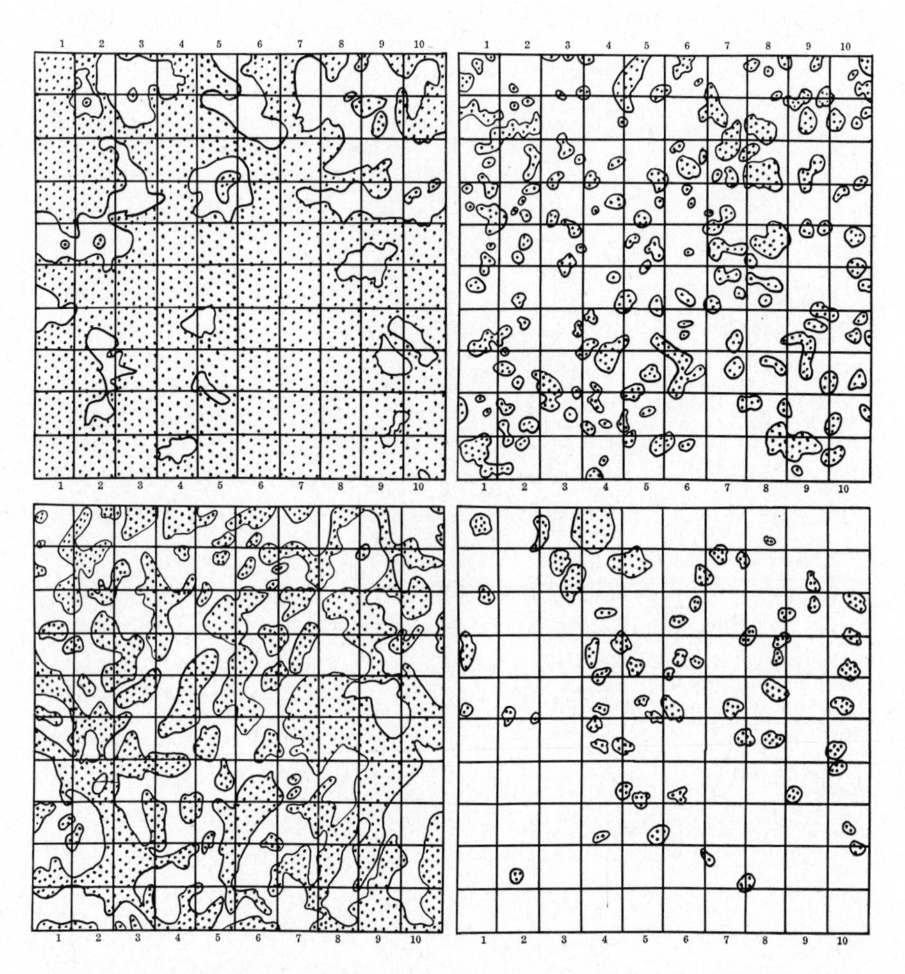

FIG. 18. (Upper) Quadrat (one square meter) in typical closed-mat type (dotted) in the blue grama-buffalo grass community showing change in cover due to drought. The basal area in 1934 (left) was 77 per cent, but this was reduced to 17 per cent (right) by the spring of 1935. (Lower) Quadrat in typical open-mat type of the short-grass community showing changes in vegetation resulting from drought. In 1932 (left) the basal cover was 43 per cent. This was reduced to about 9 per cent following the drought of 1934.

Purple three-awn and red three-awn were well established in the short-grass habitat before the drought. Although their basal cover was not large plants were rather uniformly scattered throughout. They sustained an average loss of 55 per cent (Fig. 19). Side-oats grama was often replaced by short-grasses, especially under moderate grazing (Fig. 20).

Little bluestem suffered heavy losses. These were greater where the plants grew in deep soil, which became dry, than where the roots extended into clay pockets in the underlying limestone. Average losses in the two

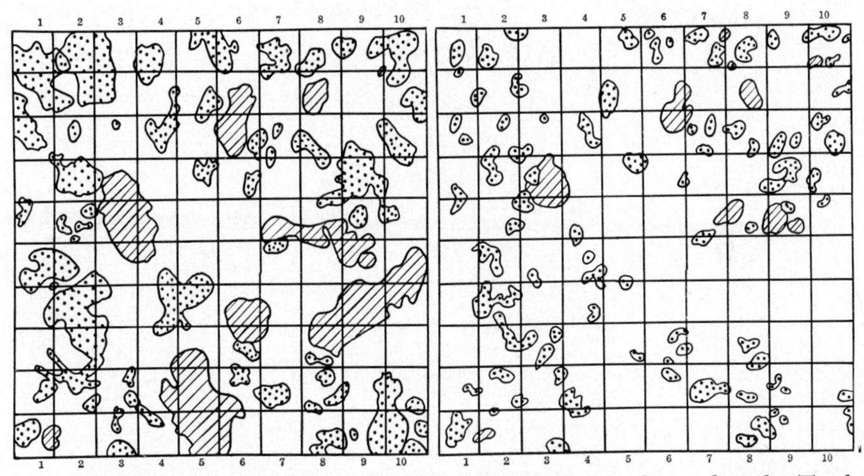

FIG. 19. (Left) Quadrat showing death of three-awn grasses due to drought. Total cover of vegetation in June, 1935, including dead three-awn (left hatch) and short grasses (dotted areas). (Right) Same quadrat on same day with all dead grasses removed. Three-awn grasses were reduced from 9 to 2 per cent, the short grasses from 21 to 11 per cent.

locations were 88 and 52 per cent, respectively. They occurred especially during the drought of the second and third year when the water in the pockets and crevices of the rocks was exhausted. Vegetation was replaced to some extent by big bluestem, whose roots extended somewhat deeper, and by the more xeric side-oats grama and tall dropseed, in places where these grasses formed a part of the original cover. However, much of the soil surface was left bare (Fig. 20). In the transitional area between little bluestem and short-grass communities, the taller grasses had spread far outward during the series of good years. Here little bluestem nearly all died and much of the area was taken over by buffalo grass.

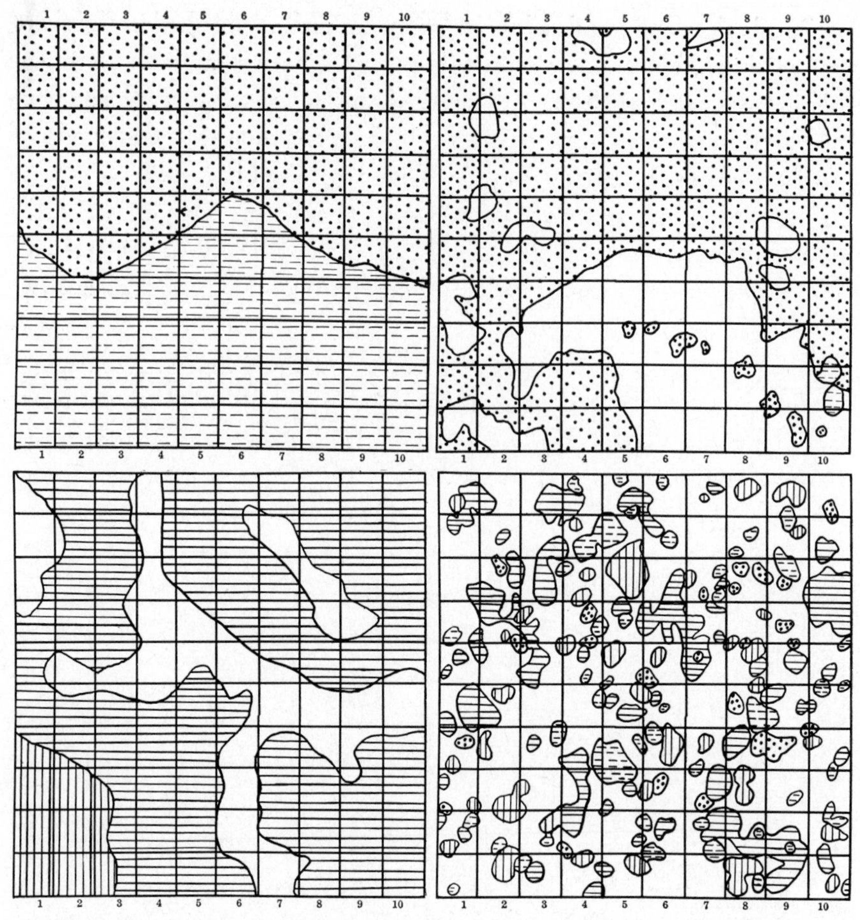

FIG. 20. (Upper) Quadrat showing replacement of side-oats grama (broken lines) by buffalo grass and blue grama (dotted areas). In 1933 (left) 54 per cent of the quadrat was covered with short grasses, but 74 per cent (right) in 1935. Less than 1 per cent of side-oats grama remained. (Lower) Quadrat in ungrazed, typical little bluestem community on hillside in 1932, and (on right) in 1935. Little bluestem (horizontal lines) decreased from 68 to 14 per cent; big bluestem (vertical lines) decreased greatly and then regained its 8 per cent area; short grasses (dotted areas) and side-oats grama (broken lines) invaded.

In the big bluestem community effects of drought had not become apparent in 1933. By 1935 there had been considerable shifting in the amounts of the different species but no loss in basal cover had been sustained. Earlier quadrat studies in several different lowland prairies had shown that big bluestem constituted about 75 per cent of the vegetation.

Fifteen per cent was added to the grass population by side-oats grama, scattered rather uniformly throughout, western wheatgrass, confined largely to the bases of slopes, and tall dropseed, in complete possession of a few small local areas. The remaining 10 per cent consisted of 6 minor species. The amount of big bluestem had decreased to 50 per cent by 1935. This loss, however, was compensated for by wider distribution and considerable increases in side-oats grama, tall dropseed and western wheatgrass. Certain other grasses also gained slightly. The forb population, however, remained practically unchanged except that many-flowered aster made very definite gains along the borders in the driest areas.

Thirty-one different areas of grassland extending across west-central Kansas were studied in 1934 and 1935. Percentage of soil surface occupied was compared with the predrought cover, as based upon previous examinations and comparisons with similar prairies at Hays. Ungrazed prairies of south-central Kansas lost 60 per cent of their basal cover; various types moderately grazed decreased 36 per cent; and others heavily grazed lost 74 per cent. Losses in the same sequence in north-central Kansas were 50, 54, and 91 per cent. Conditions were most severe in the west-central part where ungrazed prairie lost but 5 per cent of its predrought cover; moderately grazed areas, 72 per cent; and heavily grazed ones, 91 per cent. Deficient soil moisture, coupled with extremely high temperatures and low humidities and supplemented by wind and burial by dust, was the cause of the destruction.

Where the prairies were located near cultivated fields, a layer of dust 0.5 to 4 inches in depth commonly covered the vegetation. The depth often varied directly with the density of the plant cover, being greatest where it was heavy. In many places where weeds had blown into the barbed wire fences and formed a barrier to wind-blown dust, great drifts accumulated over the fences and extended outward over the grassland. Where the new deposit was more than an inch in thickness loss of vegetation was practically complete. Farther out in the prairie, deep drifts of dust accumulated over the bunches of grass and caused their death. Where the ground was nearly bare and the living portions of the grass remnants were below or just above the surface of the soil, the layer of dust was comparatively thin and losses caused directly by it were usually small. Dust, even from distant fields, carried with it myriads of seeds of the weeds common to cultivated land. Seeds of Russian thistle (*Salsola kali*), witchgrass

(*Panicum capillare*) and others scattered far by plants tumbling before the wind were even more widely distributed during the "black blizzards."

Certain grasses found regularly in the prairies of western Kansas during preceding years were so adversely affected by the drought that during 1934–35 they occurred only occasionally. Chief among these were prairie wedgegrass (*Sphenopholis obtusata*), Junegrass (*Koeleria cristata*), plains bluegrass (*Poa arida*), Scribner's panic grass (*Panicum scribnerianum*), purple three-awn (*Aristida purpurea*), six-weeks fescue (*Festuca octoflora*) and water foxtail (*Alopecurus geniculatus*).

The following forbs, although not affected to the same extent by the drought, are examples of plants that were either partially or completely eliminated from the prairies:

Milfoil
Achillea lanulosa
Western ragweed
Ambrosia psilostachya
Carolina anemone
Anemone caroliniana
Prairie cat's-foot
Antennaria neglecta
Missouri milk vetch
Astragalus missouriensis
Short's vetch
Astragalus shortianus
Daisy fleabane
Erigeron strigosus
Crazyweed
Oxytropis lambertii
White milkwort
Polygala alba
Silver-leaf psoralea
Psoralea argophylla
Silky sophora
Sophora sericea
Spermolepis
Spermolepis inermis

The decrease in basal cover occasioned by the death of the grasses and forbs resulted in an increase in the number of certain native forbs of greater drought resistance. Those that spread most conspicuously were the following: many-flowered aster (*Aster ericoides*), evax (*Evax prolifera*), purple coneflower (*Echinacea angustifolia*), broom snakeweed (*Gutierrezia sarothrae*), red false mallow (*Sphaeralcea coccinea*), yellow sheep sorrel (*Oxalis stricta*), Pursh's plantain (*Plantago purshii*), spinulose plantain (*P. spinulosa*), whorled milkwort (*Polygala verticillata*), ground cherry (*Physalis lobata*), velvety goldenrod (*Solidago mollis*) and large bracted vervain (*Verbena bracteata*).

Seeds of ruderals had been spread widely by the wind over the whole Midwest. Germination in the bared areas was prompt upon the advent of rain. Consequently most prairies and pastures were literally covered with seedlings of species of lamb's quarters (*Chenopodium*) and pigweed

(*Amaranthus*), stinkgrass (*Eragrostis cilianensis*), witchgrass (*Panicum capillare*), green bristlegrass (*Setaria viridis*), buffalo bur (*Solanum rostratum*), peppergrass (*Lepidium densiflorum*), Russian thistle (*Salsola kali*), downy chess (*Bromus tectorum*) and little barley (*Hordeum pusillum*).

So abundant were the weeds that the prairies often appeared more like abandoned fields than grassland. The tallest weeds had rather completely covered the ground, but the summer drought of 1935 had killed most of them before they were fully grown. The most conspicuous species were Russian thistle and buffalo bur. Stinkgrass and witchgrass often formed a larger percentage of the ground cover than did the native short grasses. In sandy soil the weedy population was even better developed. Large areas were often completely occupied by common sunflower (*Helianthus annuus*), lamb's quarters and pigweeds, buffalo bur and Russian thistle.

CHAPTER 6

Changes in Vegetation in Drought

MIXED PRAIRIE vegetation of western Kansas was studied through seven years of continuous drought, 1933 to 1939, inclusive. Investigations were centered at Hays but studies were made in many counties to the Colorado border. Water content of soil was determined weekly during the growing season and a record of aerial environmental factors was obtained. Reactions of the vegetation were recorded year by year in scores of permanent, widely distributed quadrats and by extensive field studies.

Moderately grazed and ungrazed prairies were in excellent condition in 1933 because of the very favorable six-year period just preceding when the average annual precipitation (27.8 in. at Hays) was approximately 5 inches above average. Other environmental factors were likewise more conducive than usual to the growth of native prairie plants. Prairies moderately grazed were in excellent condition but some that were ungrazed and unmowed accumulated so much debris that the basal cover afforded by living plants was greatly reduced. During wet years the more mesic vegetation advanced up the slopes from the moist ravines and lowlands to the more xeric hillsides and tablelands. Big bluestem for example, which normally grows in ravines, was found in considerable quantities in depressions on the nearly level uplands in 1932, at the end of the wet period. Little bluestem and three-awn grasses likewise spread from their strongholds on the hillsides into the short-grass areas of the level uplands. Scattered bunches of these occurred widely throughout the short-grass type. In general, plant production was somewhat above normal and this luxuriance of growth made the vegetation more susceptible to the drought that followed.

ENVIRONMENT DURING DROUGHT

Annual precipitation during each of the drought years was below average and during four of the seven years nearly 7 inches below. Most of this deficit occurred during the growing season. There were periods of 5 to 7 weeks in summer with practically no rainfall. An accumulated deficit of 6.7 inches in 1933 increased to 21.6 in 1936 and to 34.5 inches in 1939. The damaging effect of insufficient precipitation was intensified by the fact that during the warm season when soil moisture was most essential to growth precipitation was often much less than average. These conditions were general over western Kansas, where at many stations the normal annual precipitation was only 15 to 17 inches.

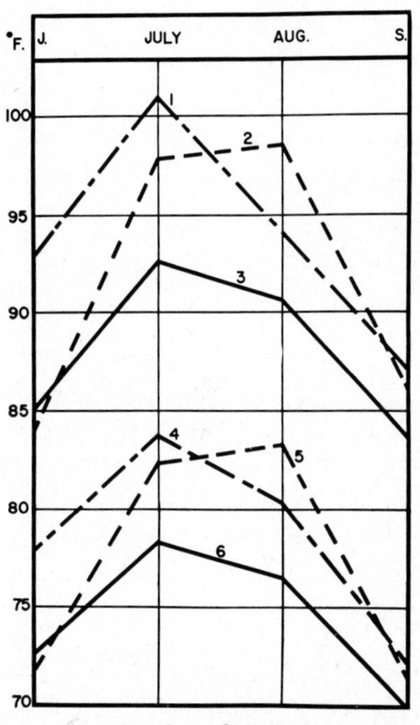

FIG. 21. Graphs showing average daily maximum temperature: 1, of the four worst drought years; 2, of the three best drought years; and 3, of predrought period (1925 to 1932). Similar data (4, 5 and 6) on average daily temperatures.

Temperatures were abnormally high during the drought and duration of periods with high temperatures unusually long (Fig. 21). Average daily maximum temperatures for June, July and August of the four driest years were 93.2°, 100.6° and 94.8° F., respectively, or 8.0°, 7.5° and 4.4° higher than for the same months during 1925–1932.

The average seasonal evaporation (April to September, inclusive) from a free water surface was 48.5 inches preceding the drought. It was always greater during the drought and was 66.4 inches in 1934. Average monthly evaporation in the drought years was 1.8 inches higher than normal in June, 2.7 inches in July and 1.7 inches in August. It was 8.5 inches above normal for the growing season. The average monthly evaporation for the 4 driest years was highest in July, 14.2 inches.

The amount of moisture in the soil is especially important in the Great Plains region since it is nearly always the limiting factor in plant production. Available soil moisture was determined weekly in the first and second 6-inch depths and in 12-inch soil cores taken with a soil tube to a depth of

5 feet. Total water content of soil minus the hygroscopic coefficient (which was determined for each soil depth) was designated as water available for growth.

There was about 2 per cent residual water available to plants at certain depths below 2 feet in 1933 but none thereafter. Water was nonavailable in the second foot after the first week in June, 1933, and continuously nonavailable except for 2 weeks in June, 1934, and during the entire month in 1935. From 1937 to 1939, inclusive, the second foot of soil had no water available for plant growth. Even water in the surface foot was depleted to an amount nonavailable for growth during three 2-week periods in 1933, one 4-week period in 1934, and one 7-week interval in 1935 (Table 1). This occurred when water was also nonavailable at any depth to 5 feet; the plants succumbed or became dormant. During 3

TABLE 1. Available soil moisture each week at the several depths in the short-grass community from 1935 (except 1936) to 1940. Numbers indicate the amount of available water; (1) 1 to 4.9%, (2) 5 to 9.9, (3) 10 to 19.9, and (4) 20% or more; otherwise there was none. From 1935 to 1940 no water was available for growth below 2 feet.

Depth Feet	May		June				July				August				Sept.	
	3	4	1	2	3	4	1	2	3	4	1	2	3	4	1	2
1935																
0–.5	2	3	3	3	3	2								1	2	2
.5–1	1	3	3	3	3	2										
1–2			1	1	2	2										
1937																
0–.5		1		2	1		1	1	2	3	1	1	2	1	1	3
.5–1		1			1				1					1	1	1
1–2																
1938																
0–.5	3	2	1	2	3	2	1						3	1		
.5–1	2	1	1	1	2	1	1							1		
1–2																
1939																
0–.5			1	1	1	3	1					2	3	2		
.5–1																
1–2																

separate weeks in 1937 they were without available water; similar periods of 5 and 2 weeks duration occurred in 1938. In 1939 there were three, including one of 4 weeks duration in July and August.

It is significant that even with showers as great as 1.5 inches comparatively little water was stored in the soil. The explanation of this doubtless lies in the fact that much of a dashing rain of this amount, because of the relatively impervious soil and scarcity of vegetation, is lost to the upland and becomes a flood hazard in the valleys below.

Wind movement was abnormally high. That of 1934 was greatest, 41,780 miles from April to September, inclusive. The lowest (1936) was 33,830 miles. The highest wind movement occurred in April and May and often resulted in great dust storms.

DUST STORMS

Combined effects of cultivation, overgrazing and drought created conditions extremely conducive to dust storms. Such storms were frequent but not severe during 1932. Many dust storms of wide extent occurred in April, 1933. Lights were necessary in the middle of the afternoon and such darkness prevailed that chickens went to roost soon after midday. The blowing of dust reached a climax in March and April of 1935. Dust storms occurred on approximately half of the days after March 15, in fact, on some occasions the air was filled with dust for a period of several days. Often a dust storm approaching from a distance had much the appearance of an extremely dark rain cloud being driven by a wind of high velocity (Fig. 22).

Visibility in the areas covered by these "dusters" was often reduced to only a few feet or even to zero. Dust penetrated every crevice in the houses; as much as a quarter of an inch of dust accumulated over the floors and furniture. The dust storm of late afternoon and night of March 15 and 16 was reported to have been the most severe and most damaging ever known in northwestern and north-central Kansas. Traffic on the highways was abandoned, trains were delayed, and, on many occasions, people were obliged to cover their faces with dampened handkerchiefs in order to breathe.

Much of the dust that was moved about was not actually suspended in the air but carried along the surface of the soil. The few growing plants that remained were often cut away as if they had been subjected to the

FIG. 22. Dust storms in southwestern Kansas, typical of the "black blizzards" of the great drought. Photos by Conard.

action of a sand blast. In sections of the dust bowl fence posts were not infrequently worn away so that only a small portion in the center remained. Enormous, tortuous drifts of soil, often 2.5 feet high, were deposited over the prairies, especially where vegetation such as yucca, sagebrush or cactus caused the accumulation of soil. Vast areas of vegetation were smothered by drifts of loose soil (Fig. 23).

FIG. 23. (Upper) Quadrat showing small scattered tufts of short grasses in well managed range at the end of drought. (Lower) Large drifts of dust, frequently 30 inches in height, were distributed over many ranges. These were later populated by Russian thistle and other annual weeds. Some were inhabited by pack rats.

Usually much of the fine silt was suspended in the air and often carried great distances and deposited where no actual blowing of the soil had occurred. During the great dust storm of March 20 to 22, 1935, the Department of Geology of the University of Wichita, at Wichita, Kansas, "weighed" the atmosphere. They estimated that 5,000,000 tons of dust were suspended over the area of 30 square miles occupied by the city in a layer of atmosphere one mile thick. This was nearly 170 thousand tons per square mile. However, the dust extended upward to a height of more than 12,000 feet and the source area of the dust was 250 miles westward (Lugn, 1939).

Extensive grasslands that were far from cultivated fields were commonly covered by a layer of this fine dust to a depth of 0.5 to 1 inch or more. "Dusting" of this nature was continued late into April, 1935, and, according to records, the air was filled with dust 15 to 25 days of the month. The rains of May and June ameliorated the condition by settling the soil and promoting the germination of weed seeds. Weeds soon covered much of the soil with a green blanket. Stabilization was temporary and on many occasions dust storms of a local nature occurred in the dust bowl. Sometimes the storms were of several days duration. Vast areas of vegetation were smothered by thin blankets of silt or by great drifts of loose earth. After the vegetation died the dust was again moved by the wind and thus supplied the silt for later "black blizzards."

Dust storms are always impressive and the "black blizzards" of the thirties often gave one the feeling that the whole surface of the affected area was blowing away. It generally requires a wind of 30 miles per hour to start even the cultivated soil of non-sandy lands (hard lands) to move. But once the soil has begun to blow, a wind velocity of only 8 to 12 miles per hour may start it to moving again (Brandon and Kezer, 1936). The writers have never observed a dust storm to originate on an area with good cover, an observation which is in agreement with that of Clements and other ecologists of long experience in grassland. Wind velocity at the soil surface under little bluestem, western wheatgrass, and other mid grasses seldom reaches 0.5 to 1 mile per hour even when air movement is 20 to 30 miles per hour above the grass level. Short grasses reduce such wind movement to one-twentieth of its velocity just above the grass. Thus, it seems improbable that dust storms could have come from anything but bare soil. It should further be noted that the terrible dust storms of the thirties were built up out of dust arising from less than one-twentieth of the surface of the dust bowl area (Finnell, 1948).

Drought and wind have always been a part of the Great Plains environment, but not the destruction of vegetation resulting from cultivating land that is permanently stable and valuable only for grazing. Such conditions induce one to consider thoughtfully the wisdom of the conclusion reached by Chilcott in 1927. "The Great Plains area has been and should continue to be devoted to stock raising, and all agencies interested in agricultural, social, and economic development of this vast region of more than 450,000 square miles should unite in bringing about conditions that will make possible the fullest development of its natural resources for stock production. Crop production should be aimed to supplement livestock production rather than to compete with it."

SOME EFFECTS OF DROUGHT

Depletion of the ranges during drought greatly intensified grazing on practically all pasture land. The carrying capacity of large areas was greatly reduced. Where formerly 1 animal unit required a grazing range of 10 to 12 acres 30 to 50 acres were now needed. The ranchers, in many instances, found it difficult to reduce the number of livestock to a conservative stocking rate; consequently, most of the grassland in the Great Plains region was seriously overgrazed. Furthermore, decreased forage caused a reduction in the quantity and quality of meat produced by the livestock. During these years it was difficult to carry livestock through the summer without supplemental feed.

Grasshoppers added further to the deterioration of the range. On numerous occasions as many as 8 to 12 per square foot were found feeding upon the weeds and grasses in the native pastures. Investigations indicated that during periods of extreme drought a large percentage of the vegetation was consumed by the hungry grasshoppers; in other areas, as we shall see, it was all destroyed.

Vegetation that is adapted to the variable climatic conditions of the Great Plains is able to become dormant or semidormant several times during a growing season. During 7 years of drought the vegetation was frequently subjected to such severe desiccation that for days at a time much wilting occurred. Often the plant cover became so dry that when trod upon it crackled underfoot.

Short grasses growing on the tablelands were the first to manifest effects of drought. The ordinary straw color accompanying dormancy usually appeared several times during the season, but in 1934 and 1939 much of the vegetation became bluish-gray, a color indicative of death. Many mesic plants disappeared completely and were replaced by others less susceptible to drought. Even the more xeric ones were often very much reduced in numbers.

ANNUAL PROGRESS OF DROUGHT

The first signs of drought were observed early in June of 1933 when the immature staminate blossoms of buffalo grass were greatly damaged and its leaves were spirally coiled and dead at the tips. The leaves of blue grama, though dark green in color, were rolled. They closely resembled those of purple three-awn. The immature blossoms of squirreltail were blasted by excessive heat. By June 15 buffalo grass had become dormant in local areas where the supply of water was least. Both short grasses were dormant by July 1. Foliage of the scattered bunches of little bluestem, purple three-awn and squirreltail was badly withered and in many instances nearly dead.

Scattered showers early in July supplied some available moisture for plant growth. Many of the grasses showed signs of life, especially in shallow depressions. Green color was restored in some instances where the leaves had not gone into complete dormancy. Usually, however, new leaves emerged from the crown, which was protected by the dormant vegetative cover; in fact, careful observations revealed that even in the periods of greatest drought small amounts of the crown remained green. Sufficient soil water was present during the last half of July to promote considerable growth. The small amount of moisture, however, was soon exhausted and by August 5 the grasses were again dormant. Growth was renewed late in August when the soil was moistened to a depth of a foot.

It was during the drought of 1934 that plants of the most exposed locations suffered greatly. The bluish-gray color of the short grasses indicated that over large areas life was completely extinct. In other places, however, where the normal straw color was retained, the plants were merely dormant. It was further observed that areas suffering greatest losses were frequently occupied by a larger percentage of buffalo grass than blue grama.

Numerous seedlings of buffalo grass and blue grama were scattered through the open places in the vegetation. In 1935 buffalo grass stolons had become so abundant that they formed a heavy mat over much of the soil. Many had reached lengths of 18 to 24 inches. The numerous small bunches of blue grama that survived the drought were now extending their cover by myriads of tillers (Riegel, 1940).

All short grasses, except those in depressions, were badly wilted by mid-July, 1935, despite their excellent development earlier in the summer when buffalo grass stolons elongated at the rate of an inch per day. Many of them were shallowly rooted or were not in contact with the soil; these had died back to the parent plant. The reactions of the grasses to the en-

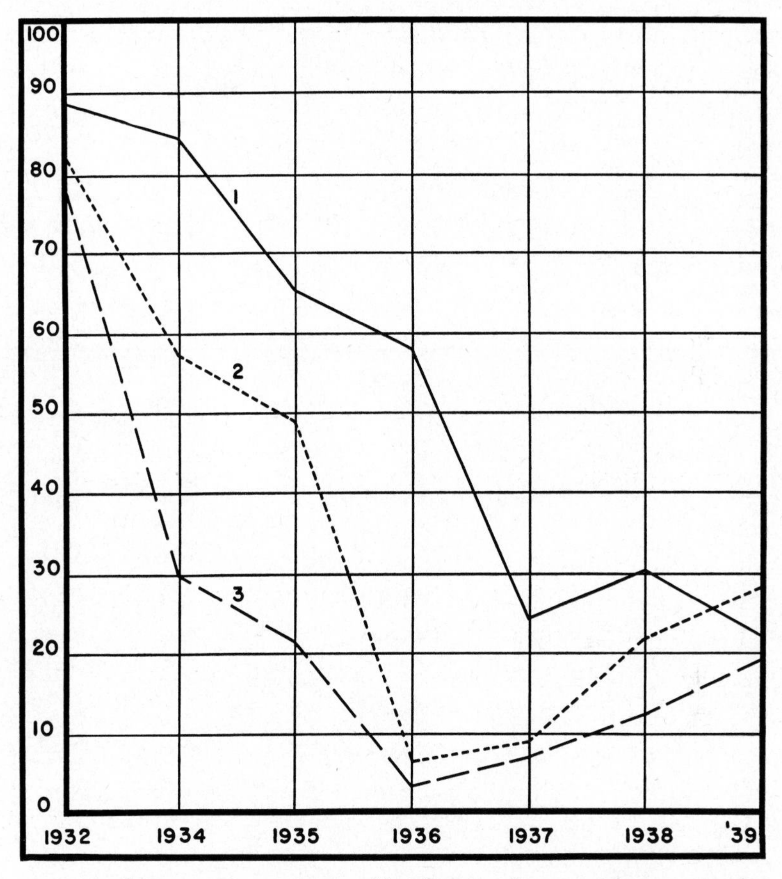

FIG. 24. Decrease in percentage of basal cover of perennial grasses in the short-grass type: (1) ungrazed, (2) moderately grazed, and (3) overgrazed.

vironmental conditions to which they were subjected indicated that under extremely adverse conditions the breakdown was rapid. Conversely, when conditions became favorable replacement was equally rapid.

The exceptionally dry months of June and July, 1936, however, forced all vegetation into dormancy and in many instances reduced the cover to nearly zero. In most places basal cover reached its minimum for the drought period during this year. Growth was only intermittent in 1937 and great drought prevailed (Fig. 24).

The rainfall of April and May, 1938 was above normal but because of excessive runoff only a comparatively small amount of water was stored in the soil. The short grasses began growth early in April and reached their maximum development during late May and early June. By June 6 numerous buffalo-grass stolons, from 3 to 8 inches long, were radiating in all directions from the parent plants. Many tillers of blue grama were added to the outside of the small tufts of living plants.

Myriads of seedlings of buffalo grass and blue grama occupied the open spaces between the bunches, often at the rate of 10 to 25 per square foot. Growth continued with no interruption until early in July when the effects of drought became apparent. By July 18 many seedlings were dead. The tufts of mature grasses were dormant and many stolons of buffalo grass had died back to the place of their origin. The rains of late August and early September stored sufficient moisture in the soil to support the production of flower stalks of blue grama. Only a little seed was produced. Side-oats grama and western wheatgrass were commonly found in buffalo wallows and other depressions. The year 1939 was the most severe of the drought. Deterioration of vegetation was very great.

During these eventful years local dust deposits exceeding 0.5 inch in depth handicapped the short grasses and a cover an inch or more in depth was usually fatal. Despite quantities of seedlings and rapid vegetative propagation of buffalo grass at various times, periods favorable for growth were usually too short to result in re-establishment. Flower stalks were sometimes formed but few seeds matured. With dusting and denudation rainfall became less efficient and runoff greatly increased.

CHANGES IN THE SHORT-GRASS COMMUNITY

Six large areas were exclosed to livestock in 1932 and numerous representative square meters of vegetation were selected for continuous study. Investigations were extended in 1935, following two years of drought and a spring of exceptionally heavy dusting. It was at this time that certain areas moderately grazed, others ungrazed for many years, and still others that were overgrazed were included. In 1937, the area for investigation was also greatly extended over western Kansas.

The exclosures in the large prairie studied in 1932 had been moderately grazed but thereafter protected from grazing. At that time blue grama and buffalo grass occurred in about equal abundance. The basal cover was 89 per cent. After two years of drought it was only slightly reduced, to 85 per cent. Sixty-six per cent cover occurred in 1935 and a year later 58. Thus, during the first four years reduction of cover took place slowly.

Decreases in basal cover in 10 representative quadrats in ungrazed blue grama–buffalo grass type were much more rapid. The original cover of 89 per cent decreased from 1934 to 1939 to the following percentages: 85, 66, 58, 25, 31, and 22, respectively. The accumulated results of the drought produced the greatest breakdown in the cover between 1935 and 1937. Cover increased somewhat in 1938 because of better growing conditions but the drought of 1939 caused another decrease.

The ravages of the drought caused great variation in the density of vegetation. In some places there occurred large barren areas almost devoid of plants. In the short-grass type moderately grazed during the drought an average basal cover of about 50 per cent was found in 1935. This was reduced to about 5 per cent in 1936; less than 0.5 per cent was buffalo grass. It then gradually increased to 28 per cent by 1939. In some areas buffalo grass, which often remained only in shallow depressions, increased more rapidly, in others the more drought-resistant codominant, blue grama. Few other species, except sand dropseed, were even of minor importance.

The results of these studies indicate that moderate grazing is no great handicap to the normal development of the short grasses; in fact, there is reason to believe that moderate grazing under normal precipitation will produce a more uniform cover than that developed under total protection (Savage, 1939).

Overgrazed short-grass ranges were reduced to a cover of 22 per cent or less than half of that under moderate grazing. Blue grama was reduced to 2 per cent, buffalo grass to less than 1 per cent, and the total basal cover to about 2.5 per cent when most depleted in 1936. Areas 10 to 15 feet in diameter and entirely bare of grass were frequent. Recovery was aided by reduced grazing presssure in 1938 and 1939 and basal cover increased year by year to 7, 13, and 19 per cent.

Basal cover in ungrazed, moderately grazed, and overgrazed short-grass ranges (where the cover in 1932 varied from 88 to 80 percent) was reduced in a somewhat parallel manner. Maximum reduction was least and a year later in ungrazed grassland. Percentages of cover were, in order, 65, 48, and 22 in 1935 but 58, 7, and 3 in 1936. By 1938 the cover was 31, 22, and 13 per cent, respectively. Further heavy losses on overgrazed ranges were recorded in 1940.

The effects of overgrazing and constant dusting on the short grasses were tragic. The vegetation in many places was reduced to less than 1 per cent and the plants were extremely weak (Fig. 24).

CHANGES IN THE LITTLE BLUESTEM COMMUNITY

The complete story of the little bluestem type was recorded. The average basal cover in 15 meter quadrats was gradually reduced from 61 per cent in 1932 to a minimum of 17 per cent in 1936. The somewhat better years of 1937 and 1938 brought some improvement. The basal cover was increased to 24 per cent in 1937 and to 30 per cent in 1938. It is evident that the accumulated benefits derived from the nearly normal year of 1938 carried over into 1939, when the rainfall was the least of any year during the entire period of drought. Decrease or increase of the various species follows:

Species	1932	1934	1935	1936	1937	1938	1939
Little bluestem	50	37	10	4	1	1	1
Big bluestem	11	6	9	5	5	3	2
Side-oats grama . . .	—	3	6	6	12	18	18
Blue grama	—	1	2	2	6	8	9
Total	61	47	27	17	24	30	30

The characteristic appearance of the little bluestem type was gradually but definitely lost soon after the onslaught of the drought in 1933. The original basal cover of about 61 per cent was composed of approximately one-sixth big bluestem and nearly all of the remainder was little bluestem. Little bluestem decreased so rapidly that only 10 per cent remained in 1935 and 1 per cent in 1939. Big bluestem was reduced to 2 per cent. Invasion of more xeric species, especially side-oats grama and blue grama resulted in the minimum basal cover of 17 per cent (1936) being increased to 30 per cent in 1939. Accumulated benefits derived from the years of least drought were often expressed by better growth the following season, even if dry. Opportune showers permitted flowering of mature plants but few viable seeds were produced.

Late in the drought large areas of level prairies were found to be completely devoid of little bluestem. Some big bluestem survived owing not only to its greater depth of root system but also to the large amounts of reserve foods in crowns and rhizomes. The deeply rooted forbs, such as lead plant and few-flowered psoralea, were turgid and green. Side-oats grama when once established in the bared areas, spread considerably, mostly by short rhizomes. The young shoots from them survived more severe drought than the seedlings. Plants of blue grama increased by tillering. The increase was slow but constant in the little bluestem habitat. Myriads of seedlings appeared in the open spaces between the bunches of living grasses. Often 50 to 75 per square foot, mostly those of side-oats grama and hairy grama, were found. These seedlings were of greatest abundance near the parent plants where the soil surface was protected from drying during the period of germination. The drought of July and early August greatly reduced the number of live seedlings. It was not uncommon to find numerous seedlings with 3 to 5 brown leaves that had withered and fallen. Examination revealed that the roots had penetrated less than 12 inches into the soil, which now had no available moisture. It was estimated that 90 per cent of the seedlings perished during this dry period.

CHANGES IN OTHER AREAS

The ecotone or transitional area between little bluestem and short grass exhibited several mixtures. Even where large amounts (40 per cent) of little bluestem were found total loss of the species usually occurred. Basal cover was reduced from 65 to 25 per cent. Owing to the entrance of side-oats grama and to a great increase in short grasses, about 50 per cent cover was present in 1939.

Drought over most of the transitional area, except where it was accompanied by dust burial, resulted in severe thinning of the short grasses rather than their complete destruction.

Side-oats grama was intermixed with short grasses in more xeric situations in the ecotone before the drought. Where it constituted 60 per cent of the cover in 1932, it decreased to 3 per cent by 1936 and scarcely gained thereafter. The short grasses were more resistant to desiccation. At first they decreased from 22 per cent to 11, but by 1939 they doubled their original basal area.

Where several mid grasses, including both purple and red three-awn were intermixed with short grasses in the transitional area, all disappeared in 1 to 3 years. The short grasses were at a low ebb in 1936 but subsequently regained the ground lost by the mid grasses. Thus, the initial basal cover of 34 per cent was again attained.

Great changes also occurred in the big bluestem type, although decrease in available soil moisture was slower here as was also decrease in abundance of vegetation. Western wheatgrass, side-oats grama and other more xeric grasses partially replaced big bluestem, tall panic grass and other mesic species. A loss of one-fourth of the vegetation resulted from drought and consequent soil erosion and deposit.

Intensive studies of ranges were made in ten additional counties in western Kansas, beginning in 1937. All were in the short-grass type. On lightly dusted and moderately grazed ranges basal cover varied from 10 to 33 per cent. Percentage of buffalo grass usually averaged higher than that of blue grama. Variations in cover were usually closely correlated with the amount of rainfall. No permanent gains occurred by 1939. Under light dusting and overgrazing a cover of 5.5 per cent increased to 18 in 1938 and to 26 in 1939. At some stations this resulted from an excellent growth of buffalo grass. Where heavy dusting and moderate grazing occurred and buffalo grass and blue grama were about equally represented, the basal cover of 6 per cent increased to 15.

Vegetation suffered the greatest losses under heavy dusting and overgrazing. An average basal cover of 1 to 2 per cent showed no increase by 1939. This much-depleted type of grassland was of very wide distribution and constituted a large portion of the vegetation near the center of the dust bowl.

Thus drought, overgrazing, and hordes of grasshoppers had caused great reduction in carrying capacity of the range. Yield of palatable forage in overgrazed pastures was less than 10 per cent of that produced in well-managed ones. It was believed that several years with normal or above normal precipitation and with the most judicious range management would be required to restore the former cover of grasses.

CHAPTER 7

Vegetation at the End of Drought

Eight years had now passed since the fateful spring of 1933. A marked change in the environment followed the extremely dry winter of 1939–40. Precipitation increased, at first gradually and then to a remarkable degree. The great drought had ended. The increased precipitation, sometimes with monthly averages of three times the normal amount, had again moistened the dry soil to depths of predrought root penetration. This, with a return to more normal atmospheric moisture, temperature and wind movement, initiated marked changes in the vegetation. Hence a resurvey of the conditions both above and below ground seemed advisable. It concluded the phase of deterioration due to desiccation and at the same time provided a clear and definite background from which the processes involved in the return of vegetation to a new dynamic stabilization might be traced.[1]

Drought and dust had wrought great changes not only in the composition of vegetation but also in its amount. They had also caused great changes of vegetational boundaries between grassland types. Movements of grass populations had been from the more xeric toward the less xeric habitats. In many localities the only plants that survived were those in moister places, such as buffalo wallows, ditches, and ravines. Reduction of cover to 2 to 10 per cent was not uncommon. Frequently large areas of nearly level grassland were covered with several inches of dust brought by the wind from adjacent cultivated fields. Under extreme conditions the wind-blown soil formed long, tortuous drifts under which the native vegetation was buried and completely destroyed.

CONDITION OF GRASSES

The first effects of drought became apparent in the permanent wilting

[1] Condensed and adapted from Weaver and Albertson, Ecological Monographs 13: 63–117, 1943. Three of the 70 illustrations have been reproduced.

of little bluestem where it occurred widely distributed as scattered bunches or in small patches among the short grasses on the tablelands. Only dormant or dead crowns remained after 1934. Even in its own type, this species was materially reduced, being replaced chiefly by side-oats grama and blue grama. Finally, only occasional bunches of little bluestem could be found even on north-facing slopes or in depressions on the hillsides where runoff water accumulated. Thus, this dominant was reduced from about 45 per cent of the total vegetation to only 1 per cent.

Effects of drought upon big bluestem became evident somewhat later than upon most other grasses associated with it. On hillsides where little bluestem dominated, it was able to survive with little loss, because of a somewhat deeper root system, several years after little bluestem had died. During later years of drought its abundance was reduced to only a fourth of its former amount. In its own community on lower slopes and in ravines big bluestem, so common before the drought, was almost entirely replaced by other species such as western wheatgrass, tall dropseed, side-oats grama, and even by buffalo grass and blue grama (Fig. 25). Thus, at the end of the drought its abundance was often only about one-fifth normal.

Side-oats grama had a wide predrought distribution in the mixed prairie. It was a chief associate of big bluestem in the postclimax type of grassland where it was a dominant species. Its bunches were also scattered widely throughout the little bluestem type on the hillsides, and it was one of the most important mid grasses that extended into the short-grass type more or less throughout western Kansas, eastern Colorado and adjacent areas. But by the end of the drought even this xeric species was enormously reduced in numbers, and over a wide territory it almost disappeared from the short grass cover. Conversely, it made steady gains in the little bluestem type and was the chief invader of the soil left bare by the death of little bluestem. An increase in amount of two or threefold was usual. Likewise, in the ravines and on lower slopes it frequently replaced big bluestem.

Three-awn grasses were most abundant and most permanently entrenched along hillsides in the little bluestem type. They also extended widely and often abundantly over the short-grass disclimax. On the heavier silt loams or very fine sandy loams these low bunch grasses were few, but they increased with coarser sand content of soil. Upon the advent of drought they were among the first to show the effects of decreased water

FIG. 25. (Upper) Increase of western wheatgrass (light color) over lower slopes and in ravines at Hays, Kansas, as it appeared in 1939. (Lower) Sod of short grass from an overgrazed range and underground materials remaining after the soil was washed away.

content. By 1935 only their dead crowns could be found in the short-grass type. Even on the hillsides they suffered a high rate of mortality and persisted only in places that were protected by other vegetation or as a result of irregular topography.

Blue grama with its codominant, buffalo grass, constituted fully four-fifths of the entire vegetation in the short-grass type. The predrought turf, of short grasses with small openings scattered throughout, had received so much abuse from edaphic and atmospheric drought, dust, overgrazing by domesticated animals, jack rabbits and grasshoppers, that it was now composed merely of isolated remnants of sod in a wilderness of bared soil.

Yet the remaining vegetation, sorely depleted as it was, consisted almost entirely of these same two short grasses. Thus, during the stress of drought most of the blue grama was killed, but that which remained grew in small tufts or bunches a few inches to many feet apart (Fig. 26). In places where runoff was great, large tracts of many square rods were completely denuded of this grass and all other vegetation. Other vast areas were bared or almost denuded by a covering of dust. In contrast to these losses which ranged from 50 to 100 per cent, gains were made by blue grama spreading on hillsides and into upper ravines where certain mid grasses had succumbed. In fact, most lowlands were also occupied by blue grama.

Buffalo grass often shared the soil more or less equally with blue grama before the great drought. In many places this stoloniferous grass entirely disappeared from the mixture during the early years of desiccation and in practically no location was it damaged only lightly. During the short periods with moist soil, the stolons developed rapidly but usually the new growth was killed by succeeding dry periods. The gains and losses of buffalo grass during this period of adversity fluctuated to a much greater extent than did those of blue grama.

The soil in the short-grass type, bared as a consequence of drought, was usually repopulated with weedy species such as little barley, peppergrass, sticktight, Russian thistle, lamb's quarters and many others. These weeds were often detrimental to the recovery of buffalo grass because of their shade and also because of their rapid absorption of water. By the end of the drought, despite rapid and repeated local recovery, buffalo grass had lost much more than the more stable blue grama. Of the 1940 cover of short grasses throughout this arid western region, buffalo grass constituted probably not more than one half as much as blue grama.

Switchgrass, although dwarfed and often unable to flower in its patches in big bluestem sod, survived the drought fairly well. Even where scattered in the little bluestem sod, its very deep rooting habit sustained it well, except for minor losses.

Western wheatgrass was widely distributed throughout in 1932. It occurred in greatest abundance in the deepest soil on the ecotone between the short-grass and little bluestem types, but also comprised a considerable portion of the vegetation on the lower slopes. By 1940, it had frequently taken complete possession of large areas on the hillsides where the soil was deep enough for it to gain a foothold. Even on the lowlands where

FIG. 26. (Upper) A formerly good range of blue grama and buffalo grass at Seibert, Colorado, in 1939. A basal cover of 85 per cent had been reduced to 18 per cent. Note the wide spacing of the tufts and that all portions of the area have some grass remnants. (Lower) Sand dropseed in much disturbed range in western Kansas. It composes about 60 per cent of the vegetation; the remainder is short grass.

big bluestem was usually dominant, it formed an important part of the vegetation (Fig. 25). It was also found in buffalo wallows scattered throughout the short-grass habitat, but here the living rhizomes remained dormant during several years with little or no growth above ground.

Sand dropseed was perhaps the most widely spread and important of the minor grasses. Under normal conditions of precipitation it was usually restricted to sandy soil, but with the destruction of climax vegetation by drought and the appearance of bare areas, this species spread rapidly on hard lands. It was not uncommonly a local dominant (Fig. 26).

Squirreltail was widely distributed but found most abundantly where the cover of short grasses was more or less interrupted as along transitional areas into mid-grass types. Its root system is shallow and it perished in the early years of drought.

Junegrass occupied a position very similar to that of squirreltail and suffered the same fate. In fact, none could be found at the close of the drought period. Sun sedge (*Carex heliophila*), frequently found in small openings in the short-grass cover, had likewise disappeared.

The occurrence of hairy grama and a hairy variety of dropseed (*Sporobolus asper pilosus*) was rather definitely limited, in western Kansas, to abrupt slopes in the little bluestem type where rocks outcropped. Both species maintained their abundance or gained slightly and were now the most important grasses in their restricted habitats.

Indian grass and wild-rye (*Elymus canadensis* and *E. virginicus*) were usually limited to local areas in the big bluestem habitat. Occasionally, however, small clumps were found ranging well up the hillsides. In these more xeric locations they succumbed, and they had not increased even on the lowlands.

Tall dropseed (*Sporobolus asper* var. *hookeri*) was limited to small, local patches on the lower hillsides and upper ravines previous to the drought. With decrease in big bluestem, however, it made rapid gains and now had full possession of many rather large areas on lowlands.

Tumblegrass (*Schedonnardus paniculatus*) and windmill grass (*Chloris verticillata*) were commonly found in disturbed places where they sometimes formed the major part of the cover. Both, however, were unable to survive the drought and were early replaced by sand dropseed. They were now found only occasionally in the short-grass type where the cover had been materially reduced by drought and accumulations of dust.

Before the dry years the only annual grasses of much importance were little barley and six-weeks fescue. Even little barley was not abundant. As the soil became bared of vegetation, however, it increased greatly and often produced a crop of forage of one to two tons per acre. Six-weeks fescue, on the other hand, suffered a high rate of mortality and at the close of the drought was seen infrequently.

Other weedy annual grasses that invaded open places were downy chess (*Bromus tectorum*), hairy chess (*B. commutatus*), Japanese chess (*B. japonicus*), witchgrass (*Panicum capillare*) and stinkgrass (*Eragrostis cilianensis*). Under most adverse conditions, where the native cover was almost entirely destroyed, these grasses produced a new but often patchy cover annually.

Data on the composition of the plant cover were ascertained throughout western Kansas from more than 100 permanent, representative quadrats. These are shown for each community in table 2 and for the transitional area to the little bluestem type as well. It should be clearly understood that these data do not indicate the amount of vegetation whether great, as before the drought, or small, as after this catastrophe, but only its percentage composition.

In the short-grass type blue grama at first composed 49 per cent of the total vegetation but finally 59. Hence while blue grama actually decreased greatly in drought buffalo grass decreased even more. This resulted in an increase of the relative abundance of blue grama. These 17 grasses (Table 2) composed 98 to 99 per cent of the entire perennial vegetation of the several communities. Perennial forbs and other perennial grasses were rare. The following species had disappeared in some communities: three-awn grasses, little bluestem and squirreltail.

The nearly equal abundance of blue grama and buffalo grass was not maintained. At the end of drought the ratio, in the same sequence, was approximately two-thirds to one-third. When the rains came following drought, buffalo grass, as shown in another large group of quadrats, soon equaled and then greatly exceeded the amount of blue grama.

The relative drought resistance of seedlings of dominant prairie grasses was determined experimentally under controlled conditions by Mueller and Weaver (1942). Seedlings were grown an inch apart. Seeds were arranged so that somewhere a plant of any species was adjacent to one of each of the other species. Mixed plantings of seedlings of 14 species of

TABLE 2. Percentage composition of the basal cover of various perennial species of four chief communities of mixed prairie vegetation before and after the great drought.

Species	Short-grass type		Ecotone		Little bluestem type		Big bluestem type	
	1932	1940	1932	1940	1932	1940	1932	1940
Blue grama	49	59	43	66	8	31	3	12
Buffalo grass	48	35	42	30	1	6	2	20
Purple and red three-awn	1	—	1	—	2	1	—	—
Sand dropseed	—	4	—	—	7	7	—	—
Squirreltail	1	—	1	1	—	—	—	—
Tumblegrass	—	1	—	—	—	—	—	—
Little bluestem	1	—	5	—	45	1	1	—
Side-oats grama	—	—	5	1	17	42	5	15
Big bluestem	—	—	2	—	17	4	76	15
Tall dropseed (var. pilosus)	—	—	—	1	1	2	—	—
Hairy grama	—	—	—	—	2	5	—	—
Switchgrass	—	—	—	—	—	—	2	2
Western wheatgrass	—	—	—	—	—	—	4	20
Indian grass	—	—	—	—	—	—	2	—
Virginia wild-rye	—	—	—	—	—	—	2	1
Tall dropseed (var. hookeri)	—	—	—	—	—	—	2	13
Total	100	99	99	99	100	99	99	98

dominant prairie grasses were tested for resistance to soil drought at ordinary summer temperatures. Only a few plants, all of which were short grasses, survived where drought was most critical. Of these blue grama showed the greatest drought resistance, three times as many plants surviving as those of hairy grama and buffalo grass which were next in order. Western wheatgrass was least able to resist drought.

There was no mortality and only slight damage to seedlings subjected to hot winds of 135° F. when soil moisture was available. Leaves of the short-grass seedlings, listed above, were scarcely injured by temperatures as high as 145° F. Neither differences of a few weeks in age nor previous exposure to drought had any significant effect on the survival of seedlings which were exposed to hot winds.

When the results of exposure to soil drought and to atmospheric drought were both taken into account, blue grama was the most drought resistant. In order of decreasing drought resistance the species were buffalo grass, hairy grama, tall dropseed, side-oats grama, needlegrass, little bluestem, big bluestem, and switchgrass. In general, species characteristic of uplands or which normally occur in mixed prairie were more resistant, and those in the lowlands or in the true prairie less resistant to drought.

In the little bluestem community, the dominant decreased to 1 per cent of the cover. Big bluestem and three-awn also greatly decreased, but side-oats grama increased its percentage of the cover from 17 to 42, and buffalo grass from 1 to 6. In the big bluestem type a great increase of the short grasses, side-oats grama (5 to 15 per cent), and western wheatgrass (4 to 20 per cent) accompanied the decline of big bluestem.

From the preceding data and years of continuous observations over the entire area, it was possible to classify the various perennial grasses in regard to their abundance at the end of the drought. The groups are: (1) species of major importance; (2) species of intermediate importance; and (3) species of minor importance. Grasses in each group are arranged approximately in the order of decreasing importance.

Short-grass type	Other types	
1. Blue grama	1. Side-oats grama	3. Little bluestem
Buffalo grass	Western wheatgrass	Three-awn grasses
2. Side-oats grama	Blue grama	Indian grass
Sand dropseed	Buffalo grass	Canada wild-rye
Western wheatgrass	Big bluestem	Virginia wild-rye
3. Three-awn grasses	Tall dropseed	Squirreltail
Tumblegrass	2. Switchgrass	Tumblegrass
Windmill grass	Sand dropseed	Plains muhly
Squirreltail	Hairy grama	Junegrass
Plains muhly	Hairy tall dropseed	

CONDITION OF FORBS

The losses of forbs were studied throughout the drought. Since many prairies were visited at regular intervals each year and hundreds of quadrats recharted annually, a comprehensive record of the actual weakening and death of forbs was obtained. The studies showed that the decrease in numbers was not gradual but sporadic, corresponding with severity of drought. Deeply rooted plants as red false mallow (*Sphaeralcea coccinea*) and false boneset (*Kuhnia eupatorioides*) held out against drought, even to the end. Prairie coneflower (*Ratibida columnifera*), Prairie cat's-foot

(*Antennaria neglecta*) and many other shallowly rooted plants were nearly all destroyed by the first great impact of drought. Others like purple coneflower (*Echinacea angustifolia*) lingered a second year; plants of most species persisted even longer and were continuously depleted in numbers with recurring periods of drought.

Drought occurred during various periods of the year—early spring, late spring, midsummer and late summer. Wilting, drying, and more or less complete defoliation of tops by grasshoppers were common phenomena later in the drought cycle among even the most deeply rooted species. Dwarfness in stature was characteristic of the more drought-resistant species which continued to grow slowly, even if intermittently. Lack of debris on the soil with little or no cover of grasses and absence of the usual shade accentuated the drought. Failure to complete vegetative growth or to blossom or ripen seed was usual. This resulted finally in a dearth of viable seed which, in conjunction with a general environment unfavorable to seedling establishment, resulted in survival of few seedlings.

Development of only a few stems from crowns of perennial species that normally supported many revealed at once the severe environment and the weakened condition of the vegetation. Often the forbs were robbed of the meager water supply in spring by the growth of a host of annual grasses, especially six-weeks fescue, little barley and various species of brome grasses. Moreover, annual forbs were plentiful.

In many prairies death by mechanical injury from blowing dust overtook aboveground parts, or both forbs and grasses were smothered under a blanket of dust a few to many inches thick.

All of the long-lived forbs in numerous representative ranges of nine counties of western Kansas were listed. Many of these ranges had not been grazed for three or more years. This was done in 1940. The lowest ebb of vegetation was reached in spring and early summer of this year, following the great drought which extended throughout the preceding fall and winter. The first ten species in the list were the most drought resistant (excepting the cacti).

All these species could be found in 1938 and 1939 in nearly every range, not abundantly and always scattered, especially after some searching. But a year later only red false mallow, false boneset, few-flowered psoralea, and wavy-leaved thistle were observed, after prolonged searching in favored spots; the rest were seen rarely. Aside from the cactus and red false mallow, only rarely was any species very abundant or even common. At each of the 15 stations they were either absent, rare or infrequent.

False boneset
Kuhnia eupatorioides
Wavy-leaved thistle
Cirsium undulatum
Rush-like lygodesmia
Lygodesmia juncea
Blazing star
Liatris punctata
Narrow-leaved four-o'clock
Mirabilis linearis
Scarlet gaura
Gaura coccinea
Red false mallow
Sphaeralcea coccinea
Few-flowered psoralea
Psoralea tenuiflora
Velvety goldenrod
Solidago mollis
Cut-leaved goldenweed
Haplopappus spinulosus
Many-flowered aster
Aster ericoides
Prairie coneflower
Ratibida columnifera
Western pricklypear
Opuntia humifusa
Woolly loco
Astragalus mollissimus
Broom snakeweed
Gutierrezia sarothrae
Large-flowered yellow flax
Linum rigidum
Brittle cactus
Opuntia fragilis

The cause of drought resistance of these species has not been studied specifically on a physiological basis. It may be found to be inherent in the protoplasm. The following observations, however, are pertinent. Nearly all are deeply rooted and thus may utilize all available water throughout the soil to the depth of water penetration. Most have storage organs consisting of thick roots or underground stems which promote early growth and rapid recovery during periods with moist soil. Most of these species do not have an abundance of foliage and with the oncoming of drought, the transpiring surface is greatly reduced by loss of many leaves. Red false mallow possesses all of these characteristics. It begins growth early, loses most of its leaves with the advent of drought, and the few that remain curl during the dry period. It is the most drought resistant of all.

The dwarfed condition of these drought-resistant survivors was very marked. This can best be appreciated when the drought form is compared directly with plants of normal stature preceding the dry years (Fig. 3).

Number of stems of forbs in two circles, 100 feet in diameter, with a combined area of approximately 15,000 square feet was ascertained at each of 14 stations in western Kansas. Red false mallow was most widely distributed and had the greatest number. Average number of stems for the 18 species found was only 23 per unit area. One marvels, however, not so much at the paucity of species and their thinly stretched web of life, as at the fact that any vegetation escaped the terrible drought and endured.

ADJUSTMENT OF ROOT DEPTH

Preceding the dry years, the two dominant short grasses, blue grama and buffalo grass, occupied the soil with a dense mass of roots to about 4 feet in depth, large numbers of much branched, thread-like roots extended to 5 feet. The sod was extremely dense, tough, and resistant to erosion. When cut a few inches deep into strips 12 to 18 inches wide, it could be rolled in the manner of bluegrass sod and, like it, used in establishing a cover of grass elsewhere.

Among the forbs scattered throughout, the roots of few-flowered psoralea, red false mallow and prairie boneset penetrated 9 to 12 feet in depth. Consequently, they obtained much of their water supply at depths far beyond the extent of the roots of the short grasses. Roots of many other common species of forbs did not penetrate beyond a depth of 5 feet and thus absorbed from the same soil levels as the grasses. The following are representative: western ragweed, cut-leaved goldenweed and narrow-leaved four-o'clock.

With continued drought, marked changes in rooting habits occurred. The roots of the two dominant short grasses were profoundly reduced in numbers and in depth of penetration. Below 2 feet, roots of these grasses were extremely scarce (Fig. 27). Investigations in widely scattered places on the depth of penetration of roots on non-sandy land in western Kansas and eastern Colorado showed that most of the roots of the two dominant grasses were limited to the upper foot of soil. In many places the cover was so reduced that only small isolated tufts 1 to 2 inches in diameter remained. Lateral spread of the surface roots was usually not more than 6 inches, and although occasionally a root penetrated to 18 inches, nearly all were in the surface foot.

Most of the fully grown forbs established before the drought had suc-

FIG. 27. Bisect showing root depth in the blue grama—buffalo grass community at the end of the great drought. The sparse roots of *Bouteloua gracilis* (Bg) and *Buchloe dactyloides* (Bd) are only 2 feet deep. Those of red false mallow (Sc) (*Sphaeralcea coccinea*) and few-flowered psoralea (Pt) (*Psoralea tenuiflora*) do not have their usual depths of 8 to 12 feet. Root depths of other upland grasses and forbs were correspondingly shallow.

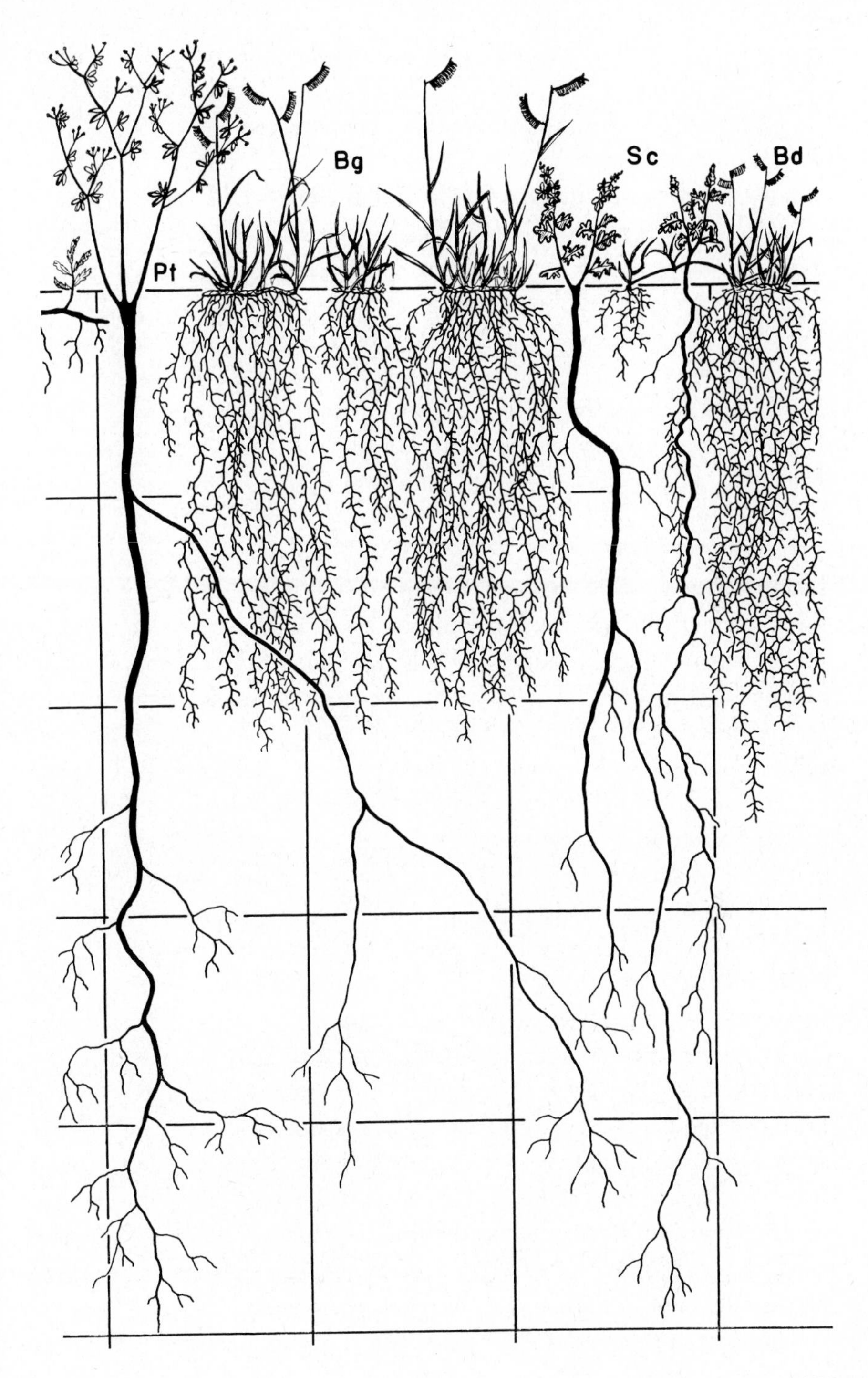
Bg
Pt
Sc
Bd

cumbed, and nearly all remaining in 1940 were either young plants when the drought began or plants that had become established during the most favorable periods during the drought. For example, the roots of few-flowered psoralea were nearly always much less in diameter than those excavated before the drought. They seldom penetrated beyond 4 feet, as compared with a previous depth of penetration of 7 to 9 feet. Red false mallow was one of the few species which increased in numbers, but did so with a greatly reduced root system. Only occasionally was a root found to extend deeper than 4 feet. Plants of false boneset in 1932 had roots to a depth of 12 feet in the short-grass sod. But after the drought they were mostly only about half this depth and none extended deeper than 9.5 feet. Little change in rooting habit occurred in forbs whose root systems were formerly limited to 4 feet of soil, although most of them suffered very heavy losses.

During the years 1934 to 1939, inclusive, there was a dry layer of soil between 2 and 5 feet in depth underlying the short grasses, at least at the numerous stations where regular soil sampling was carried on. Below this there were small amounts of residual soil moisture available throughout the drought years. The species most successful in surviving the drought were either those with roots that had previously grown into this deeper soil or those that evaded drought by limiting their activities to short periods (usually early spring) when conditions for growth were most favorable.

The amount of living underground plant parts in the surface 4 inches of soil under the short grasses was highly variable. On ranges where deferred grazing was practiced and where the location was such that little dust blew in from adjacent fields, a fairly continuous cover was sometimes maintained. As drought progressed and grazing of the weakened plants was permitted and movement of dust became greater, large areas of range land were rendered completely devoid of vegetation. The dead roots decayed, there was no new growth, and the soil became intensely susceptible to erosion by wind and water. Amount of roots and bases of stems in the surface 4 inches of soil was ascertained by Shively and Weaver (1939) from 12 samples of sod of blue grama and buffalo grass taken at 6 stations in mixed prairie of Kansas, Nebraska and Colorado. Each sample was from one-half square meter of soil. Roots of blue grama averaged 243 grams per sample, those of buffalo grass weighed 262 grams.

The roots in samples of short grasses at Hays weighed 276 grams, but after the drought, roots of similar samples had decreased 56 per cent (Fig. 25). Overgrazing and drought often result not only in the loss of the cover of grass but also of roots and later of the topsoil as well.

Root depths of various plants in the big bluestem community had been ascertained in 1932 (Albertson, 1937). Bisects were again made in 1940 to ascertain root depth and spread at the end of the drought. During increase in desiccation the root systems of most species grew into deeper soil and a greater number of rootlets developed at the deeper level. Average root depths in feet of eight important species before (1932) and near the close of the drought (1939) were as follows: big bluestem 5 and 6, western wheatgrass 6 and 8, side-oats grama 5 and 6, few-flowered psoralea 8 and 10, false boneset 10 and 12, many-flowered aster 3 and 7, Baldwin's ironweed (*Vernonia baldwini*) 4 and 8, and Pitcher's sage (*Salvia pitcheri*) 4 and 8 feet.

Thus, the roots of all of these species (and others) not only penetrated deeper into the moist subsoil, following drought in the solum, but those of *Aster, Vernonia* and *Salvia* doubled their former length. The roots of *Panicum virgatum* did not increase beyond their former 7-foot depth, but they became much more numerous than formerly in the deeper soil. Thus, changes resulting from drought in upland and lowland species were quite diverse.

PLANT YIELDS AND SOIL MOISTURE

The yields of grasses and forbs and the amount of available soil moisture were ascertained during the dry year of 1940 and the moderately wet one of 1941. Data were obtained at 3 representative stations. On each prairie enough silt had been deposited as dust to seal the soil so effectively that runoff was greatly increased. It was further accelerated by the sparse cover of grasses and consequent lack of much obstruction to running water. For example, a four-inch rain at Hays in July (1940) moistened the soil to only 8 to 10 inches. More usually in this arid climate a high monthly rainfall results from many small showers followed by bright sunshine and high winds; hence the water is soon lost from the soil by evaporation and relief from drought is slight and temporary.

It should be emphasized that blue grama and buffalo grass have the ability to renew growth during the warm season at any time showers provide available water and to become dormant again within a short period of time. Various weeds also start growth promptly and develop vigorously during these intermittent periods with moist surface soil.

In 1940 drought began in May. Usually the surface foot alone had available water, but only temporarily and at widely separated intervals. Average total yield, including weeds, was .61 ton per acre. Yield of perennial grasses, including the few native forbs, was only .19 ton. In securing the yield, the vegetation was clipped to 0.5 inch of the soil. The grasses were clipped three or four times during summer, but all clippings were made at irregular intervals. The object was to harvest at such times as to obtain the total yield without the loss of any vegetation. The crop of peppergrass (*Lepidium densiflorum*), poverty weed (*Monolepis nuttalliana*), stickseeds (*Lappula*) and little barley (*Hordeum pusillum*) was harvested early in June. These plants had completed their growth, produced seed and were drying. So severe was the drought that even Russian thistles were extremely small and wilted and the few native forbs were greatly dwarfed. Even pricklypear cactus wilted and produced no new branches.

In 1941 a good supply of soil moisture prevailed (with slight exception) at least to a depth of 2 feet. But there were few perennial grasses and forbs left to benefit from it. A very early, dense cover of little barley, germinated the preceding fall, rapidly grew to a height of 12 to 20 inches. Development of other vegetation was greatly retarded by its shade. Numerous other weeds likewise grew vigorously, except where they were held in check by little barley. Long, slender, light-green tillers of blue grama and much attenuated stolons of buffalo grass resulted from the shade. Even the pistillate flowers of buffalo grass were borne on long, slender flower stalks. By mid-summer the matured little barley had, at a distance, the color and appearance of a ripened field of grain. This dead cover still produced enough shade to retard growth of the grasses.

Yield of perennial grasses averaged only 0.65 ton per acre; that of grasses and weeds together was 1.63 tons.

CHAPTER 8

A Regional Survey

NEAR THE end of the drought it seemed advisable to compare the grasslands of the western half of Kansas with those of a much wider area which had undergone similar vicissitudes. Earlier studies in these areas furnished a background for comparison of present conditions with those of the past (Weaver, 1924; Clements and Weaver, 1924; Albertson, 1937). During August, 1939, a study was made of pastures and range lands of western Nebraska and Kansas and portions of South Dakota and of great areas in eastern Wyoming and Colorado and the panhandle of Oklahoma. Eighty-eight representative ranges were examined in the six states, including several that had been under observation for a period of ten or more years.[1]

This survey of the midwestern grasslands (exclusive of vegetation on light, sandy soils) consisted very largely in the study of two great dominants (blue grama and buffalo grass) which were, with exceptions, the most important and sometimes nearly the sole components of the vegetation. Needle-leaf sedge (*Carex eleocharis*) and thread-leaf sedge (*C. filifolia*) were important in certain areas northward; needle-and-thread (*Stipa comata*) and western wheatgrass (*Agropyron smithii*) also were often intermixed with the short grasses, especially in the more northerly ranges. But the sod-formers and not the bunch grasses had become relatively more abundant since the advent of overgrazing, and the latter had also suffered far greater losses during the drought. One of the most outstanding effects of drought upon the grasses was the usually uniform distribution of the remaining individuals.

THINNING OF THE STAND

When the great drought came, it alone rarely or never killed all of the vegetation. The effect was that of thinning the stand. In this selective

[1] Abstracted from Weaver and Albertson, Ecology 21:216–236, 1940. Four of the 27 illustrations have been re-used.

process many of the less xeric species of grasses and forbs were killed outright and only a few dwarfed relics remained in the most favorable situations. Among the most drought-resistant grasses, it seems certain that the younger and consequently more poorly rooted individuals succumbed. Likewise, the less vigorous among the older and long established plants were destroyed. Much of this thinning occurred as a result of the intense heat and extended drought of 1934, but losses continued in 1936, 1937, and again in 1939. The normal precipitation of 17 inches over the western edge of the region often fell as low as 6 inches. Amount of destruction and the extreme test experienced by the survivors may be understood when it is known that many excellent ranges with 65 to 90 per cent basal cover had been reduced usually to a scant cover ranging between 20 and 1 per cent (Fig. 26).

Death among the perennial forb population was so widespread during the initial severe period or similar recurring ones that only scattered individuals of six or eight species regularly occurred. By almost eliminating species least fitted to endure hardships and by wide spacing of those best adapted, the grassland had adjusted itself to the new environment imposed upon it. Even widely spaced survivors had barely the necessary amount of soil moisture for their existence. Such an ecological process parallels in a general way that of the human population. Extensive abandonment of ranches and emigrations of settlers had been followed by wider spacings and larger holdings of the remaining population, most of whom had learned by long experience how to endure the hardships of drought.

CAUSES OF DAMAGE TO THE RANGE

Although the ranges had been depleted in stand and vigor of vegetation and carrying capacity as a result of the great drought, damage had not been due to intense heat and desiccation alone. Overgrazing and untimely pasturing of many ranges before this great catastrophe subjected them to the onslaught of desiccation in a much weakened condition. Moreover, during this long period of adversity much pasture land had literally been stripped of the last vestige of vegetation by hungry livestock and grasshoppers. Despite these adversities, extensive areas throughout the range country would have survived with only moderate losses had it not been for partial or complete burial by dust, or for injury by wind erosion and attending disastrous consequences. Damage to grassland has been enormously increased as a consequence of injudicious breaking and unwise tilling of extensive stretches of range lands.

"Recent years of agricultural expansion destroyed vast areas of native sod. The depression which followed, coupled with severe droughts, frequently resulted in indifferent farming or outright abandonment. The bare, unprotected soil was readily moved by the preying winds. Overgrazing joined with drought and was aided in the erosional process by the abandonment of neighboring fields. Depletion of land, often complete denudation was the result" (Newport, 1937).

OVERSTOCKING AND UNDERSTOCKING

A survey of the situation revealed clearly that too close grazing of the grama-buffalo grass ranges usually occurred where stock raising was carried on in conjunction with production of farm crops. Too much grazing pressure was permitted in pastures of moderate size (80 to 160 acres or more). This occurred somewhat regularly both before and often during the drought. Overgrazing even of the extremely resistant short grasses is doubly harmful. Not only is the vigor of the tops and crowns greatly reduced and the store of reserve food therein constantly decreased, but also the root system itself is greatly weakened by reduction in depth, lateral spread, and in efficiency as an absorbing organ (Weaver and Darland, 1947). Any slight gains by stolon production may be immediately checked. On larger holdings, pastures were many square miles in area; not infrequently the sweep of unbroken, level or undulating range land extended to the horizon on all sides. Where stock raising was the chief industry, usually more attention had been given to grazing practice on these privately owned ranges. But even here the pressure of starving stock during the early drought resulted in a high degree of overgrazing, and subsequent adverse conditions had prevented much recovery even where cattle had been shipped out. Nearly all of the ranges observed had been excessively grazed.

In the midst of range lands greatly depleted by drought and dust damage, however, were found favorably located tracts of land where damage to the range, if any, must be attributed largely to grazing abuses alone. A striking example was a low-lying, almost level area north of Tribune, Kansas. It was several square miles in extent and nearly surrounded by grass-covered hills, the unbroken range extending well back over the upland. Consequently, there was no deposit of dust on the excellent growth of buffalo and grama grass which was favored by run-in water from the slopes. The basal cover was 95 per cent and the foliage almost completely concealed the soil. This, of course, was the result of good range management and decreased grazing pressure during the dry years. But portions of this lowland had suffered from overstocking. This was shown by the common occurrence and spread of cacti, by reduction of the basal cover (which was scarcely exceeded by the foliage cover) to 20 per cent, and by the presence of an abundance of weedy annuals.

Exceptions to general range damage by whatever cause sometimes occurred. These may have been due to opportune rains having permitted a previous return toward normal, to more judicious range management, or to protection from damage by dust burial.

During the extreme periods of drought of the past 7 years, it had been necessary intermittently to ship starving cattle to eastern and southern pastures. In many instances, notably in central and western Kansas and Nebraska, the herds had not been replaced (or only in part) and pastures had undergone year-long protection or, at least, light grazing. Many such ranges had somewhat recovered from drought depletion. In the eastern portion of the region with mean annual precipitation of 20 to 23 inches, increase in abundance and vigor of the vegetation was often marked. Buffalo grass, especially, had reclaimed much formerly bare area by means of rapidly spreading stolons, and mats of this grass, frequently 4 to 6 inches thick, completely concealed the soil. In the drier ranges farther westward, recovery had often been very slow even under protection, so greatly were the plants weakened and so limited had been the precipitation.

INJURY FROM DUST

Accompanying the extremely high temperatures and almost rainless summers were unusually high winds. These great storms carried enormous amounts of earth from parched fallow fields and cropped land and deposited them on other fields and pastures (Fig. 28). The depth of deposit varied greatly depending upon distance from the source of supply, topography, and nature of vegetation. Whether a good cover of native vegetation or a depleted, weedy one offered obstruction to the dust-laden wind,

FIG. 28. (Upper) Range near the Jay Em Ranch about 30 miles south of Lusk, Wyoming. The conspicuous plants are Russian thistle. Original cover consisted of blue grama, thread-leaf sedge and needle-and-thread, of which only remnants remain. Photo, 1939. (Lower) Range near Boise City, Oklahoma, on level land that had been covered with silt and again uncovered. Only enough of the original plant cover remained to identify it as native grassland. Photo, 1939.

the result was a covering of soil more or less uniformly deposited to a depth of .5 to 2 or more inches. Dust drifts and mounds sometimes 2 to 3 feet or more in height were formed. Often the grasses were only partially destroyed, but in many instances practically all vegetation was smothered. It should be emphasized that had the land not been broken decrease in amount of vegetation would have certainly resulted from the intense drought, but not such overwhelming denudation. Even when the compacted dust deposit reached a depth of only an inch, it usually killed much of the short-grass cover.

After the dust-covered vegetation died and disintegrated, the tops no longer held the soil against wind erosion. Once more the soil began to shift before the force of the wind. Much of it was transported, often to be deposited in drifts 1.5 to 2 feet or more high where centers of accumulation were afforded by the crop of annuals, most generally Russian thistles, which had previously sprung up in the pastures. Much drifting in pastures occurred in 1937 and 1938, when great areas of grassland were laid bare by the blowing away of accumulated silt. Indeed, the chief source of supply of silt for some of the worst dust storms during these years was from the earth formerly deposited on the ranges.

Abundant evidence of the sequence of deposit and subsequent erosion—sometimes by torrential rains as well as by wind—was offered by the dead crowns and decaying stolons of grasses, which usually remained plainly in view on the wind-swept, bare surface. The roots were still anchoring them in place. Other evidence was found in the crowns and taproots of forbs, a few of which often remained alive as much dwarfed survivors. In many instances two or three years elapsed before the former soil surface was uncovered.

The scarifying action of dust-laden winds contributed to the death of many pasture plants. Pastures of 80 to 160 acres in area were often wholly surrounded by cultivated fields. They suffered more injury than larger ones. Partial dust burial often caused living vegetation to reestablish its base 1 to 4 inches above the former soil level. Thus, when the loose soil was later removed, or when erosion lowered the old soil level, the plants, including various forbs, were elevated on columns quite above the surrounding soil. This exposure, of course, aggravated drought and most of the plants died.

Furrows were sometimes made in pastures in order to check the removal of blowing soil. This usually held the soil on the field and promoted an excellent growth of annual weeds but practically destroyed the native plants. So thoroughly did the soil deposits from fields and the subsequent drifting destroy the vegetation that, after the roots and rhizomes decayed, wheat was drilled on the one-time range without further preparation of a seedbed.

Some of the greatest losses to ranges by dust burial probably occurred in and adjacent to the panhandle of Oklahoma, which with considerable areas in the four adjoining states was designated as the dust bowl. This resulted from a combination of factors, one of which was the large amount of tilled land that furnished an unlimited amount of wind-blown soil. But similar damage was found throughout western Kansas and Nebraska and in Wyoming, as well as throughout eastern Colorado. It was a very general rather than a local phenomenon and is apt to recur wherever unprotected, drought-parched soil adjacent to grassland is subjected to high winds.

DAMAGE BY GRASSHOPPERS

Still another factor in reducing the vigor of vegetation was the hordes of grasshoppers which accompanied the drought. They ate the leaves and tender stems of the grasses, stripped the foliage of the ubiquitous peppergrass and Russian thistle, and devoured nearly all vegetation including the only plant cover remaining in many pastures—the mat-like poverty weed (*Monolepis nuttalliana*). Even on ranges where stock was excluded, grasshoppers had sometimes eaten practically all of the scanty growth of vegetation. Moreover, buffalo grass was especially retarded in its development not only by the injury or loss of foliage but also the always-hungry grasshoppers cut the stolons at the nodes where they are tender and where the growing tissue is sweet. Thus segregated from the parent plant, the poorly rooted, younger offspring succumbed.

CHANGES IN COMPOSITION OF VEGETATION

As a result of the combined forces causing deterioration in range and pasture, there have been marked changes in vegetational structure. The mixed prairie, distinguished by more or less distinct layers of mid grasses and short grasses, had, at least in the several thousand square miles examined, almost entirely been converted into short-grass plains. This had resulted from the loss of the mid grasses. Before the great drought, it is true, there were many ranges that had lost most of the vegetation of the upper layer through continuous overgrazing. But relics were always present and usually abundant in wet years. Moreover, adjacent grassland less severely abused showed clearly the true nature of this relationship. This grazing disclimax was now much more pronounced, and extended quite to the eastern border of mixed prairie. This conversion of mixed prairie to a short-grass disclimax was indeed one of the most interesting features of this grassland.

Over vast stretches, in 1939, red three-awn, purple three-awn, squirrel-tail, Junegrass, needle-and-thread, little bluestem and western wheatgrass appeared to be entirely absent. Undoubtedly remnants remained underground and in favored places, but the long-time drought and the grazing of the grass almost into the soil had been extremely destructive.

Many of the less xeric forbs such as ground plum (*Astragalus crassicarpus*), woolly loco (*A. mollissimus*), prairie coneflower (*Ratibida columnifera*), prairie cat's-foot (*Antennaria neglecta*), gumweed (*Grindelia squarrosa*) and others had likewise practically vanished. Certain of the most persistent native forbs were nearly always present, often as mere remnants. The most drought resistant were red false mallow (*Sphaeralcea coccinea*), cut-leaved goldenweed (*Haplopappus spinulosus*), rush-like lygodesmia (*Lygodesmia juncea*) and narrow-leaved four-o'clock (*Mirabilis linearis*). Few-flowered psoralea (*Psoralea tenuiflora*), blazing star (*Liatris punctata*) and wavy-leaved thistle (*Cirsium undulatum*) were slightly less so. False boneset (*Kuhnia eupatorioides*) was likewise very resistant to drought injury. Even these xeric forbs were always greatly dwarfed and usually only 2 to 8 inches tall. Early spring revealed an abundance of Carolina anemone (*Anemone caroliniana*) and onion (*Allium drummondi*), plants with large storage organs, but these soon disappeared aboveground.

The opening of the plant cover and the abundance of bare soil permitted the growth of hordes of short-lived annuals, some of which were so thickly placed as to quite obscure the remaining grasses. Among the most persistent and widely distributed were peppergrass (*Lepidium densiflorum*), stickseed (*Lappula occidentalis*), little barley (*Hordeum pusillum*), Pursh's plantain (*Plantago purshii*), spinulose plantain (*P. spinulosa*), poverty weed (*Monolepis nuttalliana*) and cryptantha

(*Cryptantha crassisepala*). But they were soon overtaken by drought, their dead remains giving the dull leaden-gray or, later, black color to the landscape.

Sometimes the pastures were reddened after a period with showers by a thick growth of purslane (*Portulaca oleracea*). More frequently they varied through several shades of green, depending upon the direction of the incident light, and finally to black as the ubiquitous Russian thistles proceeded through their early stages of development until they were killed and dried by drought. Large numbers of annuals—notably pigweeds (*Amaranthus retroflexus, A. blitoides,* and *A. graecizans*), lamb's quarters (*Chenopodium album*), narrow-leaved goose foot (*C. leptophyllum*) and buffalo bur (*Solanum rostratum*)—were scattered in dusted pastures or grew thickly in the deposits of silt. Their stature was determined by rainfall; they were mostly dwarfed in 1939 and only infrequently exceeded a height of 2 to 6 inches.

One of the worst perennial weeds was the cactus. Several genera are concerned but by far the most important are species of *Opuntia.* The increase in numbers accompanied the opening of the grass cover. Even before the great drought many ranges were highly infested as a result of too close grazing. Since the great destruction wrought by this recent disaster, cactus had increased almost throughout. Much branched, circular individuals 3 to 5 feet or more in diameter and spaced only 6 to 10 feet apart occupied a large portion of the range land (Fig. 29). Occupancy of 20 per cent of the soil by this pest was not uncommon. Ranges with greatly increased numbers and with only 50 to 25 per cent of soil unoccupied by cacti occurred. Some ranges were thus entirely worthless for grazing, and even jack rabbits avoided them. Propagation in bare soil is rapid; it was estimated that these plants in 1939 were 4 to 7 times as abundant as in 1934. Seedlings occurred in untold millions and were especially abundant about the parent plants. Joints of the stems are broken off by stock and frequently become rooted when the surface soil is moist, thus increasing the number (Fig. 29). Moreover many-spined opuntia (*Opuntia polyacantha*) spreads by root-offshoots.

Cacti, however, like most weeds, render certain valuable services in nature. Such are stabilizing the soil against wind and running water and furnishing oases of protection for range grasses against grazing animals. Here many species reproduce unharmed. Snow accumulates and runoff

FIG. 29. (Upper) Hard, wind-swept, level soil near Cimarron, Kansas, where only a few widely spaced tufts of buffalo grass remained. Local showers enabled them to produce stolons, but with summer drought only the older, more deeply rooted offspring survived. (Lower) Range near the South Dakota-Wyoming State line west of Custer. Cactus occupies about 20 per cent of the area and the closely grazed short grasses, threadleaf sedge, sand dropseed and western wheatgrass furnish a 20 per cent cover over the remainder.

water is dammed back until it enters the soil, which is often more permeable under the cactus. The seedling grasses and forbs grow in partial shade and evaporation from the soil surface is much reduced. Where the cactus plants merge such havens may extend several yards, often at right angles to the slope, and thus afford considerable areas for seed production by grasses and forbs. Buffalo grass is less likely to thrive because of its unfavorable reaction to shade and the accumulated debris.

So great had been the disturbance to the grassland and so regularly had ruderals taken possession that it was frequently difficult to determine, except by close study, whether or not the land had been tilled. The landscape in summer for miles about was often one of Russian thistles in field and pasture.

Reconstruction of the original cover from the dead remains is an interesting task. Fragments of rootstocks, bits of stolons, strong taproots of forbs and even grass roots themselves, together with comparison of adjacent more protected areas, make identification certain. Whether the dusting was recent or occurred during the earlier years of drought could often be determined. Previous knowledge of the area when vegetation was intact, and study during the several processes of deposit and denudation, as has been the opportunity of the writers, lent certainty to the exactness of sequence.

DEGREE OF DETERIORATION

A total of 88 well spaced, typical areas on non-sandy lands in the six states were examined and basal cover ascertained. According to the amount of remaining cover of range grasses, they have been separated into five groups. Ranges with a cover of 21 per cent or more (exclusive of weeds) formed only 16 per cent of the total. Those with 11 to 20 per cent cover constituted another 16 per cent. The largest group, 28 per cent, presented a cover of 6 to 10 per cent. The basal cover of another 16 per cent ranged from 2 to 5 per cent, while nearly one-fourth of the grasslands (24 per cent) had a basal cover of only 1 per cent or less. Distribution of the good and bad conditions was not at all uniform. This was to be expected when so many causes or combinations of causes had operated to produce degeneration. The outstanding fact was the very poor cover.

CHAPTER 9

Recovery of Vegetation

FOR EIGHT years drought had prevailed in the mid-continental grasslands. Mixed prairie vegetation westward to the Rocky Mountains had nearly or entirely disappeared. But now the parched soil was wet once more to a depth of several feet; the air was warm and moist. The terrible dust storms had ceased. A changed environment had come at last for this was the end of the long period of drought. Thus, in 1941 the long delayed recovery of vegetation began. The nature of this complex phenomenon was now to be revealed and the sequence of recovery to be recorded. It was with new hope but also with a sense of new responsibility that the writers continued their field studies. For here was nature at work repairing the damage of a great catastrophe, a catastrophe that had undoubtedly occurred many times in the long history of grassland but one of which there is no written record.[1]

THE NEW ENVIRONMENT

Although 1939, the last year of drought, was the most severe, precipitation in 1940 was approximately normal; rainfall during the two following years was far above average. Precipitation at Hays (1940–1942) was 23, 28 and 29 inches respectively, but in 1943 it was only 16 inches. Moreover, the rains were unusually well distributed (except in 1943) during each month of the growing season. This was fortunate since rainfall in summer has in this climate a greater effect in promoting growth and recovery of vegetation than has the total for the year. It was during these good years that soil moisture was replenished. Upon this reserve the vegetation continued to grow, although not luxuriantly, despite the decreased precipitation in 1943.

Amount of moisture in the soil is especially important in mixed prairie since it is nearly always the limiting factor in plant production. Soil

[1] Materials in this chapter and stages in plant succession in the following one have been adapted from Weaver and Albertson, Ecological Monographs 14:393–479, 1944. Eight illustrations have been reproduced.

samples were taken each week to a depth of 5 feet at typical locations in the upland plains type. Amount of water available for plant growth (the amount above the hygroscopic coefficient) was ascertained for each soil depth. Results at Phillipsburg and Dighton were very similar to those at Hays, which are shown in Table 3.

Wind movement decreased greatly during the period of recovery. It was 39, 20, and 16 hundred miles less during the summer of 1941, 1942, and 1943, respectively, than the average during drought. Dust storms were

TABLE 3. Available soil moisture each week at the several depths in the short-grass community. Numbers indicate the amount of available water; (1) 1 to 4.9 per cent, (2) 5 to 9.9, (3) 10 to 19.9, and (4) 20 per cent or more; otherwise there was none. In 1940 no water was available below 2 feet, and in 1941, below 3 feet.

Depth Feet	May		June				July				August				Sept.	
1940																
0–.5	3	2	1	2	1		2	2	1		3	1		1	1	
.5–1			1	1			1	2	1		1	1				
1–2									1	1						
1941																
0–.5	4	4	4	3	3	3	3	1		1		2	3	4	3	2
.5–1	3	4	4	3	3	2	3	1		1		1	3	3	3	2
1–2	3	3	4	3	2	3	2	1	1			1		1	1	
2–3	1	2	3	1	2	2	2	2	1			1				
1942																
0–.5	2	2	3	4	4	4	3	1	1	1	2	1	2		2	2
.5–1	2	1	3	3	3	4	3	2	1	1		1	1		2	2
1–2	3	2	3	3	3	3	3	2	2	2	1	1	1	1	1	2
2–3	2	2	3	3	3	3	3	2	2	2	1	1	1	1	1	1
3–4	1	1	2	2	3	3	3	2	2	2	2	1	1	1	1	1
4–5	1		2	2	3	3	3	2	2	2	2	1	2	1	1	1
1943																
0–.5	3	3	1	1	1				3	1		3	1			
.5–1	2	2	1	1	1	1				1		1				
1–2	2	2	2	1	1	1	1		1	1		1	1	1	1	
2–3	1	1	1	1										1		
3–4	1	1	1													
4–5	1	1	1	1	1	1						1		1		

far less frequent, more local, and much less severe. Evaporation at Hays from a free water surface averaged 56.9 inches during April to September 1933–1939 inclusive. It was reduced each year, 1940 to 1943, as follows: 7.7, 13.2, 15.0 and 6.4 inches, respectively. With three slight exceptions, evaporation each month was lower than during drought. The average mean maximum temperatures by weeks in June, July and August were decreased 2.6°, 4.0° and 3.9° F. Mean monthly temperatures were also very much lower.

Summarizing, the period of recovery, compared with that of drought, was one of greatly increased precipitation and soil moisture coupled with lower temperatures, less wind movement, and decreased rates of evaporation. Vegetation reacted to the changed environment by increase in number of species, greater density of cover and large gains in quantity of forage production.

A STUDY OF RECOVERY

Recovery of drought-depleted vegetation in mixed prairie has been fully studied (Fig. 30). For despite the dry-land farmer and much unwarranted exploitation of the prairie sod, the fact remained that the larger portion of this vast grassland had still been untouched by the plow (Great Plains Committee, 1937). The importance of livestock production in the United States had at this period assumed the deepest significance of historic time. The highest efficiency in animal production and range management go hand in hand with the greatest understanding of the range resources (McArdle & Costello, 1936). This must be based on the life history of vegetation and its response to the environment. In some of the eight drought years the crop of native grasses failed almost completely and early in drought thousands of cattle either starved or were shipped eastward to new pastures or to market. Any gains made by the vegetation in the period 1937 and 1938 were lost in the terrible drought of 1939–1940.

Better times had come. For three summers good rains had fallen, except in 1943 in southwestern Kansas, the Oklahoma and Texas panhandles, southern Colorado and northeastern New Mexico, in short, in the area of the old dust bowl. Even here vegetation had usually made considerable recovery and development was remarkable where rainfall was ample. It had often been moderately good even in or near the dust bowl,

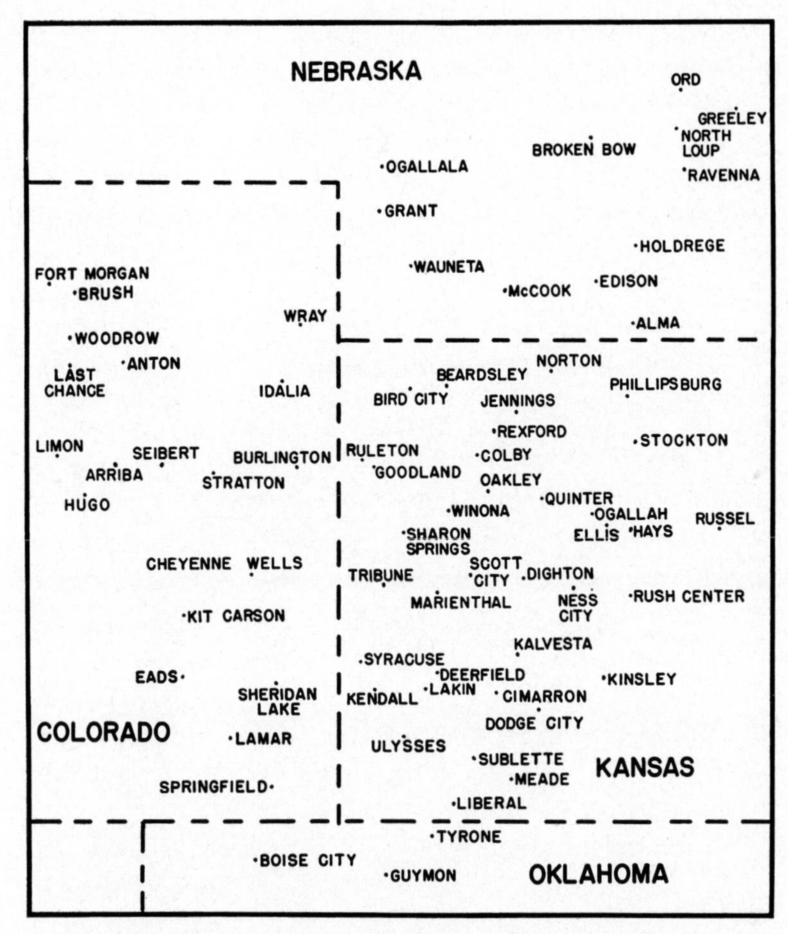

FIG. 30. Outline map of the region showing stations mentioned in the text and figures and other stations where studies were conducted.

except where deep layers of loose soil buried all of the former vegetation. There it was still covered with a stand of annual weeds (Fig. 31).

Ranges of western Kansas were not fully stocked in 1941 to 1943, inclusive, a condition which prevailed in many places elsewhere. Although emphasis was placed on production of more cattle, the herds had been so greatly depleted that, in general, renewed cover increased more rapidly than grazing animals. In most of the ranges probably not more than half of the forage was utilized and frequently only 10 to 20 per cent. Some, of course, were overgrazed; in others none of the vegetation was removed. The ranges would probably have increased their perennial cover even more rapidly if moderate grazing had been generally employed and much of the foliage which later formed excess debris had been consumed or trampled to the ground.

The major features of recovery were closely connected with the behavior of three grasses, although there were several minor ones. These were buffalo grass, blue grama and sand dropseed. Before drought the

FIG. 31. (Upper) Prairie near Ness City, Kansas, illustrative of nearly level range land which has been badly disturbed (foreground) by dust coverage. (Lower) Drifts of dust on range land near Lakin in southwestern Kansas, 1939.

first two of these, the short grasses, were fairly evenly intermixed over most of western Kansas, eastern Colorado and western Nebraska.

Buffalo grass entirely disappeared from some ranges, in others it remained alive only in the most favorable places as regards water supply. This occurred over thousands of square miles of land in the dust bowl. In addition this grass disappeared from the level areas of thousands of other pastures eastward and northward. Conversely, many ranges retained occasional tufts or small sodded patches and it was from these that regeneration proceeded so rapidly when the soil again became moist.

Blue grama is much more drought resistant than buffalo grass and it was never killed so uniformly nor so completely over a wide area. In nearly every range, unless deeply buried by dust, some bunches of blue grama persisted. These drought relics often increased greatly in diameter, sometimes to 10 or 12 inches, and were found scattered thinly in pastures where no other perennial vegetation survived.

Sand dropseed occurred widely but usually not abundantly before the drought, except in sandy soil. But when the silt loams and other types of hard land soils became bare and warm the tiny wind-blown and animal-distributed seeds of this drought-resisting bunch grass were spread everywhere and plants often occurred abundantly. They persisted tenaciously even where much dwarfed by drought.

Rate of recovery of vegetation varied greatly from place to place since several conditions were involved. Chief among these were the kind of original vegetation, the intensity of drought and consequent degree of depletion and the kind of grass relics at the end of drought. Other factors were amount of damage resulting from burial by dust and the intensity of grazing and trampling during the period of recovery, as well as the distribution of precipitation over various portions of the area during recovery. Thus, the process far from being simple was actually considerably involved.

A principle that held true throughout was that recovery was always slower where blue grama alone remained than where buffalo grass was the sole perennial grass or where it occurred with blue grama. This is well illustrated by the slow increase in cover of a range near Tribune, Kansas, where blue grama increased to only 21 per cent after three years of recovery (Fig. 32). In another range a few miles distant blue grama increased from 2 to 15 per cent in the same period.

That buffalo grass spreads much more rapidly than blue grama is well illustrated by quadrats in a dust-covered pasture near Kendall, Kansas. In 1941 buffalo grass composed about 2 per cent of the very sparse cover. But it increased to 34 per cent the next year and to 47 in 1943. During this period blue grama increased from 1 to only 3 per cent as did also sand dropseed. On a range near Marienthal, Kansas, which was only lightly

pastured after being heavily dusted, buffalo grass increased its basal cover (1940 to 1943) as follows: 2, 24, 85 and 93 per cent. Increase of blue grama was slow in the same period of years, from 1 to 5 per cent. Thus, this wonderful recovery was due almost entirely to buffalo grass.

EXAMPLES OF RECOVERY

Revegetation from a poor cover of mixed short grasses is well illustrated by quadrats in a pasture near Quinter. This range had been grazed by sheep rather continuously since 1937 and was closely grazed in 1942–43. Basal cover was composed entirely of the two short grasses. They were equally abundant both in 1940 (total basal cover 8 per cent) and 1941 (25 per cent). Blue grama increased to 28 per cent in 1942 but decreased to 16 the next year. But buffalo grass increased first to 47 per cent and then to 79. Thus, in three years recovery resulted in a 95 per cent cover of short grass.

An example of a more rapid recovery where dusting had been less extensive but drought equally severe is taken from another pasture near Quinter. Here grazing was moderate. Increase of blue grama was slow from 1940 to 1943. The percentages of cover were 6, 12, 13 and 16, respectively. Buffalo grass developed very rapidly, from 2 per cent to 34, then to 52 and finally to 80 per cent. Thus, the total cover year by year (including a little sand dropseed which entered in 1941) was 8, 46, 66 and 98 per cent, a remarkably early recovery.

When sand dropseed entered a range during the later years of drought it frequently played an important part in increasing the cover. Recovery on ranges with drifted soil was determined largely by the amount, if any, of relic vegetation. Occasionally it was rapid, usually there was a wilderness of annual weeds for a long time.

A large range near Lakin, Kansas, had been heavily dusted in 1935 and at various periods thereafter. Native vegetation had been almost completely destroyed during drought years. In the fall of 1942 only occasional bunches of buffalo grass and blue grama were found but in no instance

FIG. 32. A typical quadrat in a large range near Tribune, Kansas. In the fall of 1940 the grass was all blue grama with a basal cover of 5 per cent (upper). The same quadrat in 1942 (middle) with 18 per cent blue grama and 11 per cent sand dropseed. After three years of recovery, 1943, (lower) there was only 21 per cent basal cover of blue grama.

had they made much growth in recent years. Weeds of the early stage were plentiful, especially common sunflower which was so abundant that one walked through the pasture with great difficulty in searching for the permanent quadrats located there.

In a large pasture near Syracuse, Kansas, the soil was practically bare in the spring of 1940. In the fall of 1940 there was no short grass but there were myriads of seedlings of sand dropseed. Two years later bunches of sand dropseed 2 to 4 inches in diameter but 4 to 24 inches apart formed a cover over much of the pasture and scattered plants of buffalo grass 3 to 8 feet distant occurred as an understory. Total perennial cover did not exceed 5 per cent. Russian thistle, horseweed, sunflower and rough pigweed were very abundant. Common weeds of smaller stature were cryptantha, purslane, plantain, witchgrass and spurge.

A 360-acre range 20 miles north of Limon, Colorado, was examined in August, 1939. It had been heavily dusted and all but 1 per cent of the original cover had been destroyed. Most of the dust had been removed by wind and water after the vegetation died and thus failed to continue to hold it in place. Only widely spaced remnants of blue grama and buffalo grass remained in 1939. Most of the buffalo grass mats were small, only a foot or two in diameter. There was a very light sprinkling of sand dropseed and wheatgrass, especially about relic bunches of cactus. The population of annual weeds—plantain, peppergrass and stickseed—had died and with the fragments of small Russian thistles had been drifted together. Many square yards were entirely without a living plant.

A later stage in succession occurred on the rolling hillsides near Beardsley, Kansas, in 1942 where level land gave way to characteristic "breaks" in country dissected by streams. Many thousands of acres of such land are under grazing and will remain thus since this is not arable land. On the steep slopes runoff and erosion had become great during drought but they were less on the moderately sloping hillsides. Much of the soil was covered with an open stand of blue grama but there was also much bare soil. Erosion had removed the topsoil in places and left bunches of blue grama elevated two inches above the present soil level (Fig. 33). The many tufts of blue grama testified to a rapid recovery. Relic bunches and small patches of buffalo grass grew in the most favored places. They were not yet densely consolidated but were extending runners everywhere. Seedlings and young bunches of both three-awns and tumblegrass were

FIG. 33. (Left) Bunches of blue grama in flower on a steep hillside near Beardsley, Kansas, in July, 1942. Many are elevated 1 to 3 inches as a result of soil erosion. (Right) Range near Sheridan Lake, Colorado, showing old bunches of blue grama and numerous well established seedlings in 1942.

common. On the steepest and most abrupt slopes, locally designated as catsteps, widely spaced bunches of side-oats grama occurred plentifully. Sand dropseed was common elsewhere. The hills had not been dust-covered, but they had lost much soil by wind erosion. Soil between the bunches of grasses was hard and mostly bare since the usual soil mulch was not present. The weed stage was poorly represented by scattered plants of Russian thistle and witchgrass.

The greatly thinned cover of big bluestem in its type had been invaded by coarse weeds, especially common sunflower, lamb's quarters, horseweed, snow-on-the-mountain (*Euphorbia marginata*) and great ragweed (*Ambrosia trifida*). But these and the invading grasses—western wheatgrass, tall dropseed, side-oats grama and even short grasses—were soon replaced by shoots from the spreading rhizomes of the original dominant.

Little bluestem was all but exterminated. Yet in 1943 the hillsides and knolls where it formerly flourished were dotted with clumps of this grass. Most of these were new growth from crowns of plants which underwent deep dormancy during drought. Despite this survival, on the hillsides side-oats grama and not little bluestem retained first place among the grasses; little bluestem dominated here only during the wetter cycles.

Recovery in the ungrazed blue grama—buffalo grass community was ascertained each year in a range formerly moderately grazed near Hays. Quadrats in exclosures were staked out in 1932 and cattle excluded thereafter. The two short grasses occurred in a mixed stand in about equal amounts. The basal area was 88.6 per cent. Losses of buffalo grass were greater than those of blue grama after 1934 but it recovered in 1938 and the two grasses again occurred in approximately equal amounts. After the severe fall and winter drought of 1939–40, blue grama was once more somewhat the more abundant. But during the following period of recovery blue grama merely doubled in amount while buffalo grass increased sevenfold as follows:

Species	1939	1940	1941	1942	1943
Blue grama	13	10	14	15	22
Buffalo grass	9	9	41	80	66
Total	22	19	55	95	88

In a moderately grazed short-grass type recovery was somewhat less. Blue grama increased from 18 per cent in 1940 to 29 in 1942 and buffalo grass from 8 to 42. Buffalo grass was so aggressive that it continued to spread somewhat at the expense of blue grama, especially in 1943 when the percentages were 53 and 22. This occurred in many areas but such spreading was only temporary.

Extensive quadratting in overgrazed pastures showed an astounding increase of buffalo grass from 6 per cent in 1940 to 86 per cent two years later. This occurred somewhat at the expense of blue grama which merely doubled its 7.5 per cent of cover.

The continuous record (1932–1943) of the short-grass type where it was ungrazed, moderately grazed, and overgrazed is summarized in figure 34. Here it may be seen that the degeneration of the range showed a direct relation to the degree of grazing. An exception occurred in 1939–40 when losses on the ungrazed area with a taller and thicker cover used the available water more rapidly and consequently suffered more from the extreme drought during these years. The lag in recovery of the moderately grazed pasture in 1940 was caused by a dense stand of little barley which greatly retarded the development of the short grasses. In figure 34 the area above the individual graphs indicates bare soil or soil

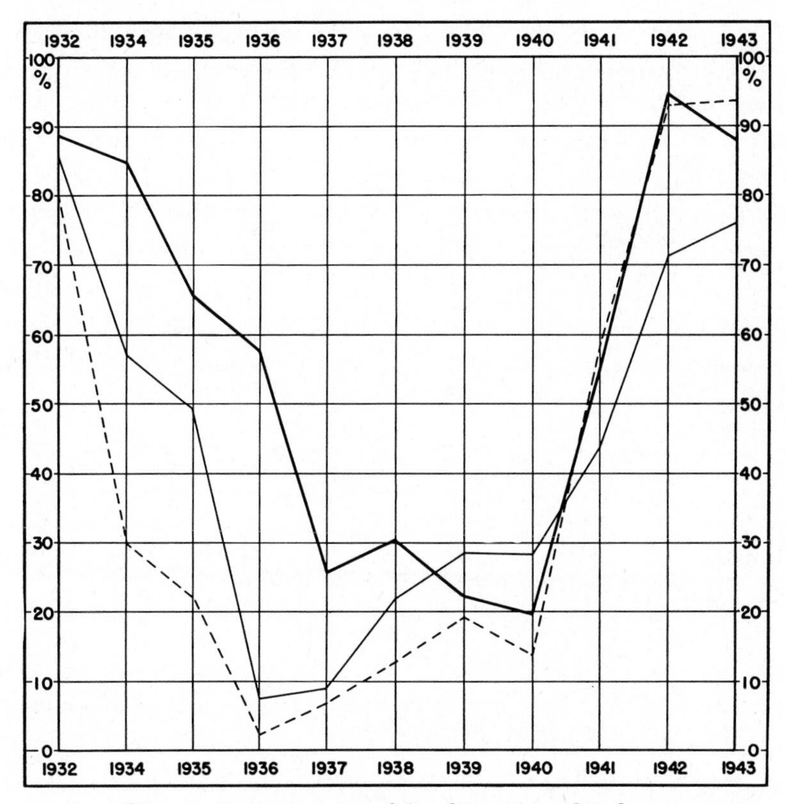

FIG. 34. Decrease in percentage of basal cover in the short-grass type during drought and increase during recovery after drought; ungrazed (heavy line), moderately grazed (light line), and overgrazed (broken line).

more or less covered with annual weeds. The great losses in cover sustained during the 8 years of drought were restored during a period of 3 good years, largely because of the wonderful recuperative powers of buffalo grass.

Vegetation in the ungrazed little bluestem type on thinner soil on rough land with a normal predrought basal cover of 60 per cent decreased to about 30. But it was 46 per cent in 1942–43. Little bluestem was entirely replaced by side-oats grama, blue grama and buffalo grass. Big bluestem nearly regained its 76 per cent of cover in its community, after being reduced to about 15, with proportional decreases in invading wheatgrass and short grasses.

The initial basal cover of vegetation (1940) at 15 well-distributed stations in western Kansas and the cover in 1943 were ascertained from numerous permanent quadrats under the following conditions of dusting and grazing:

Conditions	1940	1943
Light dusting and moderate grazing	3	76
Light dusting and overgrazing	10	69
Heavy dusting and moderate grazing	6	62
Heavy dusting and overgrazing	2	20

Recovery was most rapid in lightly dusted and moderately grazed ranges and most retarded where overgrazing had been practiced and dusting was heavy.

CONDITIONS FOR SUCCESSION

Recovery of vegetation at the end of drought was studied year by year in Kansas, Colorado and Nebraska. A series of widely separated stations was selected and examined annually (Fig. 30). Recovery over the vast area of range land was not a simple or single phenomenon. It was quite different on the level or moderately undulating uplands where the short-grass type prevailed from that on more restricted rolling and rougher areas where postclimax bluestems and other grasses dominated. The most extensive study of the subsere was made in the short-grass type. The change in a locality (or region) of one group of plants (community) to another community nearer the regional climax (original vegetation) is termed plant succession. It takes place in native ranges that are on the upgrade and is just the opposite of degeneration.

The intensity of drought was amazing. In southwestern Kansas on extremely dry years vegetation made practically no growth in spring and early summer. Sometimes the landscape was green only a few weeks during the entire growing season. Over many square miles dust from tilled land completely buried the vegetation. Coverage to an inch in depth usually killed the short grasses. Ungrazed land was not exempt, for here the presence of a good cover caused the dust to lodge in mounds and drifts. In low grade pastures weeds played a similar role. Thus, on the level land mounds and ridges of earth 1 to 5 feet deep and many feet long were a haven for weeds, the seeds having been scattered widely by the terrible dust storms. These deposits of early drought furnished the source of material for dust storms in later years after the vegetation beneath them had died. Thus, not only was the dust removed but often the original dry soil beneath as well (Fig. 31). These were conditions for the early subsere. There remains also the fact that in the drier southwestern area such an environment, as regards lack or scarcity of perennial vegetation, still persisted in 1943.

Where a moderate amount of precipitation was well distributed (1940–1943) growth was more or less continuous throughout the season and the subsere was shortened. For example, at Hays in a period of three years the earlier stages in the subsere had been replaced by the short grasses. But even here the earlier weed stages had persisted since the death of most of the vegetation, a period of 8 years.

Under less favorable normal climatic conditions southward and westward the drought had been much more severe and vast areas were so denuded by desiccation and erosion or deposit of soil that they were either almost or entirely bare. When rains came in 1940 to the eastern margin of the dust bowl, as they did at Hays, the long dry period continued westward, although with less severity. Hence these terribly denuded ranges remained in some early stage of succession even to the end of 1943. For here not only had an environment mostly unfavorable for growth been maintained but also perennial grasses were absent or so sparse that they produced almost no seed and spread but little by vegetative propagation. Throughout this territory buffalo grass had been rather widely exterminated and its return at first was nearly always by seed and not by extension of stolons.

A rather general cause of delay in re-establishment of perennial grasses not only during the most favorable years of drought but even during the first year of good rainfall was a dearth of seed. In 1941 samples of soil were collected at random from 40 different ranges in mixed prairie, nearly all in western Kansas and eastern Colorado (Weaver and Mueller, 1942). Three to five samples 0.5 inch deep and one square foot in area were taken at random from each range in very early spring. All viable seed in these soils was germinated under favorable conditions in a greenhouse. More than 11,000 seedlings emerged from the 151 samples of soil. Of these about 6,000 were grasses, including many weedy annuals. Approximately 75 per cent of the grass seedlings were blue grama, buffalo grass and sand dropseed. Blue grama was represented in 52 per cent of the samples and occurred at an average rate of 3.7 seedlings per square foot.

Buffalo grass was found in only 12 per cent and at the low average rate of 0.5 seedling per square foot. There was no side-oats grama or little bluestem and few other grasses except sand dropseed. It was found in 63 per cent of the samples and at the average rate of 26 seedlings per square foot.

In field studies in 14 of the more northerly of these mixed prairie stations, 25 square-foot samples were examined minutely in June of this very favorable year (1941) for germination and seedling growth. Average distribution of perennial grass seedlings in these ranges was only 2.4 per square foot. Repeated search for seedling grasses in the more northerly of the western Kansas stations in June and early July revealed only a few at certain stations. Elsewhere they were rare or none, since many of the ranges had been almost depopulated and continued drought had prevented even the relics from producing viable seed.

Over most of the mixed prairie there had been enough rainfall to moisten the soil continuously for several days, a condition necessary for seed germination. With rare exceptions the seedlings died from lack of a sufficient water supply. Hence, recovery by seedlings awaited a second year of good rainfall (1942) for the newly produced seed crop to germinate. Then both germination of seed and successful establishment of seedlings occurred in very great numbers (Fig. 33). Meanwhile buffalo grass had been making great gains by stolons.

STAGES OF SUCCESSION

The stages of succession in badly or completely denuded ranges and the chief species composing each stage were as follows:

First Weed Stage

Russian thistle
Salsola kali
Lamb's quarters
Chenopodium album
Narrow-leaved goosefoot
Chenopodium leptophyllum
Rough pigweed
Amaranthus retroflexus
Tumbleweed
Amaranthus graecizans
Prostrate pigweed
Amaranthus blitoides

Common sunflower
Helianthus annuus
Poverty weed
Monolepis nuttalliana
Purslane
Portulaca oleracea
Spurges
Euphorbia spp.
Buffalo bur
Solanum rostratum
Horseweed
Conyza canadensis

Second Weed Stage

Little barley
Hordeum pusillum
Witchgrass
Panicum capillare
Stinkgrass
Eragrostis cilianensis
Six-weeks fescue
Festuca octoflora hirtella
Brome or chess
Bromus spp.
Peppergrass
Lepidium densiflorum
Pursh's plantain
Plantago purshii
Spinulose plantain
Plantago spinulosa
Stickseed
Lappula redowskii
Stickseed
Lappula texana
Cryptantha
Cryptantha crassisepala

Early Native Grass Stage

Sand dropseed
Sporobolus cryptandrus
Western wheatgrass
Agropyron smithii
Tumblegrass
Schedonnardus paniculatus
False buffalo grass
Munroa squarrosa
Windmill grass
Chloris verticillata

Late Grass Stage

Blue grama
Bouteloua gracilis
Buffalo grass
Buchloe dactyloides
Purple three-awn
Aristida purpurea
Red three-awn
Aristida longiseta
Side-oats grama
Bouteloua curtipendula
Squirreltail
Sitanion hystrix

The stages in succession were not represented uniformly over any considerable territory nor were all parts of any large range usually in the same stage of development during a particular year, unless denudation had been general and complete. Usually there was a patchwork of patterns representing different stages in recovery toward the climax (*cf.* Shantz, 1917; Savage and Runyon, 1937; Judd and Jackson, 1939; and Tolstead, 1941). The concept of the presence of various stages and of their overlapping in time and space may best be gained from a presentation, in the following chapter, of actual revegetation of the land.

CHAPTER 10

Ten Good Years

The role of each of a few most important plants in the several stages of succession will now be given in order to make clear the development of vegetation from bare soil to predrought condition during the ten good years.

REVEGETATING THE LAND

Wherever the soil had been laid bare by drought or wind erosion or deposit, it soon became populated with annual weeds. Complete exhaustion of available soil moisture was the cause of death by drought; the high temperatures, low humidity, and excessive movement of desiccating winds combined to enormously increase water loss by promoting transpiration and direct evaporation from the soil surface. Plants that were watered did not die. Persistence of vegetation about snow guards (which were removed in summer) showed that its survival was due to the extra supply of moisture from the drifted snow. Here species of plants which died elsewhere often remained and sometimes maintained a nearly normal stature.

FIRST WEED STAGE

Russian thistle was the most abundant of the weedy annuals during the dry years. Of the densely crowded seedlings most succumbed and others were suppressed, since the dominant ones often attained large size, sometimes 3 feet or more in height, and the diameter of the more or less spherical top not infrequently reached 3 to 4 feet. But usually the plants were smaller and often dwarfed to only a few inches in height. This species has fleshy leaves and is very drought resistant. Normally the stems break off near the ground line in fall unless the plants are overtaken by drought. Then they tumble across the wide level country, scattering seed as they travel.

By late summer Russian thistles often occurred in practically pure stands since nearly all annual competitors had been overcome; some had been actually pushed aside by the enlarging crowns. This species alone or almost alone covered hundreds of square miles of the dust bowl and occurred widely in all the mixed prairie area. On many former ranges it was the early subsere, since it alone composed the vegetation.

Lamb's quarters and narrow-leaved goosefoot were perhaps the most abundant of all annual forbs on wet years. Seedlings did not appear until the soil became warm. The plants developed rapidly, forming a tall dense cover by midsummer. A common height was 3 to 5 feet when moisture was plentiful but on dry years there were dwarfed plants only 6-12 inches tall. They cast a dense shade and seedlings or recovering grasses were often greatly handicapped by their presence.

The common sunflower became very abundant in depleted ranges and largely replaced prairie sunflower on the hard lands. This native, annual species, although formerly extremely abundant, withstood drought poorly. Pure stands covered large areas of much degenerated range lands. Like most weeds it grew best when the soil became more or less permanently moist. But the size attained was rarely more than 4 to 6 feet. But this height contrasted sharply with most other weeds and especially with the patches of short grass sometimes scattered beneath.

Horseweed played an important part in the subsere almost everywhere. Although it occurred abundantly in the early stage, it was represented in later stages as well, and it persisted as long as there were small bare spots among the grasses where the seeds could reach the soil. A moist spring was usually essential for good establishment. It responded quickly to an increase in soil moisture and one could closely estimate the favorableness of the season by the height-growth of this weed.

All of the preceding annual weeds played an important role in temporarily stabilizing the loose, dry, wind-blown or water-eroded soil during the years of great drought. Practically all were grazed, in fact over thousands of acres they were the only forage available for starving cattle in the worst denuded pastures. But the food value was low and during the driest years even these weeds were dry during summer. Range examiners often estimated the carrying capacity of these weedy pastures in and near the great dust bowl as one animal unit per 80 acres.

SECOND WEED STAGE

The following species belong to the second weed stage. They usually dominated more stable areas than the preceding ones. In spring where the cover of weeds gave the appearance of excellent pasture, much of the aspect was due to little barley.

Little barley played a role of enormous importance during drought. This winter annual varied in height from 8 to 16 inches on wet years but was often only an inch or two tall on dry ones. It almost always succeeded in heading, however, before the moisture supply was exhausted. Its myriads of slender, unbranched stems covered the soil in very early spring and furnished fairly good grazing. But early in June and for many weeks thereafter dense yellowish patches or continuous stands of dried plants gave many ranges the appearance of a stubble field or a field of headed grain. The amount of little barley varied greatly by years and locality but it occurred everywhere.

Under little barley the shade was dense, often only 1 to 3 per cent of full sunshine. The dried straw continued to obstruct the light for seedlings and all low-growing vegetation. When it lodged, chance for survival of seedlings beneath it was still further reduced. Dead seedlings of sand dropseed and other grasses were found repeatedly under a cover of little barley. This weed produced 1 to 2 tons of forage per acre per year. Earlier in drought little barley occurred abundantly throughout the drought-stricken ranges but it decreased greatly after a year or more of heavy rainfall. It is a normal but small component of the short-grass cover.

In many ways the behavior of six-weeks fescue (*Festuca octoflora hirtella*) was similar to that of little barley. The densely aggregated stalks of this annual clothed the bare places, whether small or large, that occurred between the tufts of short grasses. A thin growth was also scattered in the clumps of short grass. When it dried it usually gave the range a tinge of brownish yellow even when the short grasses remained green.

Peppergrass produced continuous dense stands over many acres. Sometimes it was the sole species but usually there was an understory of an open stand of blue grama. It was widely distributed and grew in such abundance immediately following drought that it was very important in soil stabilization. The plants were 5 to 8 inches tall and usually grew so thickly that they obscured the grasses beneath them. This species was often replaced by plants of stickseed and cryptantha.

The stickseeds when green may grow so thickly as to completely cover the soil. On dried plants the leaves shrivel or fall and the much-branched stems and spiny fruits only are prominent. Cryptantha, a harsh borage, is often associated with stickseeds or alone covers much bared or partly bared soil.

All of these quickly maturing, weedy plants, except little barley, are of little value for grazing. Upon drying all become highly undesirable. Stickseeds and cryptantha were not eaten nor was the grass under a dense stand of these weeds. Yet the preceding weeds usually formed, during drought, the major components of the plant cover. Studies on the yield of ranges in western Kansas near the end of the drought have shown that while a ton or more per acre of peppergrass, stickseed, Russian thistle and other weeds was produced the yield of native grasses was often only 200 to 300 pounds.

The weed stages were present throughout the eight years of drought and in a fragmentary condition much longer. With the return of normal precipitation, and often two or three times the normal in spring and summer, grasses began to reclaim more of the area and bare spaces for annual weeds rapidly decreased. In this change of plant population not only did the climax grasses play a part but also a number of species which composed the early native grass stage.

EARLY NATIVE GRASS STAGE

With the appearance and increase of perennial grasses of the early native grass stage good progress toward stabilization had been made. For these plants are not only longer-lived but they also maintained a much better cover from year to year than did their predecessors. Their fibrous roots more firmly held the soil than did the short taproots of the preceding weeds or the shallow fibrous roots of the annual grasses. Nor did they grow so thickly and shade the soil with its seedling populations so greatly as the annual weeds.

Sand dropseed was the most widely spread and most abundant of the minor perennial grasses when the good years returned. Previous to the drought it was usually restricted to sandy soil. With the advent of the dry period vast areas of soil were laid bare. Into this warm, loose, usually dry soil sand dropseed spread widely, especially after 1939 when the plant cover was again greatly reduced. It increased very greatly since the drought and was now exceeded in abundance only by blue grama and buffalo grass. Although on some ranges only a few bunches were seen, more often it was found abundantly and not uncommonly in almost pure stands. It thrived in dusted pastures. Where open spaces occurred it was still spreading in 1943 by an enormous crop of seedlings. In fact, seedlings often occurred so thickly that they seemed to have been sown by man. Percentage of the basal cover where sand dropseed was intermixed with short grasses was commonly 5 to 20. Where disturbance was greater or soil type lighter, this rapidly increased to 50 per cent or more, and many ranges with 80 to 90 per cent sand dropseed and only remnants of short grasses have been examined.

Sand dropseed yielded readily to buffalo grass when it formed a dense sod. At first it became dwarfed in size, then fewer and fewer stems developed in spring. Finally old crowns without new stems revealed the last stages of its suppression. It yielded much more slowly over the years to blue grama.

Western wheatgrass often increased rapidly when the short-grass sod was opened by drought. Its rhizomes were present in the soil in numerous slightly more moist places even when development above ground was much retarded by competition. Its very early growth in spring when a little water was often available was a great advantage. Trampling, drought, and dusting were the keys that unlocked an area for the entrance or spread of wheatgrass.

Tumblegrass (Fig. 9) was commonly found, especially in disturbed places, before the drought, but it was unable to survive in drought. With the return of a normal supply of soil moisture, seedlings and tufts of tumblegrass became very abundant in the bare spaces between bunches of blue grama or mats of buffalo grass. Thus, much bare or weed-infested soil was again populated with a perennial grass. But this species formed only a temporary cover since it was easily replaced by sand dropseed, wheatgrass, and, of course, by the short grasses as well even before a complete cover was attained.

Squirreltail survived the drought poorly and only in rough or rocky terrain.

LATE GRASS STAGE

The development of the late grass stage is primarily a story of the return of blue grama and buffalo grass. Before the drought mid grasses were scattered throughout, mostly sparingly on the grazed hard lands. But during the drought cycle they practically disappeared. After three years favorable for recovery, they were only beginning to return. It was the short grasses that persisted as relics and they almost alone were replacing the cover of this great grazing disclimax.

During the great drought where all other native vegetation had succumbed one could nearly always find scattered bunches of blue grama. Sometimes they were as much as 20 feet apart, but in certain ranges they remained in considerable abundance even if widely spread. The bunches were separated in winter by bare soil and in summer by a mixed stand of annual weeds. These bunches often grew to very large size, 10 to 12 or more inches in diameter. They were important in holding the soil and later became the source of much seed.

As a result of good rains seedlings were found in abundance almost everywhere and their establishment was fairly certain. Thus, this stable species began slowly to return. Blue grama also spreads from rejuvenated tufts which result from the death of the central and often some peripheral portions of old bunches. The increase of blue grama and other grasses varied from season to season depending primarily upon amount of precipitation but also upon competition with weeds for light and water.

Where the cover of vegetation was dense, seed had difficulty in contacting the soil. In fact, it often did not reach the soil surface but instead was held above it. Moreover, growth of the seedling grasses was retarded by excessive shade. Tillering of blue grama and other established plants did not occur nor did the bunches enlarge where light was greatly reduced.

When the dense mats of buffalo grass covered the soil they soon became free of weeds and other grasses, except blue grama. In 1943 ungrazed ranges had a more or less continuous cover of short grass 8 inches in depth with 3 inches of dead mulch. When buffalo grass sod covered the soil about the bases of annual weeds they first became much dwarfed. The next season they were kept out because the seed either did not reach the soil or the soil was too dry or too much shaded for their growth.

The intermingling of buffalo grass with blue grama has been studied with great interest. Alternating patches of the two grasses were often well established before this occurred. At first the stolons spread between and among the bunches of blue grama. This resulted in a denser sod. Since the established bunches greatly overtopped the mats of buffalo grass the cover appeared very irregular. Later the buffalo grass grew close to the bunches and even spread its stolons through them. As a result blue grama tillered less and partly lost its bunchy appearance. Its growth was also less rank because of increased competition. Thus, the cover became much denser—often 95 per cent or more—and quite uniform in height, especially under grazing. Other species were mostly excluded where the sod was densest, but openings permitted the usual scattered growth of three-awn grasses, squirreltail and side-oats grama.

A transition from buffalo grass to other grassland types occurred in buffalo wallows. These are shallow, normally wet depressions varying from a few square yards to several acres in area and scattered irregularly throughout the level or undulating plains. They were so wet before the drought that they were inhabited mostly by big bluestem, side-oats grama, wild-rye, western wheatgrass and purple three-awn. Because of the shade buffalo grass grew but thinly in and around the edges of the wallow. But during the drought, it formed an almost continuous carpet with only remnants of the taller grasses. With the return of years with good rainfall the relic tall grasses renewed growth from their dormant underground parts, became re-established, and shaded out the buffalo grass.

RETURN OF FORBS

During the great drought, red false mallow (*Sphaeralcea coccinea*) was the only generally distributed, native, non-grassy species, aside from cactus, that increased in Kansas mixed prairie. It did this by vegetative propagation of underground parts when competition with the grasses was so greatly reduced. It thus increased in numbers manyfold. Its early growth in spring and its habit of semidormancy during drought enabled it to endure. A group of forbs which suffered great losses but were never completely exterminated included few-flowered psoralea (*Psoralea tenuiflora*), cut-leaved goldenweed (*Haplopappus spinulosus*), rush-leaved lygodesmia (*Lygodesmia juncea*), wavy-leaved thistle (*Cirsium undulatum*), yellow-spined thistle (*C. ochrocentrum*), scarlet gaura (*Gaura coccinea*), velvety goldenrod (*Solidago mollis*), false boneset (*Kuhnia eupatorioides*), narrow-leaved four-o'clock (*Mirabilis linearis*) and blazing star (*Liatris punctata*). But even these most xeric forbs became almost rare in 1939–40.

Following periods of good rainfall forbs began to increase not only in numbers but in stature as well. With some, this increase was from rhizomes; sometimes it was from seed from relic plants; but perhaps more frequently from seed that had lain dormant in the soil since the beginning of drought. The spread of velvety goldenrod and wavy-leaved thistle furnished examples of increase by rhizomes. Conversely, old plants of cut-leaved goldenweed have been found surrounded by offspring from recently produced seed. In badly broken prairie cover 50 to 100 seedlings were found within a radius of two feet from the parent plant. Few-flowered psoralea served as the best example of increase from seed that had lain on or in the soil for 7 or more years. This legume was greatly reduced in numbers early in drought even where the original cover was fairly well maintained. It rarely blossomed and probably seldom produced viable seed during the long dry period.

Most of the native forbs in climax grassland disappeared from the cover. Among these were prairie coneflower (*Ratibida columnifera*), woolly loco (*Astragalus mollissimus*), Venus' looking glass (*Specularia perfoliata* and *S. leptocarpa*). When the soil was again rather continuously moist at the end of the drought, myriads of seeds of these species, which had lain dormant for many years, finally germinated. Then the openings in the prairie sod were densely populated with the seedlings of many forbs. Foremost among them were prairie coneflower. There was thus great irregularity and sporadic distribution of many forbs rather than their more general and sparser occurrence. This maintained even where the cover of grasses was nearly complete.

Among the species which disappeared early was broom snakeweed (*Gutierrezia sarothrae*) which because of its extreme abundance and unpalatable nature became a chief indicator of overgrazing. But like most such species it returned promptly and often in great abundance. Many forbs were first observed after drought on north hillsides, in depressions, and in other favorable refuges from which they were extending their range. Return of western ragweed (*Ambrosia psilostachya*) was confined largely to the eastern and more moist portion of mixed prairie. Few-flowered psoralea (*Psoralea tenuiflora*) and cut-leaved goldenweed (*Haplopappus spinulosus*) made an early, marked recovery. But the recovery of most forbs was only partial during the first good years. Many-flowered aster (*Aster ericoides*), prairie cat's-foot (*Antennaria neglecta*) and prairie turnip (*Psoralea esculenta*) are examples of species that returned sparingly and only after several years. Conversely, red false mallow

(*Sphaeralcea coccinea*), with the return of more mesic conditions and a much extended cover of grasses, decreased in numbers and resumed more nearly its predrought abundance.

MORE SOIL MOISTURE AND GREATER YIELDS

Increase in dry weight is a good measure of growth and consequently of recovery of vegetation from drought as well. To ascertain yields, barbed wire exclosures to cattle were made on representative areas of short grasses moderately grazed, short grasses that had been overgrazed, and big bluestem. These were near Hays, Kansas. Production in the big bluestem type in 1942 was 2.4 times as great as in 1940; in the moderately grazed, short-grass type it was 3 times as great and in the overgrazed short-grass type, where buffalo grass was abundant, the increase was nineteenfold.

Mean annual precipitation following the drought to 1954 is shown in figure 35. From 1944 to 1950 it was approximately normal. Then the greatly increased rainfall (43 inches) in 1951 was followed by only 14 inches in 1952 and remained below normal in 1953 and 1954. This resulted in a new drought cycle. Water content of soil available for plant growth is shown throughout practically the entire growing season from 1935 to 1954 in tables 1, 3 and 4. No water was available at any time beyond a depth of 2 feet until 1941. Water was available to 5 feet throughout 1942 but low rainfall in 1943 was clearly reflected in the dry soil. A good to moderate supply of moisture occurred from 1944 to 1950, inclusive. Twice the normal rainfall in 1951 resulted in wet to moderately moist soil (Table 4).

The seasonal supply of moisture was, in general, clearly reflected in the basal cover of the vegetation (Fig. 35). The 95 per cent cover of short grasses attained in 1944 varied considerably but remained fairly high until after 1951. Then it decreased sharply to about 28 per cent by 1954. After the cover was once re-established in 1944, there was a close relationship between amount of cover and yield, if yield is interpreted also in relation to the precipitation (Fig. 35). The drought yield of 500 pounds per acre (1939) increased to 2,500 pounds when the cover reached 50 per cent. A maximum yield of about 3,800 pounds was attained when a complete cover (90 per cent) and high water content of soil were combined in 1950 and 1951.

Cover in an ungrazed area of short grass has been ascertained yearly

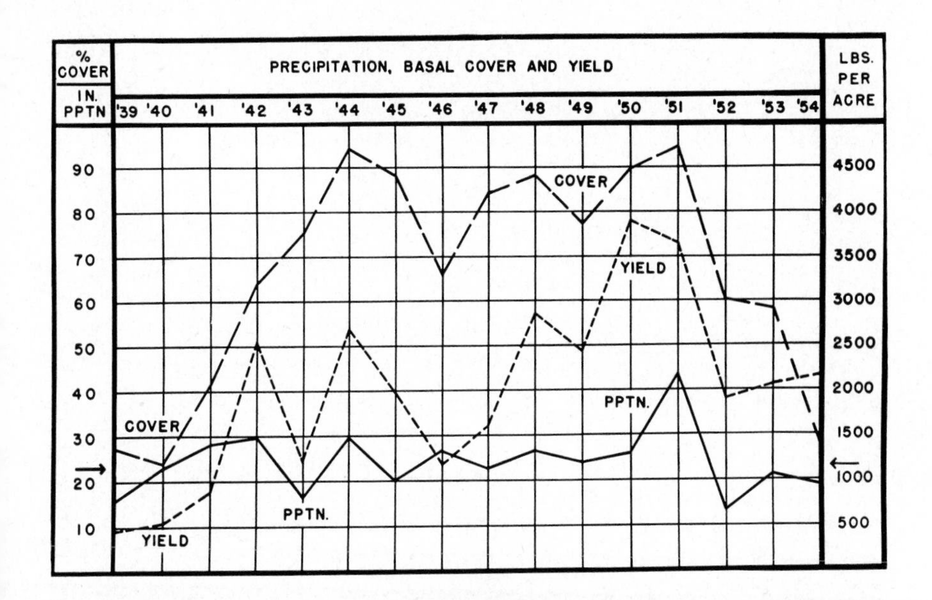

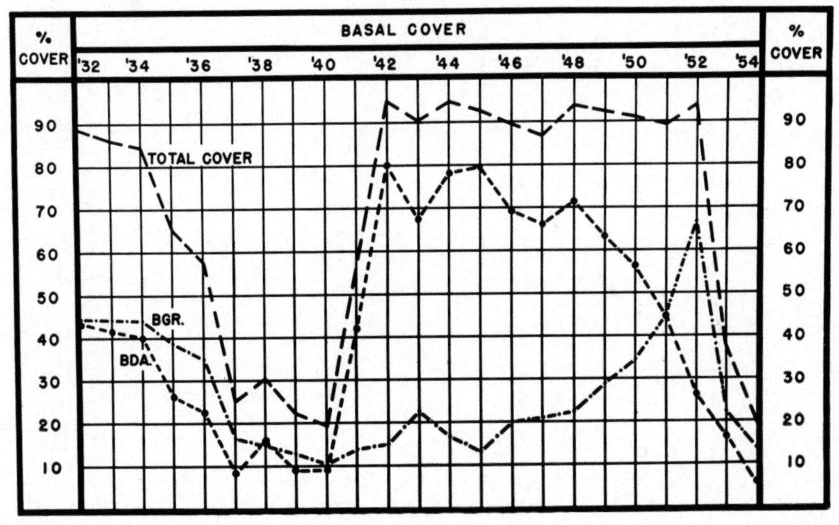

FIG. 35. (Upper) Annual precipitation, basal cover and yield in a moderately grazed range of short grasses at Hays, Kansas. Arrows indicate the mean annual rainfall of about 23 inches. (Lower) Total basal cover of short grasses in a prairie near Hays ungrazed since 1932. The partial covers furnished by blue grama (Bgr.) and buffalo grass (Bda.) are shown separately.

over a period of more than two decades (Fig. 35). The predrought cover, 88 per cent, decreased almost regularly year by year for a period of 8 years until at the end of drought it was only 20 per cent. During two years of

TABLE 4. Available soil moisture each week at the several depths in the shortgrass community. Numbers indicate the amount of available water; (1) 1 to 4.9%, (2) 5 to 9.9, (3) 10 to 19.9, and (4) 20% or more, otherwise there was none. Dashes indicate weeks when samples were not taken.

Depth feet	May				June				July				August				September			
1944																				
0–.5	3	3	3	3	3	3	1	1	1	3	4	4	3	2	3	4		3	–	–
.5–1	3	3	3	3	3	2	2	1	1	3	3	3	3	3	3	4		3	–	–
1–2	3	3	3	3	3	3	2	1	1	1	2	2	3	3	3	3		2	–	–
2–3	3	3	3	3	3	2	2	2	2	1	1	1	1	2	2	2		2	–	–
3–4	3	3	3	3	3	3	3	2	2	2	2	2	2	2	2	2		1	–	–
4–5	2	2	2	2	2	2	2	2	2	2	2	2	2	2	2	2		1	–	–
1945																				
0–.5	3	3	2	1	1	1	2	3	2	2	2	1	3	2	1				1	1
.5–1	3	3	3	3	3	2	2	2	3	3	2	2	3	2	1	1				1
1–2	3	3	3	3	3	2	2	2	2	2	2	2	1	1	2	1				
2–3	3	3	3	3	3	2	2	2	2	2	2	2	1	1	1	1	1	1	1	
3–4	2	1	2	3	2	2	1	1	1	2	2	1	1	1	1	1	1	1		
4–5	1		1	2	2	1	1	1	1	1	1	1	1	1	1	1				
1946																				
0–.5	3	4	3	4	4	2	2			2	1	1				2	1	4	2	3
.5–1	3	3	3	3	4	3	2	1		1	1	1	1	1	1	1	1	3	3	2
1–2	2	2	2	2	3	3	2	1	1		1	1	1			1	1	1	2	2
2–3	1		1	1	2	1	1	1			1								1	1
3–4				1	1	1														1
4–5	1	1	1	1	1	1														
1947																				
0–.5	3	3	4	4	4	3	4	3	1	1	2	1	1	1	1	2	1			
.5–1	3	3	4	4	3	3	3	3	2	1	1	1	1	1	1	1	1	1		
1–2	3	3	3	3	3	3	3	3	2	2	1	1	1	1	1	1				
2–3	3	2	2	3	3	3	3	3	2	2	2	1	1			1				
3–4	2	2	2	2	3	3	3	3	2	2	2	1	1							
4–5	2	2	2	2	2	3	2	2	2	2	2	2								
1948																				
0–.5	4	3	1	1	4	3	3	4	3	3	4	3	2	3	3	1		2		
.5–1	3	2	1	2	2	2	2	3	3	3	3	3	2	1	2	2	1	1	1	
1–2	2	3	3	3	2	2	1	2	3	3	3	3	2	1	3	2	1	2	1	1
2–3	2	3	2	2	2	2	1	2	3	2	3	2	1	1	2	2	1	1	1	1
3–4		1	1	1	1	1	1	1	2	1	1	1	1	1	1	1	1	1		
4–5						1	1		1						1		1			

1949

0–.5	4	4	4	3	4	4	4	3	2	2	1		1		1	1	2	1	–	–
.5–1	3	3	3	3	3	4	3	3	2	2	1	1	1		1	1	1	1	–	–
1–2	3	3	3	3	3	3	3	3	3	3	2	1	1	1	1	1	1		–	–
2–3	1	1	1	2	3	3	3	2	2	2	2	1	1	1	1	1	1		–	–
3–4				1	1	1	1	1	2	2	2		1	1	1	1	1		–	–
4–5				1	1	1				2	2		1				2		–	–

1950

0–.5	4	3	3	3	3	1	1	1	2	1	1	3	3	3	3	3	3	2	–	–
.5–1	3	3	3	3	3	1	1	1	1				2	3	2	3	3	2	–	–
1–2	3	1	3	1	2		1	1	1	1				2	1	3	2	2	–	–
2–3	1	1	1		1	1	1									2	1	1	–	–
3–4	1	1	1		1		1										1	1	–	–
4–5	1	1	1		1		1										1	1	–	–

1951

0–.5	3	4	4	3	4	4	4	4	3	4	3	4	1	2	3	3	4	3	3	3
.5–1	3	3	4	4	4	3	3	4	4	4	3	3	2	2	2	2	4	3	3	2
1–2	3	3	4	4	3	3	3	3	3	3	3	4	2	2	2	2	3	3	2	2
2–3	3	3	3	3	3	2	3	3	3	3	3	3	2	2	2	2	2	2	2	2
3–4	2	2	3	3	2	2	2	3	2	3	3	3	2	2	2	2	2	2	2	2
4–5	2	2	3	2	2	2	2	2	2	2	2	3	2	2	2	2	2	2	2	2

1952

0–.5	–	–	1	–	–	1	1	1			1		1	1						
.5–1	–	–	1	–	–	1	1	1			1		1	1						
1–2	–	–	1	–	–	2	1	1		1	1	1	1							
2–3	–	–	1	–	–	2	1	1					1							
3–4	–	–	1	–	–	2	2	2							1					
4–5	–	–		–	–	2	2	2					1	1	1					

1953

0–.5	1	2	3	1	1	1		3	1	3	3		1	2	1		1	1		
.5–1		3	3	1	1	1		1		3	3	1		1				1		
1–2	1	3	3	2	1	1	1	1		1	1	1		1	1					
2–3																				
3–4																				
4–5																				

1954

0–.5	–	–	–	–	3	–	1						3	3	1	3			2	1
.5–1	–	–	–	–	3	–	1							1					1	
1–2	–	–	–	–	3	–	2	1	1											
2–3	–	–	–	–	1	–		1												
3–4	–	–	–	–		–														
4–5	–	–	–	–		–														

far-above-normal rainfall it rapidly improved and actually exceeded its original amount (Fig. 35). This cover (87 to 94 per cent) was then maintained during 10 years. Drought in 1952–54 again reduced it to 20 per cent and thus initiated a new dry cycle.

The graph of blue grama (Fig. 35) shows that it yielded to drought (1933–40) much slower than buffalo grass. Likewise it increased during years favorable to growth only slowly. The rapid response of buffalo grass by stolon production during the moist early summer of 1938 is characteristic. Within two years following drought (1940 to 1942) this grass increased from a 10 per cent cover to one of 80 per cent. Thereafter its yearly fluctuations were greater than those of blue grama. After 1945, as the more stable blue grama steadily increased, the amount of buffalo grass declined. In 1951, 11 years after the end of the dry cycle and just before the beginning of another one, the two grasses occurred in equal amounts just as they had occurred 20 years earlier.

Development of vegetation during ten good years (1941 to 1951) will be illustrated by two examples from western Kansas. At Kendall, a greatly overgrazed and heavily dusted range was examined in 1937. Large drifts of topsoil had accumulated around dead Russian thistles. There were no perennial grasses over any part except on steep slopes and in ravines; here remnants of them were found. By 1944–48 sand dropseed, tumblegrass and false buffalo grass had reappeared and were spreading slowly through a mixed population of annual weeds. Several species of perennial forbs were found and an occasional patch of buffalo grass. It was clear that the climax grasses were spreading from their refuges in the ravines. Twelve years after the end of drought, vegetation in this ungrazed range was only midway in the process of restoring the predrought plant cover. This long, slow, though certain process was now interrupted by plowing the land in preparation for growing wheat.

An excellent, moderately grazed pasture near Oakley consisted, in 1937, of tufts of blue grama and buffalo grass 1 to 3 inches in width but 3 to 12 inches apart. Interspaces were populated with peppergrass and other weeds. In 1942 sand dropseed was also common as were some native forbs (Fig. 36). The cover continued to thicken, largely by the spread of buffalo grass and sand dropseed, and attained a density of 60 per cent in 1945. Under light grazing recovery continued until 1952 and the basal cover was maintained at about 90 per cent. Most of the mid grasses had returned at least in small amounts, wheatgrass formed fairly dense stands on gentle slopes. The population of prairie forbs had also been largely replaced and fine societies were formed by a few species. A sage (*Artemisia carruthii*), first observed in 1942, had also considerably in-

FIG. 36. (Upper) Recovery of drought-stricken, moderately grazed range at Oakley, Kansas, under complete protection. Photo 1942. The tall plants are horseweed (*Conyza canadensis*). (Lower) Condition of same range after two dry years, 1953 and 1954. Invasion of sage (*Artemisia carruthii*) was first noticed 12 years earlier.

creased. Growth was retarded by deficient moisture in 1953 and a second dry year (1954) caused the cover to become quite open. Many annual weeds reappeared (Fig. 36).

In recovery after severe drought restoration of the basal area of vegetation was first to occur. Restoration of the former composition of the cover requires a much longer time. The rate varies, under conditions favorable for growth, according to the abundance of remnants remaining from the predrought vegetation. Degree of restoration can be determined by comparison of less disturbed relic vegetation and especially by reference to known conditions on the same area before the drought.

Photographs and field notes taken by the writers in 1926 to 1932 showed that little bluestem was abundant on hillsides and in depressions on level land (Fig. 37). Bunches and patches occurred over the uplands. This grass did not form a complete cover but was intermixed with short grasses. It had not returned in quantity even after 10 good years. Nearly all mid grasses, such as Junegrass, squirreltail, side-oats grama and many others, were also far less abundant than formerly. Several species of forbs had utterly disappeared. Many were only sparsely represented. There were more weedy and fewer edible forbs than formerly. Relics of many species, once of general occurrence, were now much localized. Damage from the long drought cycle had only partly been repaired.

As one studies a particular area year after year—for 22 years in this research—he sees the general changes and obtains the details from the quadrats. Each species plays a part. Some are ephemeral and demand bare soil. Others are of longer life span, yet they succumb when conditions worsen. Buffalo grass retreats before great drought but returns rapidly when it passes. Blue grama and a dozen sturdy forbs are rarely entirely routed. All play their role under the master hand of climate. But weather constantly shifts the vegetation, determines the amount of forage, and largely controls the profits or losses of the cattleman.

A single decade was long enough for little bluestem only to begin to re-establish its former communities. It and other mid-grasses were spreading slowly among the ungrazed short grasses. Many drought-enduring forbs had spread widely and nearly all species showed some degree of increase. Nature was slow in putting back the kind of vegetation that was there before the terrible drought; but showy flowers of many forbs were beginning to redecorate the landscape.

Development is the key to an understanding of vegetation. A study of a community at a particular time and place is in itself not sufficient for a complete comprehension of its significance. The continuous tracing

FIG. 37. (Upper) Little bluestem (dark) on gentle slopes of a range near Hays, Kansas, in 1930. Short grasses (light) with scattered mid grasses occur in the foreground and on other drier sites on hilltops. Photo by L. D. Wooster. (Lower) Dust drift several feet high spreading outward over range land near Woodrow, Colorado, 1954. Chief weeds are Russian thistle, prairie sunflower and puncturevine (*Tribulus terrestris*).

of succession and other changes over long periods of time have greatly aided in an understanding of the dynamic flow of processes and that vegetation is not static but always undergoing change. Seventeen years were required for greatly damaged true prairie to recover incompletely and approach a dynamic climax (Weaver, 1954a); the present study has extended over an even longer period. By such studies one comes to realize that each grass-covered area is a page on which is written the history of the past, conditions of the present, and predictions of the future.

DROUGHT STRIKES AGAIN

Destruction of grassland in 1955 was greater in eastern Colorado and parts of western Kansas and Nebraska than in 1939 and 1940. Total rainfall deficit at Hays, Kansas, was greater in 1952 to 1954 than in any three-year period during the preceding drought. The current drought was especially severe in east-central Colorado but it covered the entire Colorado prairie from north to south. The grasses were nearly all dead in early summer, excepting a few, small, peripheral tillers. Vegetation was sparse and ranges were terribly overstocked. Ranchers kept their cattle and hoped that rains would come. Meanwhile the last remnants of vegetation were eaten and the soil trampled; rains did not come. During the great drought of the thirties, after ranchers were forced to sell or starve their livestock, most ranges had a period rather free from grazing and trampling. Moreover, much more plowed land by 1952 was a constant source of dust (Fig. 37).

An extensive survey of the entire area by Albertson and Tomanek during summer and fall of 1955 revealed that in the various parts of mixed prairie in Kansas losses from the predrought cover were generally least in non-grazed areas, intermediate in those moderately grazed, and always highest in heavily grazed ranges. They ranged, in the preceding sequence, from 20 to 31, 21 to 48, and 41 to 68 per cent.

In northwestern Kansas, southwestern Nebraska and eastern Colorado into Wyoming losses were even more pronounced. In non-grazed areas they ranged from 29 to 67 per cent. Under moderate grazing the range was 55 to 78 per cent; but under heavy grazing, which was the common practice, losses of vegetation from predrought condition amounted to 80 to 90 per cent. Southward, however, damage by drought and overgrazing, despite more injury by dust, was not so pronounced. In northwestern

Oklahoma, including the panhandle, decrease in vegetation averaged, in the preceding sequence, 30, 52 and 78 per cent. In the northern Texas panhandle losses were 41, 46 and 59 per cent. Thus, the disastrous effects of overstocking are here again clearly illustrated.

Recurrence of drought is always dreaded, yet unless one works against nature's plan one need not despair. Extended periods of drought are a part of the plains climate. The grasslands have survived throughout the ages. Slowly but surely the depleted vegetation was always restored. Enough of each species remains somewhere on the wind-swept land to furnish seed for re-establishment of the cover over a period of time. It is only when man aids in the destruction by overgrazing and trampling and by plowing that conditions are worsened and the vegetation is destroyed.

Water is the limiting factor; man's activities usually result in reducing the water supply. Under a complete cover of vegetation the stems and leaves intercept part of the rainfall. They hold the litter in place and silt and fine organic matter are also retained. Water movement on the soil surface is greatly retarded. Destructive grazing by herds of cattle removes the plant cover, destroys the vegetal mulch and reduces the depth of penetration of roots. The dusty soil is left poorly protected from dashing rains, extremes in temperature and desiccating hot winds. Its nutrient content and good structure decrease. Into unmulched, trampled soil water penetrates slowly and less deeply. Water is lost through excessive runoff and increased evaporation. Water for the forage and forage for the livestock are both reduced. When the balance between climate and vegetation is so delicate as it is in the semiarid plains, a clear understanding of the plant and soil water relationships should be had and every possible method should be employed to maintain nature's rather meager water supply. The best method is to leave the plant cover unbroken and graze it moderately, not excessively (Campbell *et al.*, 1948). Fortunately this type of grazing gives the highest yearly yields of forage.

The environment described in this and preceding chapters is not in accord with theory advocated by Sauer (1950) and Stewart (1953) that the grassland is not a climatic climax but rather that it is saved from replacement by trees and shrubs only as a result of fire. The viewpoint of the authors after long experience and study has been expressed in North American Prairie as follows. Fire is less destructive to grasses than to woody vegetation and it may sometimes benefit prairie where debris has accumulated over several years. This undoubtedly occurred where fires were set by lightning. The prairie and indeed the entire area of North American Grassland at the time of settlement consisted of a climax vegetation, the extent of which was controlled by climate. Fire was only one of the many environmental factors. The grasses produced large amounts of dead, dry, inflammable material. Lightning often started fires. "Thus the Grassland climates favor fire, just as they favor grass whether there are fires or not. . . . Fire, if not primitive man, himself, would simply have been one part of the ecological complex of a region with the climate of the Grassland. . . . Also, the precipitation pattern of eastern America during major drought years can explain why the influence of fire was restricted to the grassland. The climate of the forests generally did not favor burning" (Borchert, 1950). After extended study of the climate of Central North America, Borchert concludes: "The geographical pattern of postulated post-glacial fluctuation of the Grassland fits the facts of the recorded climate. The pattern of the Grassland at the time of white settlement also fits those facts. The patterns, themselves, suggest very strongly that they were, in the words of an earlier author, dictated by the master hand of climate." (*cf.* Albertson and Weaver, 1945).

CHAPTER 11

Sand Hills of Nebraska

MANY AREAS of sandy soil and sand dunes occur in every state in the Great Plains, but the largest and perhaps best known sand-hill region is found in Nebraska. An area of dune topography of more than 18,000 square miles lies mostly north of the Platte River and west and north of the Loess Hills and Plains (Fig. 38). The altitude is about 4,000 feet on the western border but only about 2,000 on the eastern margin.

NATURE AND ORIGIN

The Sand Hills have been described by Pool (1912) as follows: "The hills are all round-topped or conical and smooth, clearly showing that they have been shaped by the wind. . . . There are many depressions between the hills, many of which assume the proportions of valleys more than a mile in width and sometimes many miles in length. From these well-developed valleys the low places decrease in width and length until they are mere narrow, saucer-shaped basins or "pockets" a few hundred yards across. The well-pronounced valleys are, as a rule, about parallel and trend in a southeast and northwest direction. Such valleys are frequently enclosed by ranges of hills and in this way effectively separated from adjacent valleys, though such may not be more than a half mile distant. Sometimes instead of the valleys being separated by round-topped hills this is accomplished by a continuous rounded ridge. The sides of these hills are often very steep, making difficult the direct passage from one valley to another. . . . In the regions characterized by short valleys and basins the general landscape is strikingly different because in such places the hills rise on all sides without any regularity. Low hills, intermediate hills and high hills are closely associated, with no long separating valleys. The result is a very abruptly rolling surface with rounded or oblong depressions of varying depth, with the rounded or conical dunes above." Height of the hills varies from a few feet to 150 feet or more. A single hill may occupy only a few acres of land but a large one may extend over a square mile in area (Fig. 39).

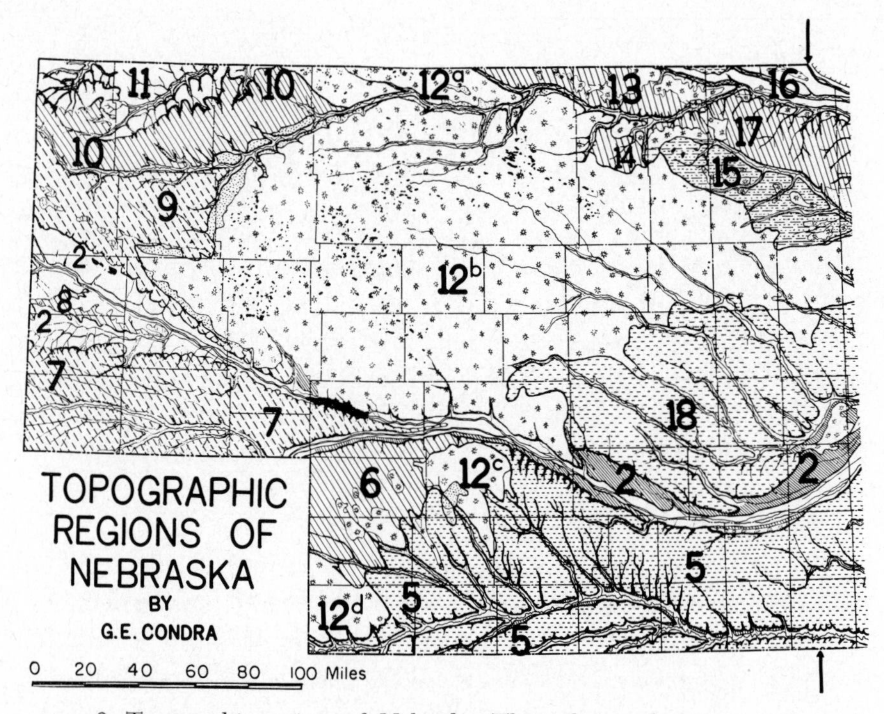

FIG. 38. Topographic regions of Nebraska. Those discussed are: 12 a, b, c, d, Sand Hills; 15, Prairie Plain; 18, Loess Hills and Plains; 5, Loess Plains; 6, Perkins Plain; 7, Cheyenne Plain; 8, Wildcat Ridge; 9, Box Butte Plain; 10, Pine Ridge; and 11, Pierre Hills. Arrows show approximate eastern limit of mixed prairie.

"The Sand-Hill Region of Nebraska is a plains region that has been excessively modified by the force of the wind. It is a region of changed environment caused by wind, a region of dune sand hills, sandy basins and valleys, exposed groundwater lakes and marshes, and little surface runoff. The few streams are in valleys with alluvium and are fed by groundwater underflow" (Condra *et al.*, 1950). Most of the sediments forming the hills were blown from the easily eroded underlying sandy formations by strong northwestern winds during dry times. The hills were mostly formed during the glacial (Pleistocene) time.

Because of wind erosion, little soil formation has occurred. The hills are composed mostly of fine-grained sand of a light-yellow color. The sand on the tops of dunes has a coarser texture than that on the sides and adjacent dry meadows. This is the result of the selective action of wind erosion. Little or no organic matter occurs in dune sands, but in

FIG. 39. (Upper) View of sand hills, looking southeast, near Seneca, Nebraska. Note small soapweed (*Yucca glauca*) in foreground and small blowouts on the hillside. Photo 1918. (Lower) North slopes of low sand hills near Dewey Lake in Nebraska. The shelters contain weather bureau instruments; the vegetation has been little grazed for several years. Photo 1936.

the more stabilized dry meadows at their base small quantities of humus are present in the surface soil.

Precipitation varies from about 23 inches on the eastern border to only 18 westward. Most of this falls during the period from April to June, inclusive, and late summer drought is common. Almost all of the rainfall immediately enters the coarse-textured sand and there is practically no runoff even from the heaviest showers. The sandy soil is wet to a much greater depth than fine-textured loam adjacent to the sand hills. As soon as a storm passes, evaporation dries out the surface sand with great rapidity, but to a slight depth only. This surface layer of dry sand forms an excellent mulch which has a great retarding effect upon further evaporation. At a depth of a few inches below the surface the sand is always moist. Since the cover of vegetation is usually sparse, water loss by transpiration is probably much less than from plants in loam soil.

Through these coarse soils sufficient water filters to characterize the region with subsurface drainage and to maintain a water table deep beneath the surface. Streams and rivers constantly receive drainage from the ground water. Since drainage is immature in many areas, the resulting high water table has formed many lakes in the depressions. The streams have a continuous flow throughout the year and fluctuations in water level are never more than a few inches. Water in undrained lakes, however, fluctuates greatly. Some have water only intermittently. Amount of available soil moisture for the different plant communities will be discussed as the vegetation is described.

Wind is one of the most important environmental factors affecting sandhill vegetation. It has molded the hills in the past and is a constant menace today. Only in the moister habitats, as in valleys, does the vegetation grow thickly. It is sparse on the hillsides and very thinly spread on the hilltops; the light-colored sand is not concealed between the bunches and open stands of plants (Fig. 39). Summer winds are mostly southerly but in winter they blow strongly and often violently from the west and northwest. Winds of 40 to 60 miles an hour are not uncommon. In the most exposed places where the vegetation is thin, often as the result of grazing or fire, the wind picks up the sand and blows it away. Since greatest wind erosion occurs during winter, the sand is removed and blowouts occur mostly on the west and northwest sides of the hills. Often wind velocity is high during several consecutive days and much sand is removed. The crater-like depressions usually, but not always, occur below the summit of the hill. "They are rounded or more commonly irregularly conical depressions of varying depth and diameter, formed by the blowing of sand and vegetation from certain areas on the upper slopes and crests of hills and ridges. The more or less conical depression is sometimes almost circular in outline. An irregular form is, however, more common both as to the perimeter of the top and the configuration of the inner slopes. One side of the rim is usually considerably lower than the opposite side because of the slope of the hill or ridge within which the blowout has been formed. . . . In the beginning blowouts cover a few square yards and are but a few inches in depth, but in extreme cases they become hollowed out to a depth probably exceeding 100 feet while the greatest circumference may be more than 600 feet" (Pool, 1914).

On the windward side of the blowout is an area of sand erosion, and on the leeward side of the rim is an area of sand deposit. The coarsest materials are deposited first and the finer particles are blown to varying distances beyond. At first both areas are places of disturbance, but ultimately they are stabilized.

Fire was a chief cause of the destruction of the cover of vegetation in the past—fires set by lightning or by the Indians. Driven by strong winds, such prairie fires swept over enormous areas, burning the tops and crowns of the bunch grasses, consuming herbs and shrubs, and destroying exposed roots of plants as well. Several years were then probably required to produce sufficient vegetation and debris for another fire. Such a catastrophe greatly aided wind erosion. It is a historical fact that the sand dunes were not so well vegetated in the early years of settlement as they are today. Pioneer vegetation was more plentiful and blowouts were more common. Increase in intensity of grazing has checked the accumulation of debris, and with the development of ranching, fires (with exceptions) have usually been kept under control.

BLOWOUT COMMUNITY

Vegetation first becomes established in the bottom or on the lower slopes of the blowout, however, only after the wind becomes ineffective in further increasing its depth. Then the sand that slides down its slopes remains in place. Two of the earliest and most important pioneers are blowout grass (*Redfieldia flexuosa*) and a legume, lance-leaved psoralea (*Psoralea lanceolata*). This grass is at home in the sand hills. Indeed, it is the most abundant and controlling species of blowout pioneers (Fig.

44). Although it may be mixed with other species, it is often the only plant present in such situations.

At first, only a few of the abundant seedlings which appear in early spring become permanently established. When once a foothold is gained, spreading by means of much branched rhizomes is rapid throughout the following years. Pound and Clements (1900) observed that there was seldom anything to be seen in recent blowouts but this grass. Arising from the underground stems are erect tufts with only a few leaves. The flexuous culms are tough and 2 to 3 feet tall. The blades of the long, flexuous, narrow leaves are glabrous and inrolled and taper to a fine point. They endure wind-whipping for long periods without injury. The large, oblong panicle is from a third to half the entire length of the stem.

The usually sparse and rather small clumps are connected by means of very long, tough, coarse rhizomes. They are frequently many feet in length and have been traced to a distance of 20 to 40 feet on the surface in places where the sand had been blown away from them. Because of the shifting sand, the depths at which they occur is variable. Living rhizomes with vertically descending branches were found at a depth of 3 feet and they were rather abundant between this depth and the sand surface, some running horizontally, others obliquely and still others almost vertically upward (Figs. 40, 46).[1]

The environment in blowouts, according to Tolstead (1942), is one with bright light, high temperatures and strong winds, but competition for water is almost nil. Blowout grass also grows on both the windward and leeward sides of dunes and in other disturbed situations, such as around stock-watering places and on much trampled ground. The stand is always open and usually very sparse. It is not readily grazed where other forage is present but in autumn after most grasses have matured and dried it remains green for a time and is then eaten by livestock. This grass was far more abundant 50 years ago when fires and blowing sand were more common phenomena than they are today.

Roots often arise in whorls from the nodes of rhizomes, usually in groups of 2 to 5 or more (Fig. 40). At first they are fleshy and 2 to 4 mm. in diameter. Older roots were well branched to the very tips with much-divided laterals 1 to 3 inches long. Some reached depths of more than 5

[1] Root descriptions, much abbreviated, and drawings are from Carnegie Institution of Washington publications 286 (1919) and 292 (1920).

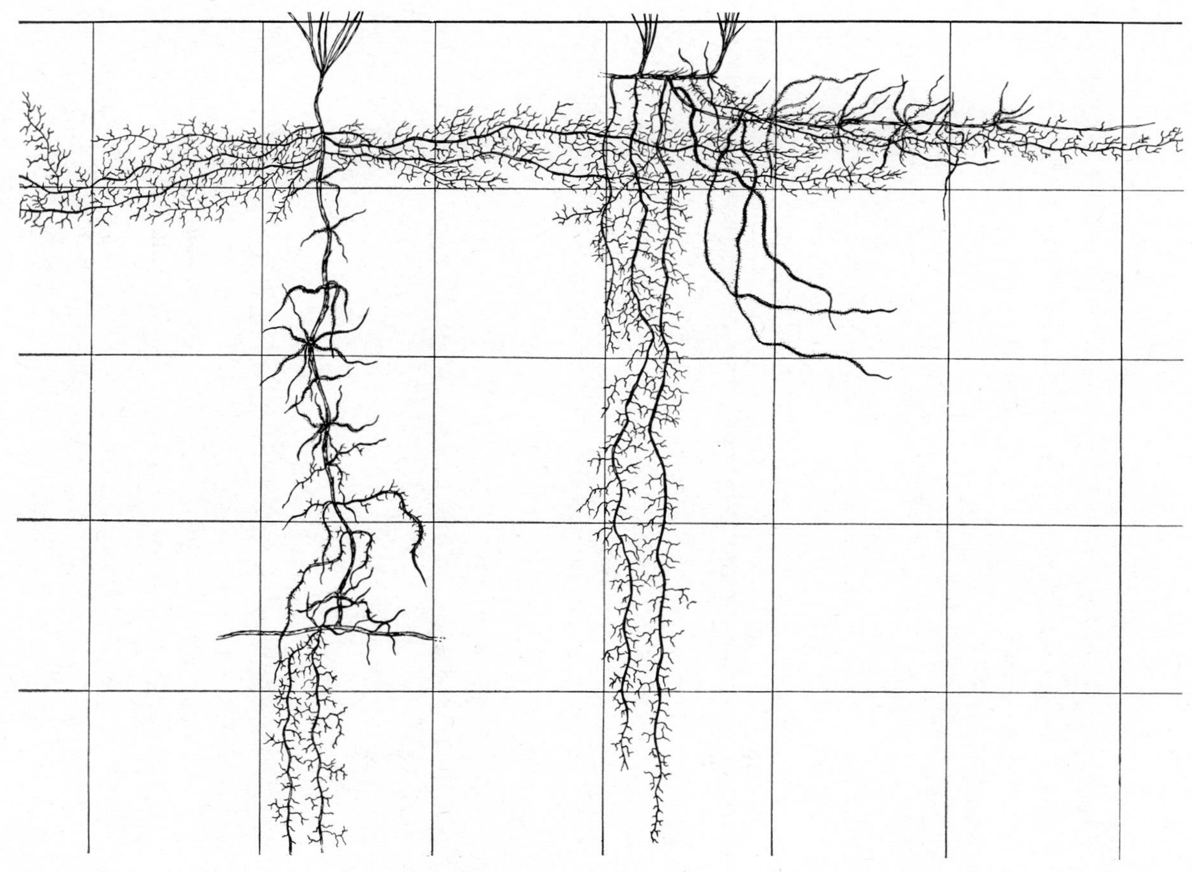

FIG. 40. Roots and rhizomes of blowout grass (*Redfieldia flexuosa*). Scale in feet.

feet. Roots extended not only vertically downward but also diverged at all angles, even to the horizontal. Long, well-branched roots were traced to more than 3 feet from the base of the plant at depths of only 4 to 8 inches. Their laterals frequently ascended vertically upward and ended in well-branched termini only 2 to 3 inches below the sand surface. Thus, the length, position, and abundance of branches on this coarse root system, together with the rhizomes, equip this grass in an effective manner for life in the shifting but moist soil of the sand dune. It is a pioneer and is rarely found on stabilized soil.

Psoralea lanceolata sometimes replaces, and is often associated with, blowout grass as a pioneer in shifting sand. It thrives in blowouts or other disturbed places but is also often abundant on sand hills and in dry meadows. Lance-leaved psoralea is a much-branched upright or ascending plant, light green in color and 1 to 2 feet high. Each leaf consists of three rather long, narrow leaflets. It has dense, short and thick spikes of bluish white flowers. The leaves and pods have an offensive odor. Its underground parts eminently fit it to succeed in a habitat where the sand surface is constantly lowered by wind erosion or built up by the same agency (Fig. 41).

The individual plants, which may be a few inches or several feet apart, are usually connected by a more or less horizontal system of rhizomes, which varies in depth from 2 inches to more than 2 feet. These underground stems, 2 to 12 mm. in diameter, may extend outward to distances of 10 to 30 feet or more. At irregular intervals along their course new plants arise. Beneath the erect stems and also at other places along the rhizome, strong, rather vertically descending roots occur, many of which reach depths of 8 to 9 feet. The upper portion of the root system was poorly furnished with branches or had none. The main system of branches began in the fourth foot of sand and extended to depths of 8 to 9 feet. Large root nodules, 1 to 3 mm. in diameter, occurred in the deep sand. The taproot, still 4 mm. in diameter, was not followed farther because of caving of the sand-walled trench.

A few tufts of Indian ricegrass (*Oryzopsis hymenoides*) and individual plants of sand lovegrass (*Eragrostis trichodes*), needle-and-thread (*Stipa*

FIG. 41. Underground parts of lance-leaved psoralea (*Psoralea lanceolata*) showing root tubercles at a depth of 8 feet. (Insert) Root system of hairy prairie clover (*Petalostemum villosum*) with portion of left branch removed. Scale in feet.

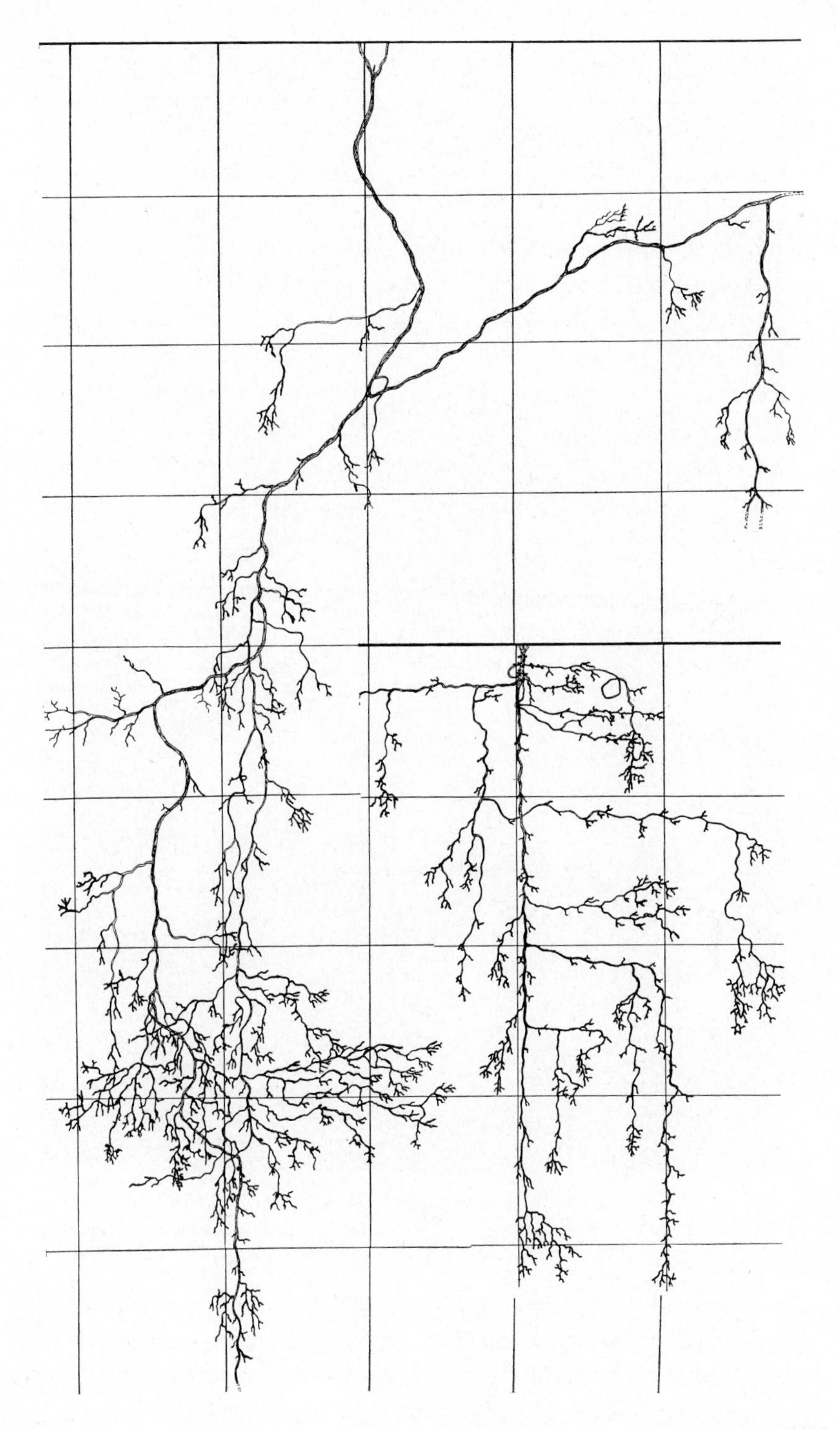

FIG. 42. (Upper) Plants of spiderwort (*Tradescantia occidentalis*) with blue to rose-colored flowers. (Lower) Tooth-leaved primrose (*Oenothera serrulata*) with yellow blossoms.

comata) or sand reed (*Calamovilfa longifolia*) may appear in the thin stand of *Redfieldia*. The vegetation, even after several years, is extremely sparse. Although sandhill muhly (*Muhlenbergia pungens*) may invade the upper slopes, little bluestem and other bunch grasses are not found there. "But seven species of ordinary sand-hills inhabitants habitually invade blowouts after blowout grasses have obtained control. These are: [spider-wort] *Tradescantia virginiana,* [annual umbrella plant] *Eriogonum annuum,* [tooth-leaved primrose] *Oenothera serrulata,* [showy peavine] *Lathyrus ornatus flavescens,* [rattlepod] *Phaca longifolia,* [white-flowered spurge] *Euphorbia petaloidea,* and [woolly yellow hymenopappus] *Hymenopappus filifolius*" (Pound and Clements, 1900). They are well adapted underground for growth here and over the sands hills generally (Fig. 42).

Spiderwort (*Tradescantia virginiana*) has a rather fleshy root system which may spread 2 to 2.5 feet on all sides of the plant but is nearly confined to the surface foot of soil. *T. occidentalis,* which also occurs on the hills, is shallowly rooted. Likewise, roots of *Commelina virginica,* the day-flower, are also fleshy and, though spreading widely, occur mostly in the upper 2 feet of soil. Annual umbrella plant has a 5-foot, well branched taproot; many branches 2 to 3 feet long spread horizontally in the surface 6 inches of soil.

Tooth-leaved primrose is a summer bloomer of wide distribution. It reaches its best development and forms the most marked societies in true prairie. In drier areas on hard lands or sandy soil it is usually much dwarfed and the bright yellow flowers are much smaller. Several plants were examined. The woody taproots were about a half-inch thick. The propagation of the plant by its widely spreading underground parts is shown in figure 43. All the larger roots were characterized by their lax and meandering courses. Large branches were frequent, smaller ones were not very abundant, but usually the root-ends were well branched.

Additional species of blowouts are James' cristatella (*Cristatella jamesii*), beardtongue (*Penstemon haydeni*), and clammy weed (*Polanisia trachysperma*). Following these pioneers, year by year a host of other species from the general sand-hill prairie gradually become established. With increasing competition the pioneer grasses and forbs very gradually disappear and the vegetation finally assumes the character of the more stable bunch-grass prairie.

SANDHILL MUHLY COMMUNITY

A community regularly dominated by *Muhlenbergia pungens* occurs on upland areas of relatively stable dune sands. It also often covers large areas around blowouts. Sandy wastes, whether resulting from fire or from exces-

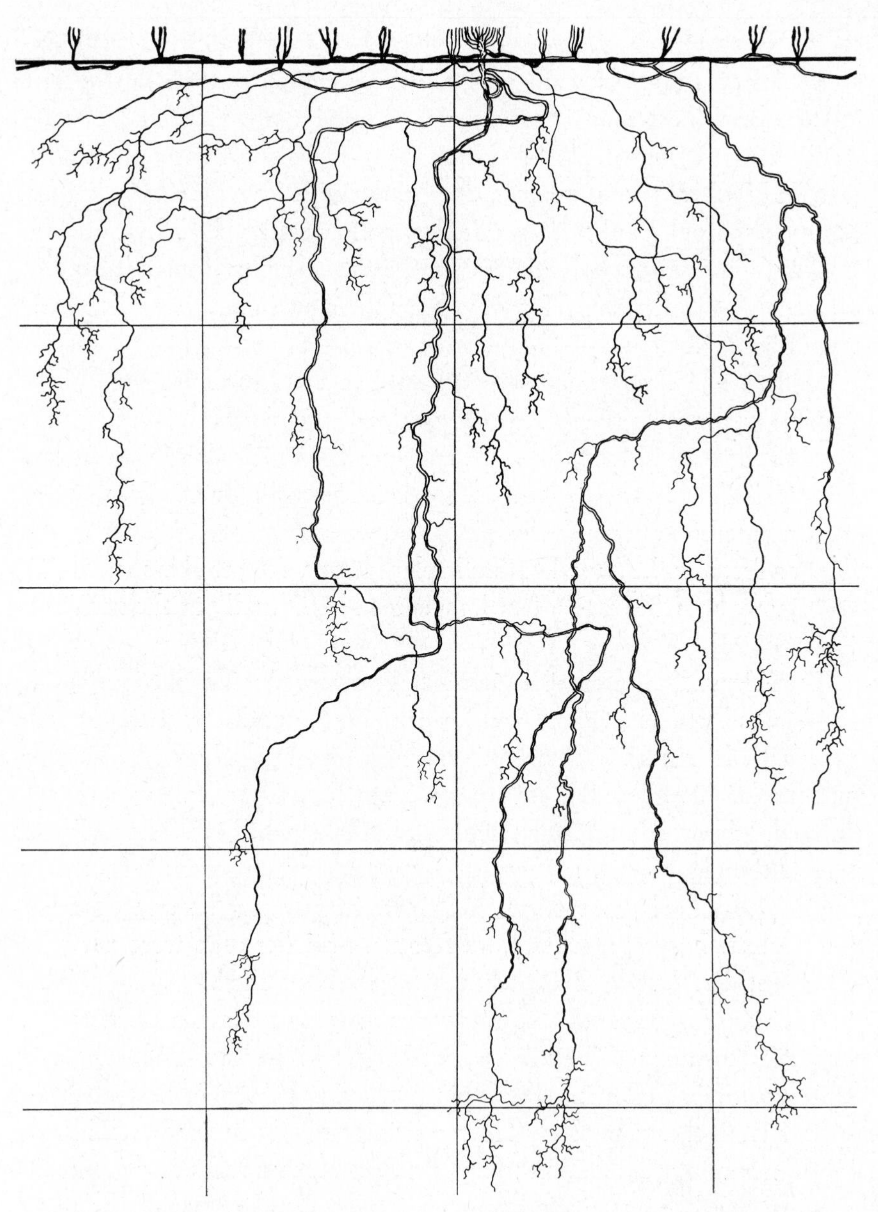

FIG. 43. Root system of tooth-leaved primrose (*Oenothera serrulata*) in sand.

sive grazing and trampling, are often characterized by this dominant. It remains in badly overgrazed ranges, since the stiff, sharp-pointed leaves are not readily grazed.

This grass is characterized by tufted stems and glaucous, narrow, rigid leaves, which are usually only 1 to 3 inches long. The stems, which arise from strong rootstocks, become erect from a decumbent leafy base. The

FIG. 44. (Upper) Blowout grass (*Redfieldia flexuosa*) in bloom in its natural habitat of loose, wind-blown sand. (Lower) Clump of sandhill muhly (*Muhlenbergia pungens*) with old flower stalks.

bunches are 4 to 15 inches wide with stems 8 to 14 or more inches high (Fig. 44).

The root system was examined on the rim and grass-covered top of a blowout where these plants were growing abundantly. Clusters of roots arose from the short rootstocks, which were 2 to 6 inches long. Some of the tough wire-like roots penetrated rather vertically downward to a depth of about 3 feet; others ran off obliquely at various angles, some almost parallel with the surface soil. Lateral spread varied from 10 to 25 inches on all sides of the plants. Below the surface inch of sand the glistening white roots were densely covered with multitudes of very fine absorbing laterals, frequently 75 per inch of main root. Many were only a few mm. long, others reached a length of 6 to 10 inches. All were profusely and minutely branched, the larger ones to the third and fourth order. Thus, the root system penetrated all portions of the sand to absorb the available water and nutrients. Both roots and tops formed an effective means of preventing sand from blowing. Soil sampling on a hilltop dominated by sandhill muhly and a common companion species, hairy grama, showed that available soil moisture was present at least in the third to fifth foot of sand even during two drought years (Tolstead, 1942).

This *Muhlenbergia* acts as a successor to blowout grass since it is a pioneer on stable sands. By its dense growth in bunches and more compact root system it gradually replaces this sand binder of loose soil. The tufts and bunches of sand muhly are spaced fairly closely when the community is well developed. With stability such species as hairy grama, small soapweed, lance-leaved psoralea, sand cherry (*Prunus besseyi*) and many others may occur. A more complete cover results, as well as gradual change in composition. Finally, annual species gradually disappear and the pioneer grasses and forbs decrease greatly as competition becomes more severe. Sandhill muhly, which thrives in the open community, becomes weakened and suppressed. For a time it remains as low-growing mats but finally disappears as a prairie of taller grasses and forbs occupy the area.

BUNCH GRASS COMMUNITY

The prevailing and most characteristic vegetation of the sand-hill region is the bunch grass community. "It covers hill after hill and ridge after ridge over areas of great extent. . . . The most noticeable character of sand-hill vegetation, after one has become accustomed to the great variety of species which the sparse vegetation of each hill affords, is its extreme monotony. . . . Not only has every hill the same species as every other hill, but they occur in the same manner and have the same relation, and in consequence one hill, as a rule, has the same appearance as another" (Pound and Clements, 1900).

The most important grasses are little bluestem (*Andropogon scoparius*), sand bluestem (*A. hallii*), sand reed (*Calamovilfa longifolia*) and needle-and-thread (*Stipa comata*). It is their constant and uniform appearance that gives character to the landscape. The most characteristic species, aside from the grasses, is the little soapweed (*Yucca glauca*).

Little bluestem, also a chief dominant in true prairie, was the most frequent and abundant grass until the great drought (1933–40). It was thus considered by Pound and Clements (1900) and Pool (1914). Its abundance has been observed many times (1916 to 1933) by one of the authors, after which its losses (95 per cent or more) equalled or exceeded those in eastern Nebraska. This plant develops distinct bunches, often 6 to 12 inches in diameter, and very numerous, leafy, closely crowded stems which reach heights of 1 to 2.5 feet (Fig. 45). Since it is scarcely grazed by livestock in the sand hills, the old stems and leaves persist for several years and furnish abundant fuel for prairie fires. Small wonder that the cattlemen, who regarded it as worthless for grazing, were not much concerned by its loss in severe drought. In moderately grazed areas and especially in protected places, it has slowly returned.

In true prairie and on loam soils in mixed prairie, the bulk of the roots of little bluestem penetrate rather vertically downward 4 to 6 feet and the lateral spread in the upper soil is rarely more than .5 to 1.5 feet. On stable sandy loams, where it also occurs abundantly, the root habit is greatly modified. It has been studied in several sand-hill areas. Here half of the root system is spread laterally in the surface 1 to 1.5 feet of soil. Some roots ended in the first foot but at distances of more than 3 feet from the base of the plant. Others penetrated laterally at various depths more than 4 feet. All were well branched. Some of the deeper oblique roots developed more or less vertical branches which ended near the soil surface. Although many of the roots ran out obliquely at all angles between the vertical and horizontal and thus furnished an excellent surface-absorbing system, others penetrated straight downward. These, with the oblique roots, which often turned downward and reached a depth of several feet, provided for absorption in the deeper soil. Branching was very profuse throughout, the root-ends usually being well supplied with branches. This grass absorbs to depths of 6 to 8 feet in sand. Although the bunches are not closely spaced, it is very effective in stabilizing the soil.

FIG. 45. Sand hill near Seneca with stabilized vegetation. The most conspicuous species is little bluestem (*Andropogon scoparius*). Photo in 1918.

Sand bluestem (*Andropogon hallii*) is a coarse, glaucous grass with only a few stems in the loose open bunches, but these reach a height of 3 to 5 feet (Fig. 46). The forked racemes which appear after midsummer are conspicuously villous, the hairs varying in color from grayish to pale golden. It grows on the tops of the sand hills everywhere, and in certain areas it may replace little bluestem, but it is far less conspicuous. It also occurs as a pioneer in shifting sand to mature communities on protected

FIG. 46. Four sand-hill grasses. (Upper) Sand lovegrass (*Eragrostis trichodes*) and sand reed (*Calamovilfa longifolia*). (Lower) Sand bluestem (*Andropogon hallii*) and blowout grass (*Redfieldia flexuosa*).

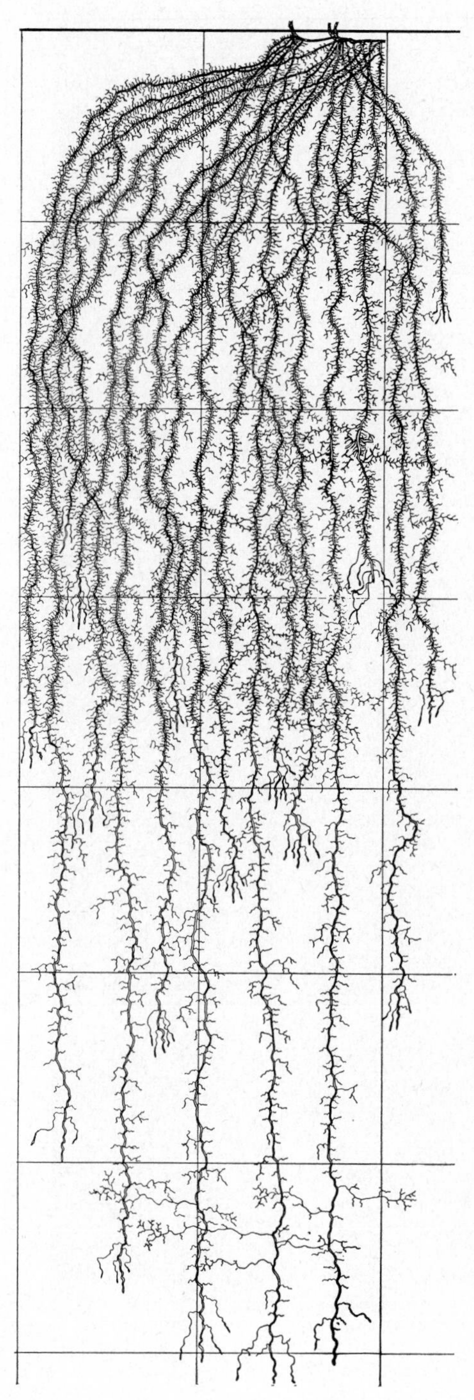

south hillsides. Basal cover is always small. The broad tender leaves, usually 6 to 9 per stem and 12 to 16 inches long, furnish forage of such high preference by livestock that the grass is far less abundant today than a half-century ago. In protected areas it has increased in abundance since the decline in little bluestem.

The rhizomes vary from 4 to 8 inches in length. They grow rapidly in spring and the stem-scars on the old rhizomes have been traced back through a period of 3 to 5 years. From the rhizomes, many roots take their origin. Some spread laterally, others penetrate almost vertically downward, and still others pursue an oblique course (Fig. 47). The roots grow rapidly and some reach depths of 4 to 6 feet in only 3 to 4 months. A usual depth of penetration of the 9 plants examined was 6 to 10 feet. Thus, it is similar in its rooting habits to the closely related big bluestem (*Andropogon gerardi*).

Sand reed (*Calamovilfa longifolia*) has stems which mostly arise singly from strong scaly rootstocks and attain

FIG. 47. Root system of sand bluestem (*Andropogon hallii*).

heights of 30 to 50 or more inches (Fig. 46). Well developed culms have 10 to 12 leaves with flat or inrolled blades 15 to 24 inches long which taper to a long fine point. Growth is renewed late in April, and the broad panicles, 6 to 12 inches long, unfold and blossoming occurs from July to September. This grass is drought resistant. It is frequently found associated with blowout grass and lance-leaved psoralea in blowouts and other shifting sands but also occurs with sand-hills bluestem and other grasses in the well developed plant cover. It propagates almost entirely by rhizomes and has occupied so much of the area lost by little bluestem that it is now perhaps the most characteristic grass of the sand hills. It furnishes nearly half of the total forage. Although it ranges widely, it develops best on south slopes of dunes and in broad dry valleys. In pure stands the basal area is only 1 to 2 per cent; even when other species are present it is rarely over 5 per cent. Chief associated dominants are needle-and-thread, hairy grama and sand dropseed, the last becoming abundant under disturbance caused by close grazing.

Under a good stand of sand reed there was a tangled mat of roots and rhizomes to a depth of 3 feet. An abundance of tough, wiry, much-branched rhizomes formed an underground network connecting the widely spaced plants. The rhizomes are thickly covered with long scales and tipped with buds about an inch in length and with sharp, hard points. The network of rhizomes occurred at all depths from the surface to 3 feet, the deeper ones undoubtedly having been buried by wind-blown sand. Multitudes of tough wiry roots, about 1 to 2 mm. in diameter, arose from them and penetrated the soil in all directions from horizontally to vertically downward. Many reached depths of 4.5 to 5 feet. From a depth of an inch to their very tips they were abundantly supplied with laterals which extended outward at right angles to distances of 1 to more than 2 inches (Fig. 48). Branching occurred to the third and fourth orders. The roots completely thread the soil and help to hold it firmly in place.

Needle-and-thread was ranked, 50 years ago, as second in importance to little bluestem on the ridges and slopes of the Sand Hills (Pound and Clements, 1900). Its few-stemmed bunches or tufts were scattered thickly between those of the bluestems and other grasses. *Stipa* is so palatable and renews growth so early in spring that it has been grazed out in many areas. This dominant, widespread throughout the northern and central plains, has been described. The roots spread widely and are 3 to 5 feet deep.

Small soapweed (*Yucca glauca*) is one of the few non-grasses which are outstanding among the bunch grasses. Although common, it does not occur in all parts of the region but is often very abundant on upper slopes. The sand is frequently blown away from the thick underground stems, yet the plant continues to thrive and often develops new rosettes of thick, sharp-pointed leaves from the exposed stems. Little soapweed is also common elsewhere on the Great Plains (Fig. 48). It has a remarkable ability to hold the soil against wind erosion.

FIG. 48. Roots of sand reed at depths of 2 to 3 feet (left), and plant of small soapweed (*Yucca glauca*) showing the much branched underground stem, about two feet deep, from which the roots arise.

The bush morning-glory (*Ipomoea leptophylla*) is a common plant of the Great Plains and a definite indicator of sandy soil. The large hemispherical tops, conspicuous because of their size and the profuse purple blossoms, cover many square feet of soil (Fig. 49). Two plants which were growing together were examined. The intermingled tops measured 7 feet in diameter and were 2.5 feet high. At a depth of 9 inches the taproots became greatly enlarged, reaching a diameter of 6 to 8 inches (but some others were 18 to 24 inches thick). They maintained this size for a distance of 12 inches; then they tapered gradually so that at a depth of 4 feet they

FIG. 49. (Upper) Bush morning-glory (*Ipomoea leptophylla*) with purple flowers. (Lower) Sand sage (*Artemisia filifolia*) with needle-and-thread in overgrazed sand-hill range.

were only an inch or two in diameter. Below this point the taproots lost their dominance, breaking up into large numbers of deeply penetrating and widely spreading branches (Fig. 50).

In the first foot of soil scarcely any laterals originated, but below this level both large and small branches occurred in great abundance. These varied in diameter from less than a mm. to half an inch. Although a few ran somewhat vertically or obliquely downward, the general course of most of them was nearly parallel with the soil surface. The lateral spread was enormous, the roots running off to distances of 15 to 25 feet or more in various directions from the base of the plant. Because of repeated and profuse branching, the surface foot of soil and the 10 feet below it were well filled with glistening white, brittle branches of this remarkable root system. Because of the caving of the sandy soil the roots were not followed to greater depths. However, because of their diameters of 2 to 4 mm. at the 11-foot level and the nature of other roots examined, it is highly probable that they penetrated many feet deeper. The enlarged portion of the taproot furnishes not only an enormous reservoir of food but also a storehouse of water upon which the plant may exist during drought.

Sand lovegrass (*Eragrostis trichodes*) is a bunch grass of considerable importance throughout this region (Fig. 46). The bunches are widely spaced, often only 5 to 8 per square yard. Once abundant, it is so palatable that it has undergone severe damage from grazing. This perennial is 2 to more than 3 feet tall. It grows best on the north slopes of dunes which protect it from the dry south winds of summer. It is found in mixtures with sand reed on lower slopes and with sand-hill bluestem, sand muhly and other grasses nearer the hilltops. In places where stands are well developed, other grasses, both short and tall, are few. Experiments in sandy soils at Woodward, Oklahoma, by Savage (1947) have shown that sand lovegrass possesses many fine qualities. It renews growth early in spring, produces more forage than most native grasses and is very palatable. It remains green late in fall, after most other grasses have dried. It is equal to the short grasses in average content of both protein and minerals. Moreover, like blue grama and buffalo grass it retains about half of its nutrients when winter cured.

Sand dropseed (*Sporobolus cryptandrus*), an important dominant of mixed prairie elsewhere, was originally not common in the sand hills. With grazing, it has greatly increased in abundance along with sand reed. It

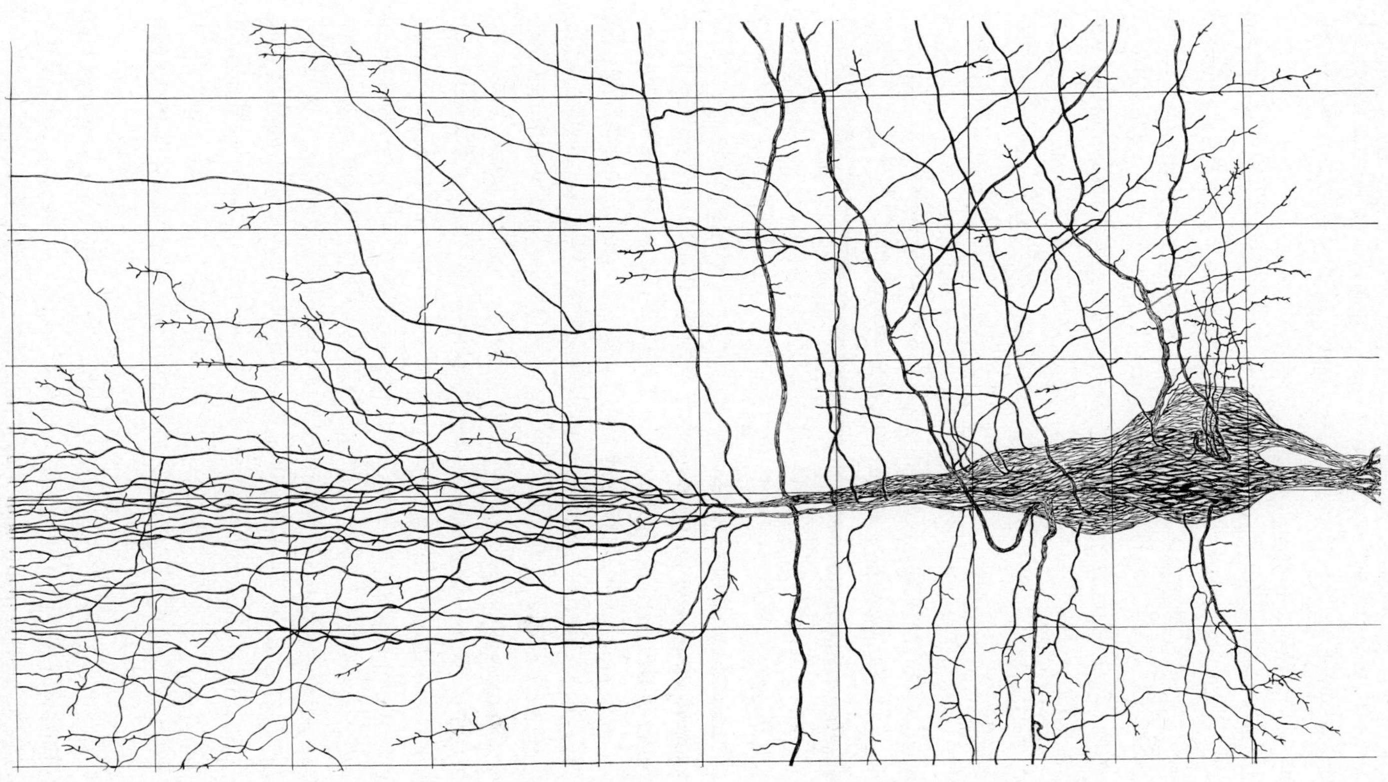

FIG. 50. Bush morning-glory (*Ipomoea leptophylla*) showing a portion of the very extensive root system. Scale in feet.

forms rather open bunches and is 2 to 3 feet tall. It produces an abundance of seed each year and thus maintains itself in places where the cover is disturbed. The fine, extremely well branched roots are abundant and roots of the fourth order occur. The spreading roots extend outward about 2 feet and with other more vertically descending ones occupy the first 2 to 3 feet of soil. According to Tolstead (1942), the three stages in the degeneration of sand-hill ranges are decrease of the most palatable species, dominance of sand reed and sand dropseed, and finally the dominance of sandhill muhly.

Changes in the original composition of sand-hill vegetation resulting from grazing and drought were pointed out by Frolic and Shepherd (1940). Little bluestem and needle-and-thread had materially decreased in abundance, as had also sand bluestem. Sand reed had increased, and hairy grama and sand dropseed, formerly of minor importance, had increased to the rank of important species. In their studies of range lands in Cherry County, sand reed ranked highest in density, hairy grama second, and sand dropseed third.

Sedges of several species make up a part of the vegetation. Plants of *Cyperus schweinitzii* growing singly are commonly associated with the bunch grasses throughout the region. This perennial, perhaps more commonly a component of stabilized vegetation, is also frequently found among the pioneers in the shifting sands of blowouts. It consists of a few tufts of grass-like, spreading stems which form a very open bunch. Height is approximately 2 feet. The plant has short, woody, much branched rhizomes. Great numbers of fine, fibrous, dark-brown roots began to branch near the soil surface and gave rise to great clusters of exceedingly fine and minutely branched laterals which permeated the soil in all directions. They were especially well developed in mat-like areas in the surface soil. In fact, most of the root system occurred in the surface foot and practically all of the roots were in the first 2 feet. Lateral spread was very great. Roots grew parallel with the soil surface for distances of 3.5 feet on all sides of the plants.

Sun sedge (*Carex heliophila*), which is only a few inches high, was common in well developed vegetation. It spreads by means of rhizomes. Growth begins early in spring and seeds are ripened in about 60 days. The plant is dormant during the hot summer.

Blue grama is well distributed over the dunes, especially in heavier soil, and hairy grama is found in many localities and is an important species of the understory. Indian ricegrass (*Oryzopsis hymenoides*) is also common. Many other grasses occur but mostly in smaller amounts.

Hairy prairie clover (*Petalostemum villosum*) is a low, finely branched legume. With its dense cover of silvery leaflets it stands out as a prominent object in the sand-hills flora. It sometimes plays the role of a pioneer in the blowouts but is regularly found in various locations on the hills. This plant is 12 to 18 inches tall. Of the half-dozen mature plants examined all had strong taproots nearly half an inch in diameter, a much branched root system, and a root penetration of 4 to 5 feet (Fig. 41). Nodules were abundant especially in the surface soil. The numerous surface laterals often extended outward 2 to 3 feet in the first foot of soil. A profuse network of finely branched rootlets at the root-ends was characteristic of this species.

Fleabane (*Erigeron bellidiastrum*), a much-branched annual composite with light-pink or lavender flowers, frequently forms extensive societies. The plants examined were 12 to 15 inches tall and in blossom. The taproots reached depths of about 3 feet. Beginning an inch below the soil surface, branches came off in great profusion. This species had a widely spreading but not deeply seated root system.

Gilia longiflora is a white- to pink-flowered annual gilia. It had a root-pattern similar to that of fleabane but with at least three times as many main branches, which thoroughly occupied both the first and second foot of soil.

Sand milkweed (*Asclepias arenaria*) is a widely distributed component of the vegetation although it seldom occurred in abundance. Three specimens, each 2 feet high and in full bloom, were examined on a fairly well vegetated hillside. The fleshy taproots were about a half-inch in diameter; all were characterized by a tortuous course and very few branches. Several roots were traced to a depth of 8 feet; it is probable that they penetrated 2 to 3 feet deeper. A few other sand-hill plants, such as bractless mentzelia (*Mentzelia nuda*), have similar deeply penetrating but poorly branched roots.

Sand sage (*Artemisia filifolia*) is an abundant shrub especially in the southwestern and western portions of the sand hills. It associates with sand reed and sand-hill bluestem. Often it occurs with, or nearly replaces, needle-and-thread over broad sandy belts in undulating sand hills (Fig.

49). Its density increases with overuse of the preceding grasses. This much branched, bushy shrub is 1 to 2 feet in width and approximately 16 to 26 inches in height. The plants have a dark-green color. Roots of three plants were examined. They were growing on a stabilized area near a sand dune. The largest had a taproot 1.5 inches in diameter from which arose a large number of stems to a height of 2 feet, forming a bush about 18 inches wide. In the third foot of soil the taproot broke up into 3 parts. One of these was traced to a depth of 9 feet where it was still 4 mm. in diameter. The extensive branching in the first 4 feet of soil and the course of the deeper roots are shown in figure 51. Thus, it may be seen that this 10-year-old plant had a highly developed absorbing and soil-binding root system characteristic of the general group of sand-hill plants.

Umbrella plant (*Eriogonum microthecum*), a perennial, somewhat woody-based plant, frequently controls local areas of sandy slopes and occurs rather widely throughout the sandy plains. It has a very deep taproot and branches widely in a manner very similar to that of the sand sage.

Canada sage (*Artemisia canadensis*) is an herbaceous plant with erect stems 1 to 2 feet high. It is widely distributed in the sand hills and frequently occurs in abundance. It had a rather small taproot which reached a depth of 8 feet. Long branches extended outward 2 to 2.5 feet from the base of the plant and then ran vertically downward 4 to 6 feet. Branching was so profuse throughout that over a surface area of at least 20 square feet and to a depth of 6 feet the soil was threaded with the roots of this sage.

Sufficient data have been presented to show that among the grasses of sand hills the rhizome habit was extremely well developed. Several forbs had a similar means of spreading through the sand. Most of the plants had wide-spreading main roots or lateral branches in the soil surface and to several feet in depth. The following summary is based on 45 species of sand-hill plants examined at five widely separated stations—Seneca, Haigler, and Central City in Nebraska, and Yuma and an area southeast of Colorado Springs in Colorado. "Only 9 per cent of the species have roots confined to the surface foot or two of soil, 18 per cent have few or no roots which carry on absorption in this area, while 73 per cent of the species are supplied with an absorbing system of such a character as to get water and solutes from both the shallower and deeper soil layers, many species having roots which extend as deep as the fifth to the eighth foot of soil" (Weaver, 1920).

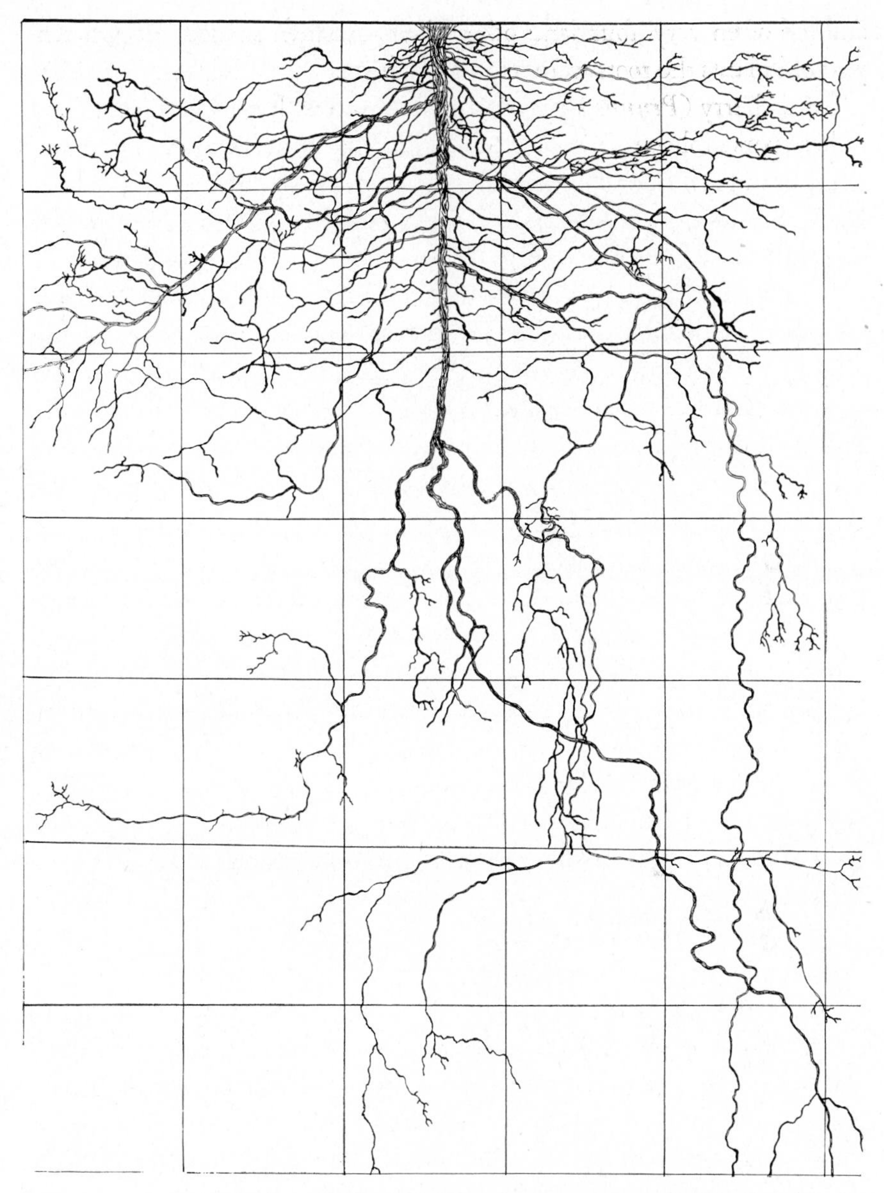

FIG. 51. Root system of a ten-year-old sand sage (*Artemisia filifolia*) 8 feet deep.

Only a few species of shrubs, in addition to sand sage, are found in sand hills. Redroot (*Ceanothus ovatus*) is represented by many-stemmed, bushy plants about 2 feet in height. They occur singly or in small to large patches and are often very abundant; other plants are then shaded out. On ten-year-old plants the roots were 9 to 12 feet deep.

Sand cherry (*Prunus besseyi*) is a low shrub with numerous stems and rather sparse foliage. It is conspicuous in May because of the numerous white or pinkish-colored flowers and again in late summer when the large black cherries have ripened. This shrub may be found on almost every sand hill.

Prairie rose (*Rosa suffulta*) has extremely deep roots and abundant underground stems and forms dense patches. Sometimes these are acres in extent on hillsides protected from the wind. Locally most bunch grasses and other herbs are then excluded. The large showy flowers are beautiful to behold during May and the cherry-red fruits, in autumn. Lead plant (*Amorpha canescens*) is another common shrub. It is characteristic of firm soils.

Total herbaceous flora of the sand hills is very large. Many species are characteristic of true prairie eastward, some are more typical of the mixed prairie to the west, and many are found only in sandy soils of the central United States. Together they compose a very diversified flora. Despite the climate, the dominants are mostly tall grasses. The sand receives and retains enough water to produce a wonderfully luxuriant vegetation on years with good rainfall. In dry and drought years the plants, as elsewhere on the Great Plains, are less vigorous, dwarfed and dried. The carpet of green over the hills is thinner and bleached and the sand is held less firmly in place.

LAKES AND WET MEADOWS

Many lakes occur in various parts of the sand hills. They vary greatly in size from mere ponds to a mile or even more in width and 1 to 5 miles in length. A few are saline, most are freshwater, but all are shallow. They are nearly all rich in submerged and floating plants and in emergent plants such as bulrushes, arrowheads, cattails, and wild rice which form well defined zones to the edge of the wet meadow. The following data are from the work of Tolstead (1942). The zone along the lower edge of the wet meadow is flooded each spring. Here bluejoint (*Calamagrostis canadensis*), numerous species of sedges, and certain tall forbs such as water hemlock (*Cicuta maculata*) and swamp milkweed (*Asclepias incarnata*) composed the vegetation. The middle portion of the wet meadow was occupied largely by big bluestem, Indian grass, switchgrass and slender wheatgrass (*Agropyron trachycaulum*). Sloughgrass (*Spartina pectinata*) was found in the wettest places. This community occurred extensively in all sand-hill valleys where the maximum water table was only a foot or two below the soil surface and the minimum level was about 3 to 5 feet deep.

The postclimax, true-prairie community was usually confined to a zone where the minimum depth of the water table was between 4.5 and 6.5 feet. It occupied the upper portions of the wet meadows. It is a westward extension of true prairie and only the most xerophytic species of this prairie are present. Characteristic grasses were tall dropseed, little bluestem, June-grass and western wheatgrass. Common forbs were stiff sunflower and smooth goldenrod but many others occurred here as well as on the dunes.

On the slopes and tops of the dunes, quite beyond the reach of the water table, the grasses and forbs of the bunch-grass community prevailed.

Various modifications of the meadow communities occur throughout the vast expanse of sand-hill country, as pointed out by Pool (1914). His "Hay Meadow Association" occupied essentially the area just described between the marshes on the wet side and the tall grasses typical of the sand hills. "The many broad valleys of the northern half of the sand-hill region, and less so the valleys of the southern portion, reveal the presence of wide expanses of flat, but relatively dry soil above that of all the lowland associations. . . . Some narrow valleys with finger lakes show practically no flat land. . . . In many cases, however, much of the valley floor . . . is covered in the main by grasses and other plants which are annually mowed by ranchmen along with parts of the wetter meadow for hay. . . . The upland forage crop is seldom cut for hay."

Northeast of the main body of sand hills is a large wet meadow area designated in figure 38 as Prairie Plain. The land is nearly level except for the occasional occurrence of sandhills. From the Sand-Hills Region, water for subirrigation supplements the precipitation. The ground water lies near the surface over much of the area. The vegetation varies from that of ponds and small lakes, which are abundant, through wet meadow to the big bluestem type of grassland. Keim *et al.* (1932) have shown that the structure of the vegetation is closely correlated with the depth of the water table. Over much of the Prairie Plain the wet meadow type prevails. This is one of the leading prairie-hay districts in the United States. In the meadows the vegetation forms a nearly complete and typically closed cover which contrasts strikingly with the open cover of the sand-hill vegetation.

Thus, the Sand-Hill Region is a vast prairie and one of the most important cattle raising districts in the United States. In addition to the three great enemies of grassland—overgrazing, fire, and drought—this prairie has a fourth one, drifting sand. The ranches are large, 1,000 to 100,000 acres in area, and a livestock density of one cow for 10 to 20 acres is usual; 17 acres per steer is perhaps an average stocking rate. Winter grazing is not extensive. The dry meadows, which produce only 0.5 to 1 ton per acre of hay, are usually grazed but the wet meadows furnish an abundance of hay for winter use. Haymaking takes place from July to September.

Areas of sand also occur in southwestern Nebraska south of the Platte, but the Sand-Hills Region gives way quite abruptly on the southeast to the Loess Hills and Plains. Westward the transition from sand hills to the hard lands of the High Plains is usually quickly made and scattered ranges of sand hills or even isolated hills are few. This is also true northward. These adjacent regions, in Nebraska, will now be described.

CHAPTER 12

Nebraska Plains Around the Sand Hills

LYING SOUTHEAST of the Sand Hills in Nebraska but north of the Platte River, there is an extensive hilly area of loess and remnants of the high level plain from which the hills have originated (Fig. 38). South of this region, across the Platte, the land is nearly level except where it is deeply eroded by the Republican River. The parts of these areas not in the eastern third of the state (as indicated by the arrows on the map) have a cover of mixed-prairie grasses.

LOESS HILLS AND PLAINS

The greater part of this upland plain, because of stream erosion and wind action, is a hilly region; the hills are often 100 to 150 feet higher than the valleys between them (Fig. 52). The light yellow to brownish yellow loess, composed largely of particles of silt, is uniform in texture, mellow and very deep. Lime is abundant usually at depths of about 3 feet. The soil is easily eroded and depletion of the plant cover and reduction of the vegetal mulch quickly result in the loss of much soil. Moreover, natural recovery is slow and land once broken is reseeded only with great difficulty (Voigt, 1951). Under an annual rainfall of 23 inches water penetrates deeply, and most grasses and forbs extend 2 to 3 or more feet deeper than under a similar rainfall on more compacted and heavier types of soil. Western wheatgrass, for example, extended its roots downward more than 10 feet and few-flowered psoralea reached 18 feet in depth. Nearly half of the area in 1950 was still covered with the native prairie sod; a part was undisturbed except by mowing, the rest was used as range land.

The mixed prairie is naturally divided into three main communities. Blue grama, or blue grama with small amounts of buffalo grass, was dominant in the short-grass type which occurred on hilltops and extended some distance down the hillsides, on dry slopes sometimes to near the base of the hill. A postclimax type of tall and mid grasses of true prairie clothed the typically broad flat bottoms of ravines, low terraces, and lower slopes of the hills. Here the dominant grasses were big bluestem, side-oats grama, and western wheatgrass, with smaller amounts of switchgrass and Canada wild-rye.

FIG. 52. (Upper) Typical range land in the Loess Hills near Broken Bow, Nebraska. Most abundant grass on this silt loam soil is blue grama. (Lower) A small flat-bottomed valley and three bare canyon walls resulting from erosion and slipping of the soil. Western wheatgrass is on the valley floor.

A third community of mixed short and taller grasses occupied the hillsides where the short grasses from the hilltops and upper slopes mingled with the mid and tall grasses from the lower land. This two-layered community is a typical expression of mixed prairie. Following the great losses of little bluestem during drought and its replacement to a considerable degree by big bluestem, the dominant taller grasses were side-oats grama, big bluestem and western wheatgrass. The understory was composed chiefly of blue grama but also of some buffalo grass and various low-growing sedges.

Western wheatgrass spread extensively during the great drought. Its original abundance in the area is not known. After 1944, it was found in various amounts in every prairie examined. This varied from almost complete replacement of other vegetation, where aided by dust deposits, to patches so small or stands so thin that they had little effect upon the plant cover.

The most abundant grasses and sedges of secondary importance were plains muhly (*Muhlenbergia cuspidata*), Kentucky bluegrass, Junegrass, sand dropseed, Scribner's panic grass, penn sedge, tall dropseed and little bluestem. Needle-leaf sedge (*Carex eleocharis*), needle-and-thread and red and purple three-awn were less abundant.

Forbs were plentiful. Those most abundant and forming marked societies were red false mallow (*Sphaeralcea coccinea*), cut-leaved goldenweed (*Haplopappus spinulosus*), velvety goldenrod (*Solidago mollis*), large-flowered yellow flax (*Linum rigidum*), low poppymallow (*Callirrhoe involucrata*), scarlet gaura (*Gaura coccinea*), Platte milk vetch (*Astragalus plattensis*), low milk vetch (*A. lotiflorus*), Short's milk vetch (*A. shortianus*), yellow-spined thistle (*Cirsium ochrocentrum*), showy peavine (*Lathyrus ornatus*) and ball cactus (*Neomammillaria vivipara*). The preceding data are from Weaver and Bruner (1948) (Fig. 53).

Further studies by Hopkins (1951) in annually mowed but ungrazed prairies revealed that the short-grass type occupied about 33 per cent of the area. Here blue grama constituted 91 per cent of the vegetation and buffalo grass about 5 per cent. Basal cover averaged 31 per cent, and a vegetal mulch of 1,700 pounds per acre covered the soil. Another third of the prairies was occupied by the mixed-grass type. Blue grama composed approximately 50 per cent of the vegetation, side-oats grama 18, and sedges and big bluestem each 7 to 8 per cent. Basal cover was only 19 per cent, and the organic mulch about 1,200 pounds per acre. In the mid- and tall-grass type, which covered 25 per cent of the area, percentage composition was big bluestem 56, side-oats grama 13, and species of sedges 11. Basal area was only 9 per cent, and the dry mulch was 838 pounds per acre under

FIG. 53. (Upper) Cobaea beardtongue (*Pentstemon cobaea*) with white or purple flowers, and white milkwort (*Polygala alba*). (Lower) Rush-like lygodesmia or skeleton weed with the usual insect galls, and two stems of milk vetch (*Astragalus racemosus*) with yellowish-white flowers and young fruits.

annual mowing. Hopkins also studied the environment of each grassland type and layering and seasonal aspects of the vegetation as well as yield. In 1948, a season when the grasses developed normally, greatest yields were obtained in the mid- and tall-grass type, which produced 1.7 tons of air-dry forage per acre. The short-grass and mixed-grass types each yielded about a ton per acre.

DEGENERATION AND YIELDS UNDER GRAZING

A quantitative study of the degeneration of each of the preceding types of vegetation under prolonged grazing has been made (Branson, 1952; Branson and Weaver, 1953). Representative areas of excellent, good, fair, and poor ranges were selected in each grassland type and the composition of the vegetation and yields were ascertained in each of 12 locations.

The lowland sites (mid- and tall-grass type) were the most preferred by cattle for grazing. Big bluestem decreased steadily from 58 per cent in an excellent range to 29 in a good one. It disappeared in fair and poor ranges. Switchgrass and other tall grasses also decreased, some entirely disappearing in fair and poor pastures. Blue grama, bluegrass and buffalo grass all increased; buffalo grass composed 72 per cent of the vegetation in fair grade pastures. Sand dropseed was a chief invader.

On hillside sites, where the mixed-grass type prevailed, big bluestem soon disappeared as did also side-oats grama and bluegrass. Sand dropseed entered good pastures and gradually increased thereafter. The greatest changes were the gains of blue grama and buffalo grass. Blue grama increased from 64 to 75 per cent from excellent to good range, and buffalo grass from 5 to 45 per cent from an excellent range that degenerated to a fair one. Thus, continued overgrazing reduced both the vegetation of hillsides (mixed-grass type) and that of lowlands (mid- and tall-grass type) to a short-grass grazing disclimax. In the lowland type, yields of perennial grasses were reduced from 2.44 tons per acre in excellent range to 1.65 tons in a good one and finally to only .27 ton after long periods of overgrazing. On the hillsides a yield of 1.44 tons per acre was gradually decreased through the good and fair pasture stages to only .41 ton in poor ranges.

Changes in hilltop sites (short-grass type) consisted of buffalo grass increasing from 20 per cent in excellent range to 68 in a fair one, and blue grama decreasing from 75 per cent to 28 in the same ranges. A high yield of about 1.25 tons of perennial grasses per acre decreased to .65 ton in fair range but to only .41 ton in poor pasture.

Most legumes and other prairie forbs decreased or disappeared as excellent ranges were reduced to fair or poor ones. Others, such as ironweed (*Vernonia baldwini*), many-flowered aster (*Aster ericoides*) and wavy-leaved thistle (*Cirsium undulatum*), increased with grazing. Invading weeds were well represented by woolly vervain (*Verbena stricta*) and western snowberry (*Symphoricarpos occidentalis*), and later by common sunflower (*Helianthus annuus*), buffalo bur (*Solanum rostratum*), snow-on-the-mountain (*Euphorbia marginata*) and many other annuals.

The monthly and annual yield and forage utilization were ascertained by means of numerous 30-square-foot, portable exclosures in two pastures near Kearney typical of the loess hills. Forage utilization is here considered as the amount of forage removed by grazing animals, rodents, insects, and hail in relation to the total production. The first pasture consisted of 70 acres of excellent, almost pure buffalo grass. Current yield exceeded utilization in early summer, but it was usually exceeded by utilization after August. In 1945, 18 animal units of cattle utilized 1.65 tons of forage per acre of the 1.96 tons yield. The next year, which was less favorable for growth, 17 animal units utilized 99 per cent of the 1.42 tons yield per acre. The following year, which was more favorable for growth, 12 animal units utilized 1 ton of the 1.56 tons yield. Thus, under good management, a stocking rate of 6 to 7 acres per animal unit seemed to be a proper one in this pasture which was typical of many others throughout the hills (Weaver and Bruner, 1948).

The second pasture was 160 acres in extent and on hilly land. About half of it was in a 23-year-old subsere following breaking. In 1946, 36 animal units of cattle utilized 1.78 tons of forage per acre in the buffalo grass-bluegrass type of the lowlands of a 2.19 ton yield. Of the 1.26 tons yield in the buffalo grass type of the hillsides, 1.03 tons per acre were utilized. Only .71 ton of the .98 ton yield of buffalo grass-sand dropseed type of the hilltops was eaten. In the subsere of open stands of western wheatgrass, three-awn grasses, and buffalo grass, yield was only .71 ton per acre and utilization .24 ton.

About three-fourths of the ranges of the loess hills region were in only fair to poor condition.

Loess hills and level uplands also occur southwest of McCook, Nebraska, and near Atwood in northwestern Kansas. Uplands are usually not over 75 to 100 feet above the valleys and the hills are usually less steep than those described. The vegetation in Kansas has been studied by Tomanek and Albertson.

Ungrazed level uplands and gentle slopes were clothed with blue grama, side-oats grama and buffalo grass. They composed three-fourths of the cover. Small scattered patches of big bluestem occurred. Bunches of little bluestem were common on hillsides, but they were more abundant on lower slopes. Red three-awn was uniformly distributed throughout. Western wheatgrass, purple three-awn, sand dropseed and hairy grama were of minor importance.

Moderate grazing resulted in a great decrease of bluestems. Blue grama, side-oats grama and red three-awn maintained their stand, but buffalo grass, which ranked third in abundance, soon became the most abundant species. Under heavy grazing blue grama, side-oats grama and red three-awn also decreased so greatly that heavily grazed pasture was composed practically of pure buffalo grass.

Vegetation of ungrazed lowland was 70 per cent big bluestem and side-oats grama. Western wheatgrass occurred in small patches, and little bluestem (depleted as on the hillsides by drought) occurred on lower slopes. Other grasses were sand dropseed, red three-awn, buffalo grass, blue grama and, in the more moist places, Canada wild-rye and switchgrass.

Moderately grazed lowland had lost most of its big bluestem and was dominated by side-oats grama and western wheatgrass. Buffalo grass, blue grama and sand dropseed had all increased in abundance. Under heavy grazing buffalo grass increased enormously to become the chief species; western wheatgrass and side-oats grama were still common but all other grasses had practically disappeared.

Forbs were abundant in both species and numbers of plants. Most abundant species were as follows:

Scarlet globemallow
Sphaeralcea coccinea
Plains milkweed
Asclepias pumila
Many-flowered aster
Aster ericoides
Wavy-leaved thistle
Cirsium undulatum
False boneset
Kuhnia eupatorioides
Smooth goldenrod
Solidago missouriensis
Aromatic aster
Aster oblongifolius
Blazing star
Liatris punctata

Rush-like lygodesmia
Lygodesmia juncea
Few-flowered psoralea
Psoralea tenuiflora
Western ragweed
Ambrosia psilostachya
Linear-leaved sage
Artemisia dracunculus
Scarlet gaura
Gaura coccinea
Tooth-leaved primrose
Oenothera serrulata
Silver-leaf psoralea
Psoralea argophylla
Velvety goldenrod
Solidago mollis
Licorice
Glycyrrhiza lepidota

Nine other legumes, in addition to the three listed, were present in this grassland. Four were species of *Astragalus,* but slender indigo bush (*Dalea enneandra*), crazyweed (*Oxytropis lambertii*), sensitive brier (*Schrankia nuttallii*), prairie turnip (*Psoralea esculenta*) and white prairie clover (*Petalostemum candidum*) also occurred.

GRAZING PATTERNS

Grazing patterns in this hilly region are of much interest; topography, indirectly, has much to do with the kind of vegetation, its amount, and its period of development. All these factors affect the grazing habits of animals. For example, in the Nebraska hills for a period of 6 weeks after May 1 grazing was heavy in the lowland. Not only was Kentucky bluegrass the earliest perennial in beginning growth but also it was here that the winter annual, hairy chess (*Bromus commutatus*), was most abundant and made its best growth. Not until late May and early June did the new crop of buffalo grass become available on the hillsides. Then in the lowland the ripening and drying hairy chess overtopped all other grasses and equaled the height of the cool-season wheatgrass. The cattle now grazed mostly on the hillsides. In late June and July, the highly palatable sand dropseed in another grazing type made an excellent growth. Forage in the buffalo grass-sand dropseed type was usually well developed before it was much grazed in July and August. In autumn search for green forage was general; there was much trampling of the dried hairy chess on lowlands as the cattle sought out the renewed growth of bluegrass, western wheatgrass, and green seedlings of hairy chess.

An extensive study has been made of a 290-acre range on similar hilly land about 130 miles eastward in true prairie. The grazing preferences and activities of cattle and their effects on the composition and distribution of the natural vegetation were studied (Weaver and Tomanek, 1951).

Moorefield and Hopkins (1951) made similar studies on the grazing habits of cattle in a mixed-prairie pasture about 140 miles south of Kearney near Hays, Kansas.

Considerable attention has also been given to the effects of various grazing types on the behavior of both sheep and cattle in the hilly areas near Miles City, Montana (Woolfolk, 1949; Holscher and Woolfolk, 1953; Peterson and Woolfolk, 1955). These studies are discussed in chapter 20. Methods to bring about proper utilization of forage are of great importance as regards not only the welfare of the vegetation but also the gains made by livestock which consume it.

EFFECTS OF DEGREE OF UTILIZATION

A closely related problem is the effect of different degrees of grazing upon the vegetation. Such studies are often made by clipping at different heights and at different intervals. The tragic experience of the great drought of the 1930's caused federal and state agencies, as well as individual investigators, to give serious thought to the ecology and economics of overuse of grasslands. The results of a recent, intensive, six-year study of the effects of different intensities of clipping on the blue grama-buffalo grass type in west-central Kansas are given as typical (Albertson *et al.*, 1953).

The grasses in 72 square-meter quadrats were clipped (beginning on May 25 or June 5, 10 or 25) at different intervals (every 2, 3, 4 or 6 weeks) and in different amounts (over 60, 80, 90 or 100 per cent of the quadrat). Also height of clipping varied from 1 to 2 inches. Soil moisture supply was as follows:

1942	nearly optimum	1945	low, late summer drought
1943	deficient below 4–6 inches	1946	severe summer drought
1944	nearly optimum	1947	low, late summer drought

Clipping stimulated top growth, especially for 2 to 3 years. During the first growing season total elongation of tops was nearly 20 inches on closely clipped plants, 12 inches on those moderately clipped, but only 7 on unclipped ones. The stimulus resulting from clipping was still apparent under light to moderate clipping during the third year, but in closely clipped quadrats it had been greatly reduced.

After the second year the increment of top growth was always least on plants closely clipped. During the fourth and fifth years total increment of top growth decreased with intensity of clipping.

There was no great effect of top removal on basal cover except under close clipping. Here the centers of crowns died and marginal tillers were more slender and sparse than elsewhere. Following the death of the crowns, open spaces became larger and surface erosion of soil was greater. After 4 to 6 years, half-dead crowns were left on mounds nearly an inch high even on this nearly level land.

Decreased cover and less vigorous growth of closely clipped vegetation resulted, late in the study, in greatly reduced yield. Complete removal of tops late in the growing season resulted in nearly as great reduction in yield as when clipping continued throughout the season.

Roots as well as tops were greatly affected by close clipping. Amount of tops and roots suffered more than 50 per cent reduction in weight under close clipping compared with plants clipped moderately or lightly. Recovery was slow following 6 years of close clipping. Total yield, height and density of grasses were all less than normal even after 3 years of recovery.

The one favorable feature of close clipping was that through most of the season a cover of green, succulent vegetation fairly high in protein was maintained. This feature, of course, did not compensate for the numerous harmful effects of overuse.

The taller native grasses of western Kansas were found to be more greatly damaged by frequent clipping than were the short grasses (Riegel, 1947). Clipping experiments by Lang and Barnes (1942) near Cheyenne, Wyoming, gave similar results. Mid grasses and annual forbs yielded more under protection and harvesting at the end of the growing season than under frequent clipping. Conversely, short grasses and perennial forbs gave higher yields under frequent clipping than when harvested only once at the end of the growing season. They present an extensive review of the literature on the effects of clipping.

The quantity of roots in an overgrazed bluestem pasture was only about 42 per cent as great as in a similar pasture moderately grazed (Weaver, 1950).

OTHER NEBRASKA PLAINS

The Platte, Niobrara, and White Rivers and other streams have modified the original High Plain surface. They eroded it deeply. This dissection separated the old plain into a number of distinct divisions and made the valleys and rough lands. The three main divisions are the Perkins, Cheyenne and Box Butte Plains (Fig. 38). The surfaces of these vary from level to undulating, rolling, and rough. Scattered hills occur as well as many small valleys and deep canyons. In addition much of the surface of Wildcat Ridge (south of the North Platte Valley and near the Wyoming State line) and Pine Ridge, in the northwest, is rough, stony land (Condra, 1920). Thus many habitats are afforded the vegetation.

The short-grass type, as described in Kansas and to be described in Colorado, extended over much of Nebraska south and west of the Sand Hills. It once covered much of the Cheyenne and Perkins tablelands as well as large portions of the Loess Plains Region eastward to about 98° 30′ west longitude (Fig. 38). Over all this area blue grama and buffalo grass were often about equally distributed, except on lighter soils where blue grama was more plentiful. Mid grasses were especially abundant in the part of the Loess Plain Region that is greatly dissected by the Republican River and its tributaries (Fig. 54). Here little bluestem, side-oats grama, sand dropseed and other mid and even some tall grasses were important species. In fact, the vegetation was much the same as that of the loess hills. The nature of the transition of true prairie to mixed prairie over a belt of vegetation about 50 miles wide extending across eastern Nebraska and central Kansas has been fully described by Weaver and Bruner (1954).

The seemingly endless carpet of grass which extended from true prairie westward over the Loess Plains region was not uninterrupted. "Scattered throughout the nearly level prairie were depressed areas which were occupied by a very different type of vegetation. These varied greatly in size. Many were small, covering only one-fourth acre, others were 80 to 160 acres in extent. The largest were sometimes 1 to 3 miles long and 2 to 4 square miles in area. The smaller depressions were only a foot or two below the general soil level but the larger ones were depressed 10 to 15 feet. Depth of accumulated water varied greatly from year to year and from spring to autumn. The shallow depressions usually became dry by mid or late summer. In larger and deeper ones, water exceeded 3 feet in depth during wet seasons. These fresh water marshes were scattered thickly over the plain. It has been ascertained that they occupied an area of more than a hundred square miles (Condra, 1939). Their origin is not definitely known and may, in part, date back to a time preceding the

FIG. 54. (Upper) Small tributary of Republican River in southwestern Nebraska. Side-oats grama and sand dropseed are scattered through the understory of blue grama and buffalo grass (light areas). Some land (dark area) is under cultivation. (Lower) Rocky hillside on breaks of the Cheyenne Plain near Bushnell, Nebraska. The Mixed Prairie is composed largely of little bluestem, side-oats grama, Junegrass and needle-and-thread.

deposition of the Peorian loess. Soils with heavy and thick claypans have developed in these depressions, *viz.* Scott and Fillmore soils. The water seeps through the heavy soil, or more probably through great cracks formed by the shrinking of the clay, hence there is no accumulation of salts. In these places, which are more or less alternately wet and dry, only adapted species of plants can exist." The hydrophytic communities occurring in the depressed areas have been described. "Wheatgrass either in rather pure stands or with an understory of short grasses often bordered the deeper depressions and sometimes formed extensive hay meadows. On others, the muddy slopes became clothed with buffalo grass and blue grama. All of these grasses during dry years invaded the depressions at least temporarily. On the outer edge, the zone of grasses gave way to prairie" (Weaver and Bruner, 1954).

The Pine Ridge Escarpment, most conspicuous in northwestern Nebraska, extends westward through eastern Wyoming toward the Laramie Range (Fenneman, 1931). It also extends northeastward into South Dakota but soon turns eastward paralleling the White River (but some distance south of it) and continues almost to the Missouri River (Fig. 79). This region in Nebraska and South Dakota lies north of the Sand Hills. The soils of the Box Butte Plain, Pine Ridge, and the Rosebud area eastward are essentially fine sandy loams. This is in sharp contrast to the prevailing heavier soils northward which have developed from Brule and Pierre clays. The herbaceous vegetation also is similar throughout. North of the North Platte River on the Box Butte Plain and elsewhere threadleaf sedge, especially, but also needle-and-thread are far more abundant than south of the Platte. Western wheatgrass also increases in amount in this somewhat cooler more northerly climate. Western yellow or ponderosa pine is a characteristic tree on the steepest slopes bordering this great area (Fig. 55).

Stipa comata was so abundant over parts of northwestern Nebraska before 1900 that Pound and Clements described it as a separate community. "As one looks at the high rolling prairies . . . covered with *Stipa comata,* from a distance the carpet of *Stipa,* variegated with the profusely flowering astragali, lupines, and psoraleas which abound in it, appears to be a piece out of the familiar prairie of the eastern portion of the State. But even in this type . . . on closer inspection the carpet is to be found thin and patchy, while, on the sandy plains, the cover is seldom sufficiently

FIG. 55. (Upper) Range land north of Bridgeport on the Box Butte Plain west of the Sand Hills, showing an area of the great grazing disclimax. Chief grasses are blue grama, buffalo grass and needle-and-thread. (Lower) View on the Pine Ridge Escarpment, west of Chadron, Nebraska. The trees are ponderosa pine alternating with mixed prairie. Photo by W. L. Tolstead.

dense to hide the sand. This type covered large areas of rolling tablelands and of sides of ridges. Junegrass and wheatgrasses were other important mid grasses, and blue grama and buffalo grass were in the understory. Abundant and conspicuous legumes were *Astragalus mollissimus, A. adsurgens, Lupinus plattensis, Oxytropis lambertii, Psoralea argophylla, P. tenuiflora* and *P. esculenta. Erysimum asperum, Thelesperma trifidum* and *Pentstemon albidus* were common along with many other forbs well distributed over the Great Plains." Thus, these botanists give us a glimpse of the wonderful variations of vegetation in the original mixed prairie. They also emphasized the occurrence of western wheatgrass on gumbo plains. The wire-grass (three-awn) type of Shantz (to be described) was also well represented in western Nebraska in various transitional areas between hard lands and the bunch grasses (little bluestem, and others) of sandy soil. Several species of three-awn (*Aristida longiseta, A. purpurea* and *A. basiramea*) were conspicuous in or above the layer of *Bouteloua gracilis, B. hirsuta* and *Buchloe dactyloides.* Various cacti and a host of other forbs common to the short-grass type were present.

A study of relic, protected areas of grassland was made in northwestern Nebraska by Tolstead in 1939. These were on the fine sandy loams of Pine Ridge, on Brule Clay at lower elevations south of the White River, and on Pierre Clay north of the river (Fig. 38). *Stipa comata* was by far the most abundant dominant throughout. *Carex filifolia* was second in abundance. Minor quantities of western wheatgrass were common. The understory of blue grama and buffalo grass was represented by only small isolated plants. This was probably due in part to the much earlier development of the mid grasses, which not only utilized the water stored in winter but also detrimentally shaded the short grasses.

Under grazing on the fine sandy loams, both *Stipa comata* and *Carex filifolia* remained for a long time and occurred in a mixture with numerous other species. Excessive grazing resulted in a *Bouteloua gracilis–Buchloe dactyloides* community with weedy grasses and forbs. On Brule clay *Stipa* rapidly disappeared under grazing and *Carex* remained only in small amounts. The general appearance was soon one of complete dominance of blue grama and buffalo grass. On Pierre clay both *Stipa* and *Carex* were rather quickly replaced by western wheatgrass, blue grama, and buffalo grass.

CHAPTER 13

Plains Plants Underground

At least half of each of the plants that compose the vegetation of the plains and furnish forage for livestock lives in the soil. It is effectually hidden from view. This is true of cultivated plants as well (Weaver, 1926). As a consequence, the roots of plants are the least known, the least understood, and the least appreciated part of the plant. All who deal with plants and vegetation should have a vivid mental picture of the plant as a whole.[1]

Plants branch and spread their leaves widely to secure sufficient light and carbon dioxide, both needed in the process of food manufacture. They grow deeply and branch widely and often minutely to secure water and nutrients which are also essential to food making and growth. The ability of a plant to become established is often dependent upon the nature and rate of growth of its root system. Ordinarily its roots must compete with those of many other plants to obtain the necessities of life from the crowded soil. There is tremendous competition in grassland underground. One plant may lessen competition by penetrating deeply and absorbing far below the roots of grasses, as do many legumes. Another may, under favorable conditions, produce such dense masses of roots that most other species are crowded out, a common habit of western wheatgrass. One kind of plant may be a good soil binder because of its numerous fibrous roots; another may be of little soil-binding value because of its poorly branched taproot. Many problems in the grasslands can be solved and others better understood with a knowledge of the underground plant parts.

Roots of plants are often greatly modified by the environment in which they live. They respond to differences in water content, aeration, soil structure, and nutrients. In fact, the character of the root system is usually an indicator of soil conditions. Moreover, whatever affects the aboveground growth of plants, whether amount of light, degree of humidity, or the

[1] Root descriptions, much abbreviated, and drawings are from Carnegie Institution of Washington publications 286 (1919) and 292 (1920).

removal of the tops as in grazing, has, in turn, its influence upon root development (Weaver and Clements, 1938).

In an extensive survey of the root systems of vegetation, studies were made in 7 widely separated localities in mixed prairie. These ranged from Colorado Springs on the west to Yuma, Colorado, eastward and north to Ardmore, South Dakota.

The extensive studies at Colorado Springs warrant a brief statement of the composition of the vegetation. Blue grama was the chief understory dominant. Buffalo grass was not found, but ringgrass (*Muhlenbergia torreyi*) and penn sedge (*Carex pennsylvanica*) were common in the short-grass understory, which was overtopped by rather widely spaced bunches of purple three-awn (*Aristida purpurea*). The real mixed-prairie nature of the vegetation was revealed by the frequent occurrence of little bluestem, Junegrass, side-oats grama, and green needlegrass (*Stipa viridula*). Common non-grasslike plants were few-flowered psoralea (*Psoralea tenuiflora*), hairy golden aster (*Chrysopsis villosa*), puccoon (*Lithospermum incisum*) and fringed sage (*Artemisia frigida*). Often as many as 6 or 7 species of grasses and an equal number of forbs occurred in a single square meter. Hanson (1955) listed 89 species in 120 square meter samples in 8 stands in the mountain-front zone of northern Colorado. Average number of species per quadrat varied from 8.3 to 15.5.

Mean annual precipitation was slightly less than 15 inches, of which about 12 inches fall during the growing season. The soil was a light-colored loam intermixed with some sand. It was removed with difficulty and in digging the trenches a large pick was kept in constant use. Therefore, roots were unearthed only with great labor. Several specimens of mature plants of each species were usually examined, and drawings were made, always to exact measurements, as the roots were excavated. In the drawings the roots were arranged as nearly as possible in their natural position in a vertical plane.

At Limon, Colorado, 70 miles northeast, under approximately the same precipitation, many typical areas of mixed prairie occurred. The distribution of vegetation was largely determined by edaphic conditions. Where the soil consisted of a compact silt loam, there was a marked expression of the short-grass vegetation, but where it was of sandier consistency but still very compact, more mid grasses occurred. Chief among these were needle-and-thread, purple three-awn and western wheatgrass. Many others, such as Junegrass, squirreltail, needle-leaf sedge and tumblegrass, were common together with a large number of forbs.

In western South Dakota some fine mixed prairies were examined. On the uplands at Ardmore, *Agropyron smithii* reached a height of more than 2 feet and the flower stalks of *Bouteloua gracilis* a length of 12 inches, both indicating very favorable conditions for growth. Mean annual precipitation here was almost 18 inches. Although runoff is high, the Pierre clay is very retentive of water. Common mid-grass dominants were needle-and-thread, red three-awn, plains bluegrass, side-oats grama and little bluestem. The understory grasses were buffalo grass, blue grama, needle-leaf sedge and thread-leaf sedge. The presence of numerous societies was indicative of rather favorable climatic conditions. Some of the more important of these were few-flowered psoralea (*Psoralea tenuiflora*), silver-leaf psoralea (*P. argophylla*), sand sage (*Artemisia frigida*), many-spined opuntia (*Opuntia polyacantha*), woolly loco (*Astragalus mollissimus*), crazyweed (*Oxytropus lambertii*), red false mallow (*Sphaeralcea coccinea*), Pursh's plantain (*Plantago purshii*) and gumweed (*Grindelia spuarrosa*) (Fig. 56).

Typical plains hard land with a lime accumulation at a depth of 1.5 to 2.5 feet occurred at Sterling and Burlington, Colorado. Here, as at Yuma, vegetation was closely similar to that described in western Kansas. Indeed, these brief glimpses emphasize the similarity of the vegetation throughout.

BUFFALO GRASS

The following is a description of a typical root system of *Buchloe dactyloides* in Colorado. From the base of the tufts or clumps roots arose often in clusters of 3 to 10. They were less than a millimeter in diameter but very tough and wiry. Many of the surface roots spread laterally to distances of 0.8 to 1.7 feet from their origin. The roots were very numerous and occupied the soil thoroughly. The tiny laterals were usually not over half an inch in length and rebranched rather poorly. The thread-like main roots penetrated nearly vertically downward. Many reached depths of about 4 feet and some extended a foot or two deeper. The great abundance of very fine roots, their wide spreading in the surface soil, and considerable depth of penetration were the chief characteristics of the root system (Fig. 57).

Roots of buffalo grass were excavated on the hard lands at 6 widely

FIG. 56. (Upper) Western wallflower (*Erysimum asperum*), a yellow-flowered mustard, and (yellow) prairie coneflower (*Ratibida columnifera*). (Lower) Purple-flowered Missouri milk vetch (*Astragalus missouriensis*).

separated stations; all but two were in Colorado. The soils were very fine sandy loams or silt loams. Average depth and maximum depth in feet at the several stations were as follows: Yuma 5 and 7, Burlington 3 and 6.3,

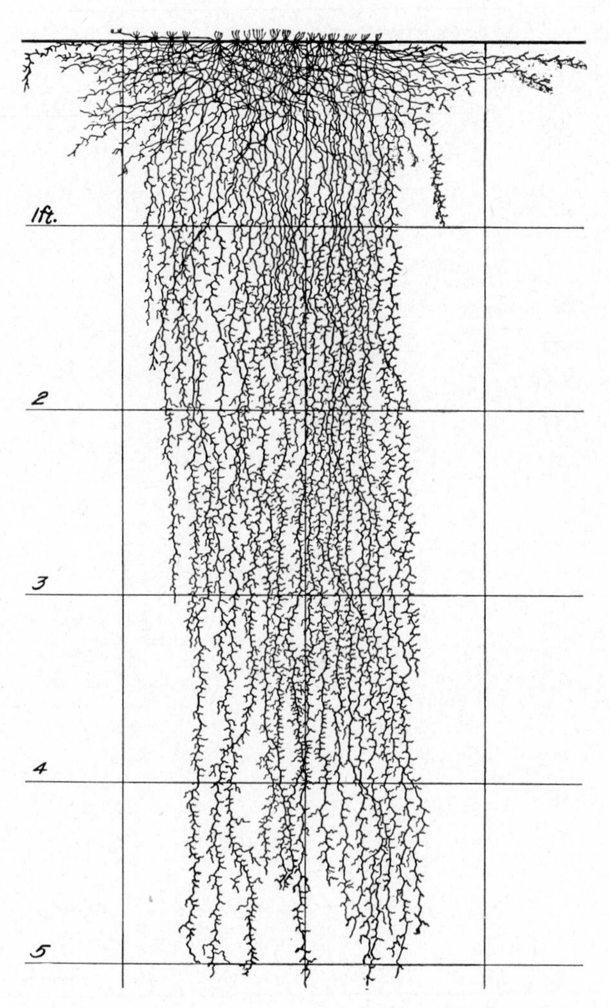

FIG. 57. A representative root system of buffalo grass growing in fine-textured, silty, clay loam soil (hard land) near Yuma, on the High Plains of Colorado.

Sterling 3.6 and 5.7, Limon 4 and 5.2, Phillipsburg, Kansas 5 and 6 and Ardmore, South Dakota 4 and 7. Depths of 4.5 and 5 feet were later ascertained at Hays, Kansas (Albertson, 1937), and 4.5 and 6 feet in the loess hills near Kearney, Nebraska (Weaver and Bruner, 1948).

BLUE GRAMA

Bouteloua gracilis was examined in the mixed prairie at Colorado Springs, where the soil was well filled with fine rootlets to a depth of 2.5

feet. In the next half-foot they were still fairly abundant, some of the longer ones penetrating to a maximum depth of 4 feet. Further examinations were made in heavy clay loam about 25 miles southeastward where blue grama was again the dominant species. Roots were very abundant to a depth of 3.3 feet and several extended to 4.3 feet. At Sterling, Colorado, the soil was well occupied with roots to a depth of 2.5 feet, and at 3.2 feet they were still abundant. Maximum depth of penetration was 4.2 feet. In the tenacious but moist Pierre clay at Ardmore, roots were abundant to a depth of 3.6 feet, and some were traced downward to nearly 4.5 feet. A depth of 5.5 feet was found at Hays, and one of 6.5 feet in the loess hills of Nebraska (Hopkins, 1951). At Nunn, Colorado, roots of blue grama have been traced to a depth of 6 feet (Costello, 1944).

The roots are fine and of great tensile strength, much like those of buffalo grass. The vertically downward penetration of most roots and the depth attained are also similar to this grass. Many roots also spread widely in the surface soil, often to distances of 12 to 18 inches. Thus, although bare places between the bunches and mats of blue grama and buffalo grass occurred, roots, beginning just beneath the surface, threaded the soil. Both of these xeric grasses are thus able to benefit from moderately light showers. Under the higher rainfall of true prairie eastward this lateral spreading of roots rarely occurred.

PURPLE THREE-AWN

Much of the Great Plains is characterized by the conspicuous bunches of *Aristida purpurea*. The strong fibrous roots were a mm. or less in diameter. These rather coarse roots either descended vertically or ran off obliquely at angles of 20 to 45 degrees with the soil surface to a distance of 5 to 8 inches before turning downward (Fig. 58). Although laterals were fairly numerous even to the maximum depth of 4 to 5 feet, the root system lacked the abundant laterals so pronounced in buffalo grass and blue grama. It has been repeatedly observed that this species is also less resistant to severe drought. A depth of 4 to 5 feet was also attained at Hays, Kansas.

NEEDLE-AND-THREAD

A root system of *Stipa comata* was examined. The exceedingly numerous fibrous roots were a mm. or less in diameter. Though many of these descended vertically, others ran off at various oblique angles; some of them had a lateral spread of more than 14 inches from the base of the plant in the surface half-foot of soil. From the very surface of the soil, the main roots were clothed with well-branched laterals 2 to 20 mm. long. Branching occurred profusely throughout, even to a depth of 5 to 5.5 feet. This

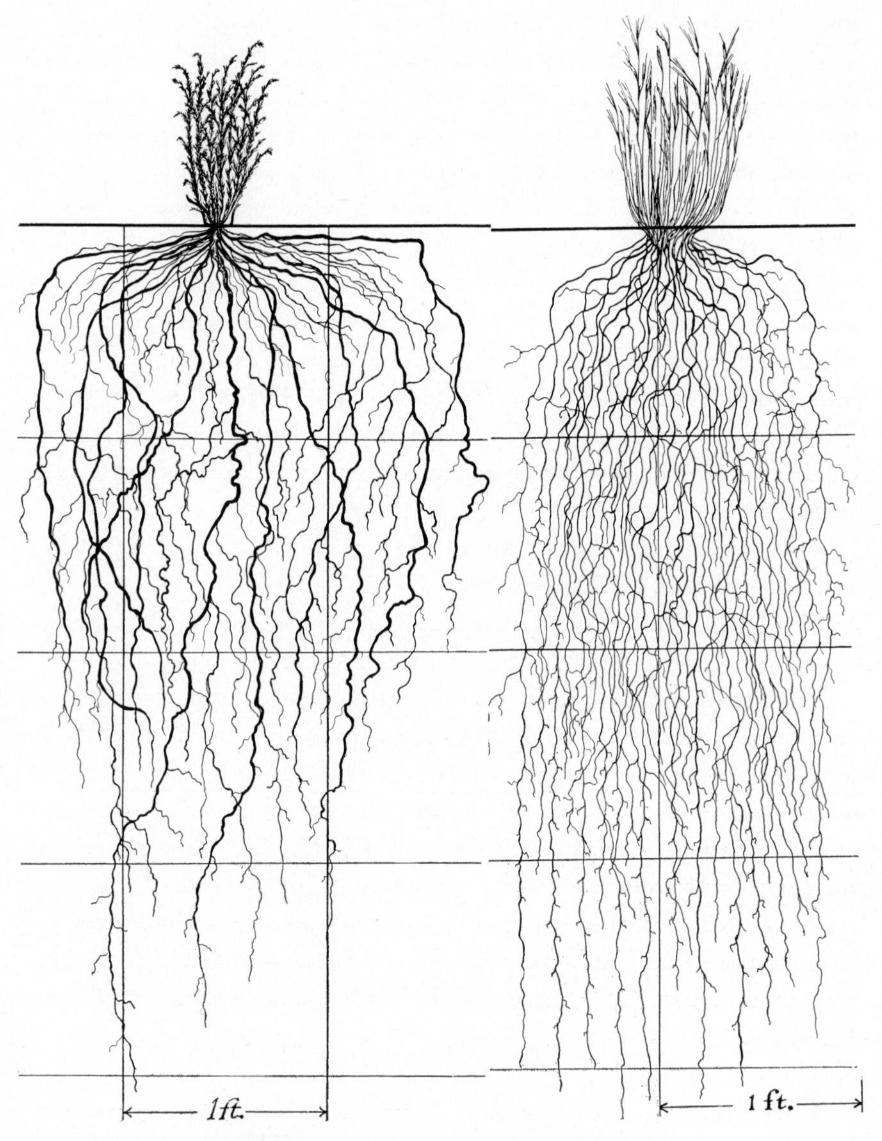

FIG. 58. Purple three-awn (*Aristida purpurea*) and fringed sage (*Artemisia frigida*) growing on hard land.

species is provided with a much finer, more branched, and more widely spreading root system than is needlegrass (*Stipa spartea*) of true prairie.

GREEN NEEDLEGRASS

Stipa viridula is usually best developed in soils which permit considerable water penetration. In Colorado it occurred in greatest abundance in broad swales; it was excavated where it grew in a nearly pure stand. The larger roots were coarse, tough and wiry, especially in the first 5 to 7 feet. Just below the soil surface some roots followed a course almost parallel with it and at a depth of only 2 to 4 inches to distances of 1 to 1.5 feet or more before turning downward. Others ran off obliquely with a maximum spread of only 8 inches on either side of the plant. The rest extended vertically downward, some to a depth of over 11 feet. Root branching was very much like that of needle-and-thread. The entire area under the plant and for a distance of more than a foot on either side was filled with the profuse and delicate branches of the second and third order. Branching continued nearly to the root ends. In this area, unlike that clothed with blue grama, the soil was moist throughout the entire growing season. The usual depth of penetration is probably very much less.

SIDE-OATS GRAMA

Bouteloua curtipendula most often occurred in tufts or small bunches, intermixed with other vegetation. It propagates by means of rather slender rhizomes, usually 2 to 4 inches long. From the base of the plant and the underground stems there arose great numbers of roots. The largest were seldom over a mm. in diameter. Many spread laterally 1 to 1.5 feet in the surface 2 to 4 inches of soil before turning downward. This root habit is very characteristic of most grasses of the Great Plains. Numerous roots pursued a course more obliquely downward, reaching a depth of 4 feet at a horizontal distance of only 8 to 10 inches from the base of the clump. Still others extended more or less vertically downward, some to 5.5 feet. All of the roots in the entire soil mass were abundantly supplied with delicate rebranched laterals not unlike those of blue grama. Similar depths have been observed at Hays, Kansas.

Plants at Ardmore were growing in Pierre clay underlaid at 2.3 feet with a sandy and somewhat gravelly subsoil. The roots occurred at 4 feet in depth and some were several inches deeper. Thus, this drought-resistant grama is characterized by a widely spreading, moderately deep but exceedingly well branched root system.

THREAD-LEAF SEDGE

The root systems of several plants of *Carex filifolia* were examined on the upland at Ardmore. Here they grew with western wheatgrass and blue grama in Pierre clay under a rainfall of about 18 inches. The sedge often grows in clumps 4 to 6 inches in diameter. Not infrequently the stems die in the center and grow only around the periphery of the bunch. This sedge does not develop rootstocks, but where the bunches grow close together they form a dense sod.

The plants were furnished with an enormous number of tough, wiry roots a mm. or less in diameter. These seldom descended vertically but extended obliquely away from as well as under the plant, forming a great tangled mat to a depth of 1.2 to 1.5 feet. Laterals were traced horizontally to a distance of 2.7 feet at a depth of only 3 to 6 inches. Although the larger and older roots were not well branched for the first few inches, a very large number of smaller, profusely branched roots absorbed in the surface soil close to the plant. All of the roots were abundantly supplied with laterals ranging in length from 0.5 to more than 3 inches. These terminated in brush-like mats of laterals, the ultimate branches being very fine. Not only was the surface soil filled with roots, but also many extended obliquely downward, criss-crossing at various angles and reaching a general depth of about 4 feet. Some reached a depth of over 5 feet. These roots also ended in brush-like branches.

The tough, brown or black, wiry roots of this sedge bind the soil so firmly and decay so slowly that new wagon roads through the grassland were very rough for several years until the clumps of roots were worn through. Where the land was broken, the dried root masses remained undecayed for many years. The black color of the roots, with their wiry, matted appearance, accounted for the vernacular name "niggerwool" which was applied to this plant.

PENN SEDGE

Carex pennsylvanica is a low-growing sedge which has a wide range throughout the grasslands. Because of its early growth and flowering habit, it is often most conspicuous in very early spring before most grasses have resumed growth. The tufts are connected by coarse rhizomes 2 to 10 inches long in the surface 3 inches of soil. Roots originate from the rhizomes as well as from the bases of the clumps. The much-branched fibrous roots possessed abundant laterals of the third and fourth order; although a few roots extended downward 3 feet, the chief absorbing area was in the first and second foot of soil.

WESTERN WHEATGRASS

Individual stems of *Agropyron smithii* are connected by tough rhizomes, 1 to 2 mm. in diameter, from a few inches to more than 1.5 feet in length. These lie 0.5 to 2 inches below the soil surface and are frequently branched, abundantly covered with scale leaves, and tipped with long, sharp-pointed buds. From the base of the plants and from the rhizomes arose numerous, short, horizontal roots. These were profusely branched and rebranched to the third and fourth orders, the ultimate branches being almost microscopic in size. Thus, there was an excellent surface-absorbing system. An abundance of coarse, tough roots, 1.5 to 2 mm. in diameter, penetrated in a more or less vertical direction and others at oblique angles to a maximum depth of 7 feet. These roots were profusely clothed with laterals from a few mm. to 2 or 3 inches long; many laterals ran off rather horizontally. Branches were abundant to the root tips. Thus, western wheatgrass is supplied with an absorbing system which thoroughly permeates all portions of the soil to a depth of 6 feet. The plants were examined near Colorado Springs, Colorado. In the true prairie at Lincoln, Nebraska, with more moist soil, the surface absorbing system was only poorly developed. At both Ardmore, South Dakota, and at Limon, Colorado, the surface absorbing system was again pronounced. Depths of penetration were 7 and 5.2 feet, respectively. Similar root extent was found at Hays, Kansas.

JUNEGRASS

Koeleria cristata has a shallow but exceedingly well developed root system. It has been examined in many soil types and in different climates. The average depth of roots is only about 18 inches but the longest ones may reach 2 feet. A great abundance of fine rootlets spread from the base of the plant and fully occupied the soil even in the surface inch to 8 inches on all sides of the bunch. The root system formed a dense mat beneath the plant in the upper 1.5 feet of soil. (See Fig. 59).

RINGGRASS

Muhlenbergia torreyi is common in many parts of the Great Plains from western Kansas and Wyoming to Texas. In places it is abundant. It makes a mat-like growth and has short curled leaves. Frequently the center of the mat is dead and only the peripheral portions produce flowers. Great clusters of roots, only 0.5 mm. or less in diameter, ran off in all directions from near the soil surface to more than 2 feet in depth. All roots were supplied with short, much rebranched laterals. The roots have a wide lateral spread. Most of the dense network of roots and fine branches occurred in the upper 2.5 feet of soil, but a few were traced to 4.5 feet.

TUMBLEGRASS

Schedonnardus paniculatus is an annual or short-lived perennial which is nearly always present in small amounts in the short-grass sod (Fig. 9). It was examined on the plains near Sterling, Colorado, where bunches were growing in an open sod of buffalo grass and blue grama. The root system was relatively shallow, reaching a depth of only 2 to 2.5 feet. Many roots spread from the base of the clump 1 to 1.5 feet in the surface 6 inches of soil. Others penetrated almost vertically downward.

LITTLE BLUESTEM

Andropogon scoparius is an important species of plains vegetation. Plants examined at Phillipsburg, Kansas, in silt loam, produced a very large number of roots from 0.1 to 0.8 mm. in diameter. Most of them penetrated almost vertically downward. They were abundant to 4.5 feet and not a few reached a depth of 5.2 feet. Some spread laterally nearly parallel with the soil surface but more often they ran obliquely downward to distances of 1 to 1.2 feet before turning directly downward. Many of the profuse lateral branches were 2.5 feet long and all were rebranched to the third and fourth order. The surface soil was especially well occupied with dense masses of finely branched roots, but branching occurred on all roots and continued nearly to the root tips. At Colorado Springs the sur-

FIG. 59. (Upper) A pricklypear cactus (*Opuntia macrorhiza*) with yellow flowers. (Lower) Bractless mentzelia (*Mentzelia nuda*) in sandy soil, with large white flowers ready to open, and prairie sunflower (*Helianthus petiolaris*).

face portion of the root system was again well developed. Lateral roots spread 1 to 1.2 feet on all sides of the bunches in the surface 4 inches of soil. Below and within the mass of soil delimited by them, great numbers of roots penetrated at all angles to vertically downward. Most of these reached a depth of 3.5 feet; maximum depth of penetration was 6 feet.

We shall next consider representative species other than grasses.

CACTI

Comanche cactus (*Opuntia camanchica*) is a very widely distributed cactus in the plains grasslands. Like other cacti it is favored in its competition with the grasses by grazing, and its development in great abundance is frequently indicative of overgrazing.

A single, representative plant of average size was examined. As is characteristic of many cacti, the root system consisted of two distinct parts—a few vertically descending, deep roots and a much more extensive and shallow absorbing system. The glistening white, deeper roots were only 4 in number. At their origin they were 2.5 to 3 mm. in diameter. They grew vertically downward, tapering gradually and branching, to a depth of 3 feet. The surface roots ran outward in the soil, usually at a depth of about an inch and seldom deeper than 3 inches, to distances varying from 6 inches to 6 feet (Fig. 60). The largest were 5 mm. in diameter and tapered very slowly in spite of the repeated branching. All of these roots ended in brush-like termini. These shallow roots were brownish in color and very tough.

Western pricklypear (*Opuntia humifusa*) had a similar root system, except that the 6 or 7 downwardly penetrating roots were less than a foot in length and the lateral spread was 2.5 to 3 feet.

Brittle opuntia (*Opuntia fragilis*) has a distinctly shallow root system. About 20 roots extended outward approximately 16 inches in the first 3 inches of soil. The remainder descended at wide angles or vertically to depths of only 8 to 15 inches. Great mats and tufts of roots were interspersed throughout the soil, the whole forming a very excellent system for surface absorption.

Ball cactus (*Neomammillaria vivipara*) had a very similar although far less extensive absorbing system. New plants developed from the widespread roots of many-spined cactus (*Opuntia polyacantha*), thus making this species especially difficult to eradicate. Some of these roots were 5.5

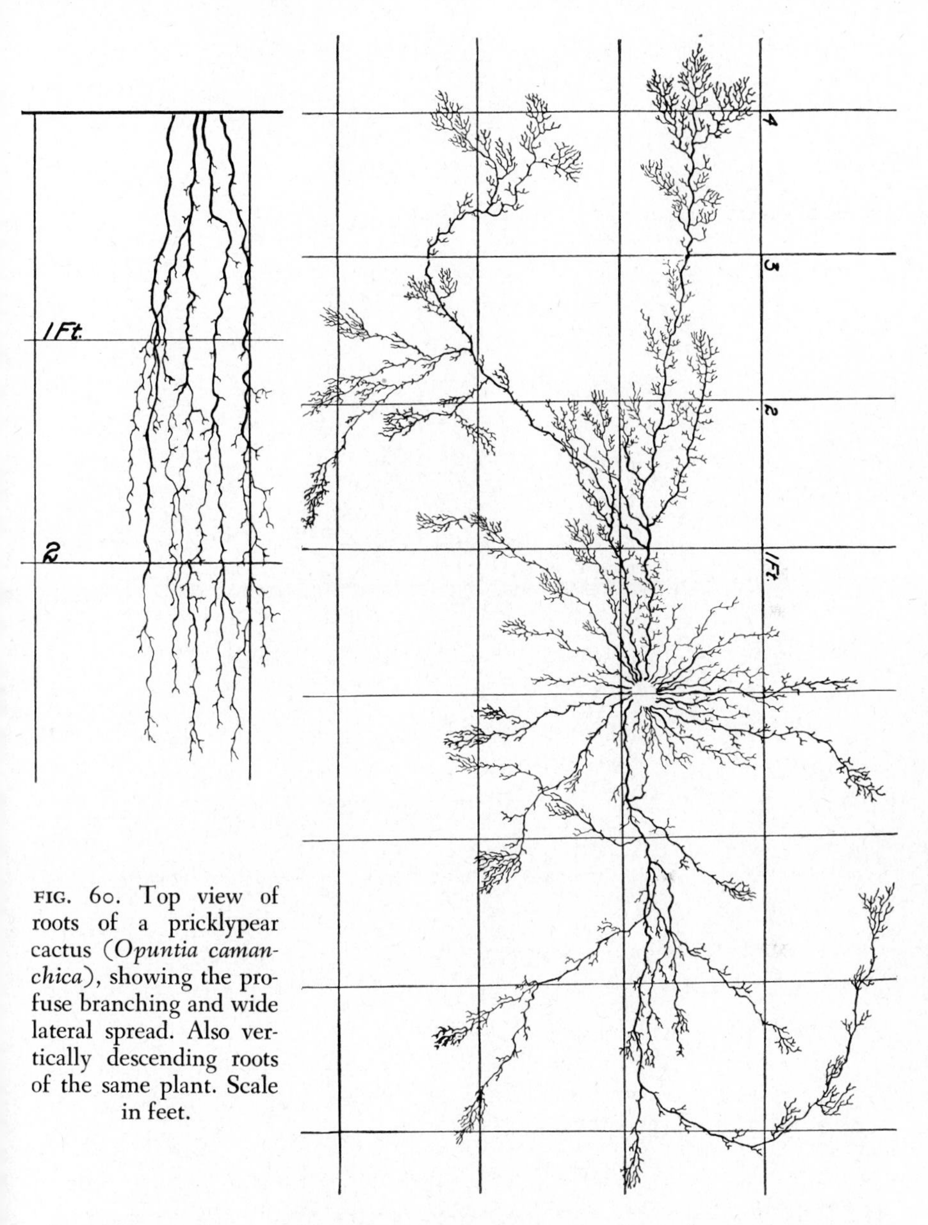

FIG. 60. Top view of roots of a pricklypear cactus (*Opuntia camanchica*), showing the profuse branching and wide lateral spread. Also vertically descending roots of the same plant. Scale in feet.

feet long and new plants arose at several places along a single root. Greatest depth of penetration was only 2 feet. As a whole, the root system was strikingly like that of Comanche cactus and distinctly superficial in its position in the soil. Thus, the cacti compete successfully with the grasses for the moisture in the surface soil afforded by summer showers.

RAGWORT

Senecio oblanceolatus Rydb. is a common and often abundant species, frequently forming vernal societies in the grassland. A drawing of one of the four root systems examined is shown in figure 61. The plants were well adapted for absorption in the surface soil and to a depth of 3 feet.

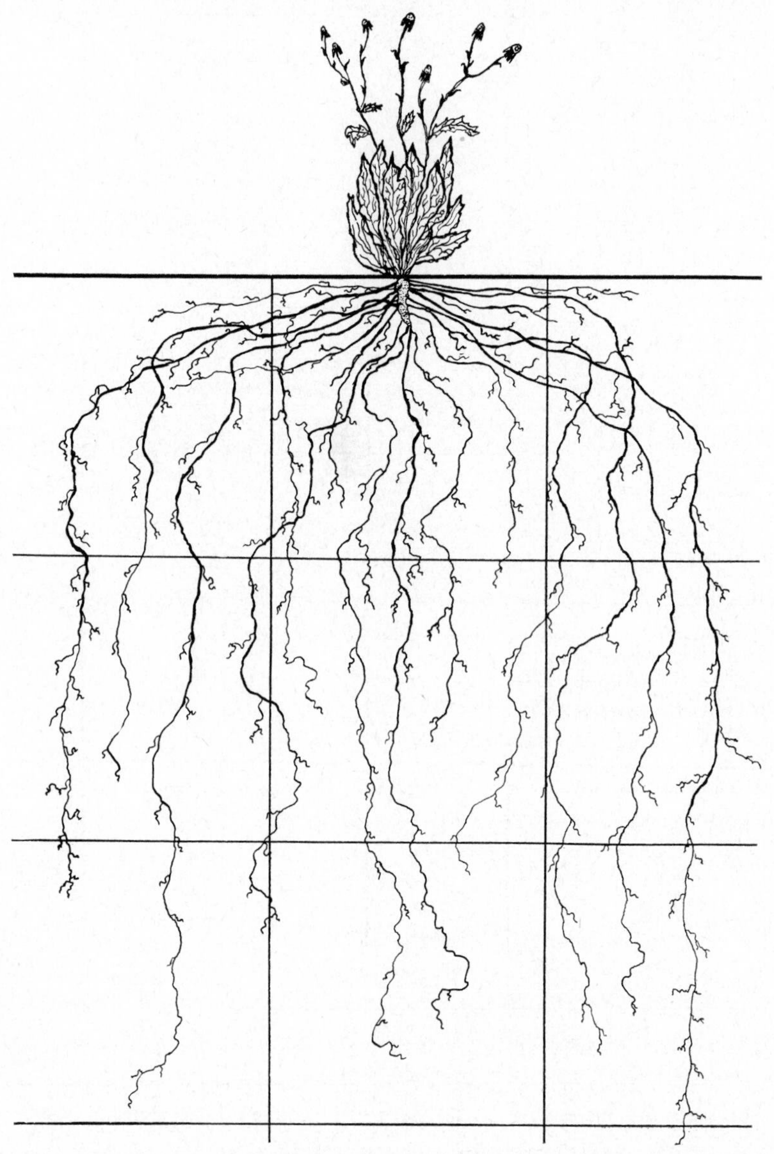

FIG. 61. Ragwort (*Senecio oblanceolatus*) from the High Plains.

PRAIRIE CONEFLOWER

Ratibida columnifera is a species of composite widely distributed throughout the grassland where it forms societies dominating large areas. These plants possess strong, well branched taproots none of which penetrated deeper than about two feet in the hard lands of Colorado and Kansas (Fig. 62). In the loess hills of Nebraska a depth of 5 to 6 feet was attained (Hopkins, 1951). This perennial, unlike the cacti, was temporarily nearly exterminated by the great drought. Aside from annuals, few forbs of the plains are so shallowly rooted.

PLAINS MILKWEED

Asclepias pumila is a dwarf milkweed generally distributed throughout the hard lands of the plains. The plants varied from 3 to 5 inches in height and were connected by extensive underground parts which were 1 to 2 mm. in diameter. The roots are finely and often profusely branched and especially well provided for absorption in the surface foot of soil (Fig. 62).

BROOM SNAKEWEED

Gutierrezia sarothrae, a low half-shrub, occurs throughout the plains region, although it is usually more abundant in areas of less thoroughly disintegrated soil or in overgrazed ranges. It frequently forms extensive societies. Numerous stems arose from a strong taproot 5 to 8 mm. thick. The numerous widely spread laterals which arose in the surface sod are shown in figure 63. From the soil surface to 18 inches depth, especially, the taproot and its many laterals were profusely furnished with finely branched and rebranched, thread-like rootlets. The deeper roots were often unbranched for a distance of a foot or more, or laterals only 2 to 3 inches long occurred in groups. Roots of a similar nature 5 feet deep were excavated in western Kansas.

FRINGED SAGE

Artemisia frigida is a competitor of the plains grasses, especially northward, for the rather meager supply of water. Near the mountains, in rocky or gravelly situations, it frequently forms extensive societies. From the base of the clustered woody stems a taproot arose. It was from 5 to about 10 mm. in diameter and descended rather vertically to a distance

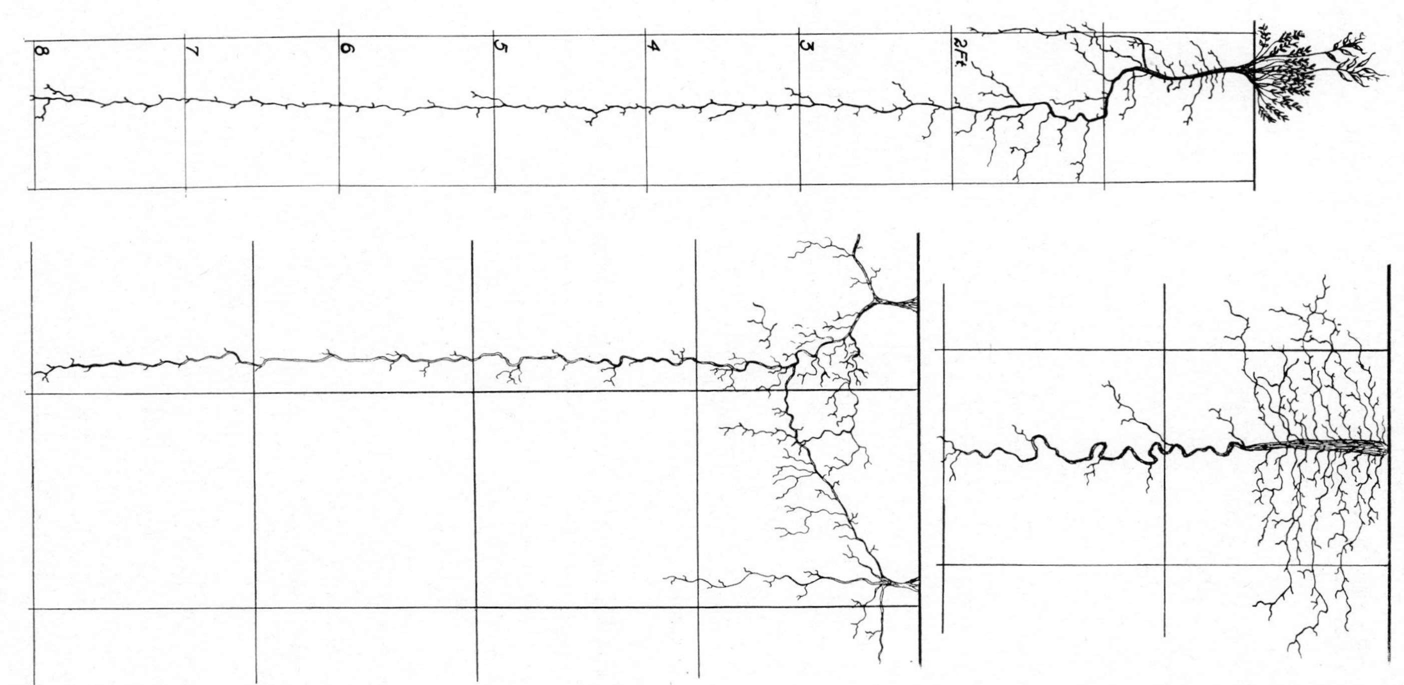

FIG. 62. Roots of prairie coneflower (*Ratibida columnifera*) (upper right), and plains milkweed (*Asclepias pumila*) (below). (Left) Plant of crazyweed (*Oxytropis lambertii*) with roots 8 feet deep.

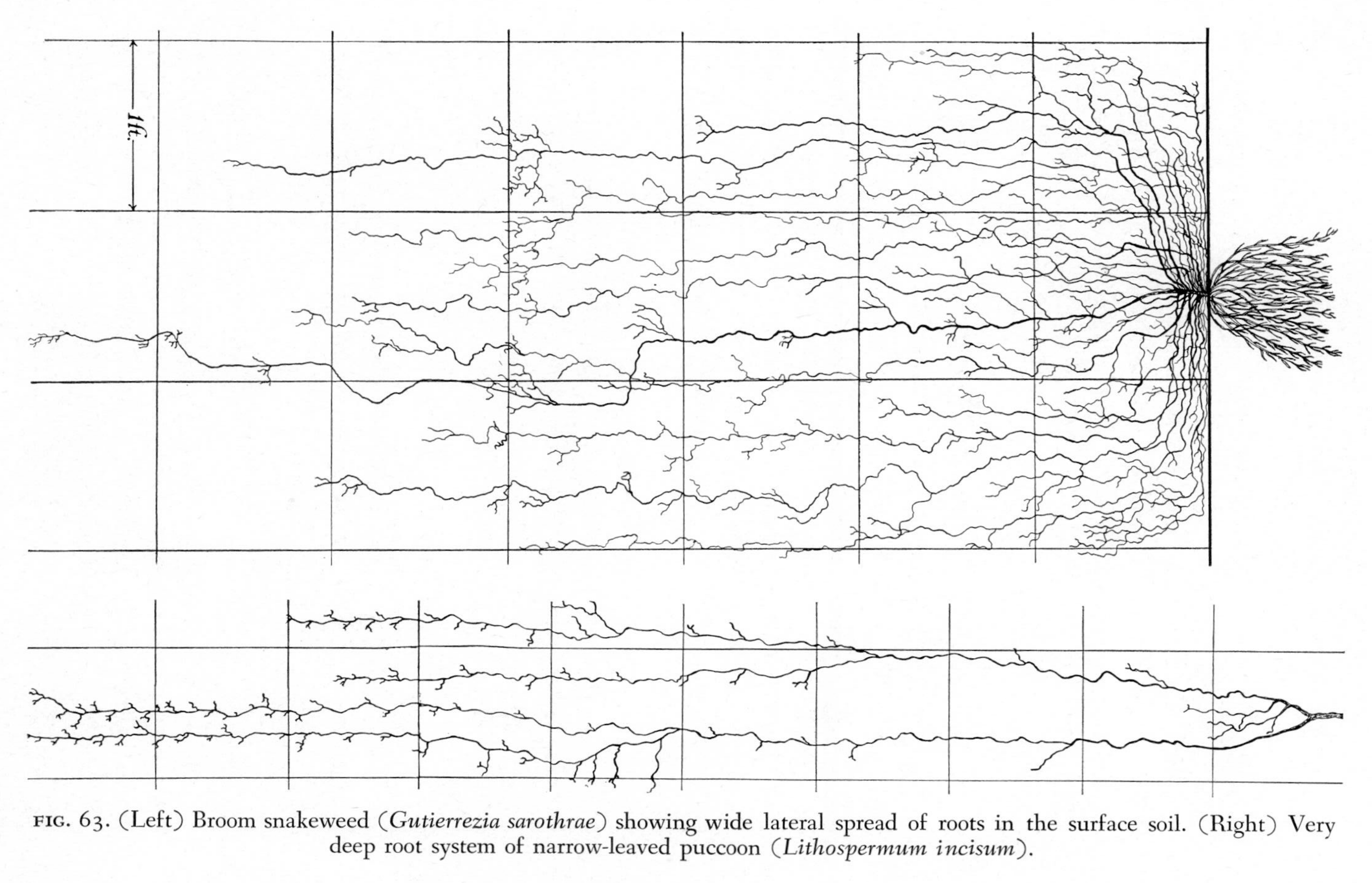

FIG. 63. (Left) Broom snakeweed (*Gutierrezia sarothrae*) showing wide lateral spread of roots in the surface soil. (Right) Very deep root system of narrow-leaved puccoon (*Lithospermum incisum*).

4 to more than 6 feet. The course of the many widely spreading laterals, which were almost as prominent as the taproot, may be seen in figure 58. The woody base of the stem, as well as the first 6 to 10 inches of the taproot, gave rise also to very abundant rootlets, 1 mm. or less in diameter, which thoroughly occupied the surface soil. They branched and rebranched into thread-like termini and furnished this sage, as is true of so many plains plants, with a splendid surface absorbing system. The deeper roots, although branching from time to time and pursuing a rather tortuous course, were characterized by the absence of numerous laterals.

PRICKLY POPPY

Argemone platyceras, conspicuous because of its large size and showy flowers, is found as a frequent component of plains vegetation. Usually it is more abundant in disturbed areas, often becoming ruderal. This plant has a fleshy, dark-brown taproot, sometimes an inch in diameter. At a foot in depth it branched into 2 equal parts. The branches diverged not more than 6 to 8 inches and pursued a downward course. It continued to branch in this manner at irregular intervals throughout the first 8 feet, the whole trend being downward. At about 8 feet a layer of moist sand occurred and here a few branches spread farther outward. Other roots penetrated to a depth of 12 feet, partly through a sandy clay. There were almost no small branches to a depth of 4 feet. At greater depths laterals 2 to 4 mm. in diameter and 4 to 14 inches long occurred sparingly. Clearly this root system is adapted for absorption only in deep soil.

NARROW-LEAVED PUCCOON

Lithospermum incisum is a common component of plains vegetation. Its deeply rooting habit and poor adaptation for absorption in the upper 4 feet of soil is shown in figure 63.

CRAZYWEED

Root systems of several species of legumes were examined. *Oxytropis lambertii* is a poisonous plant—one of several loco weeds. It is widely distributed throughout mixed prairie and is especially conspicuous when it blossoms in spring and early summer. It had a thick taproot which tapered rapidly and penetrated 8 feet deep (Fig. 62). This plant is normally unpalatable to livestock. When desirable forage is scarce or absent, cattle, horses and sheep eat it freely.

DRUMMOND VETCH

Astragalus drummondi was examined in Pierre clay underlaid below 4 feet with sand and gravel so compacted that it was necessary to use a large pick in removing it. The taproots were a half-inch in diameter. They descended rather vertically and tapered rapidly. Depths of only 4 to 4.3 feet were attained, undoubtedly because of the compacted soil. Large, widely spreading branches were numerous; these originated mostly in the first 2 to 18 inches of soil. Some reached depths equal to that of the taproot. Branches of smaller size were abundant. Clusters of tubercles were found at various depths, forming X, Y, and H patterns 5 to 6 mm. in diameter.

PRAIRIE CLOVERS

Petalostemum candidum and *P. purpureum* are examples of legumes with taproots which extended 6 or more feet into the soil, branched widely, and were well provided for absorbing moisture from many cubic feet of soil beneath each plant.

FEW-FLOWERED PSORALEA

Psoralea tenuiflora is a widely distributed legume and one of the most important forbs of mixed prairie. A large bushy plant 2 feet high with a taproot an inch in diameter was excavated near Yuma, Colorado. Although there was an absence of any laterals in the surface 1.7 feet of soil, widely spreading but poorly branched deeper roots were found. Roots were traced to a depth of 9 feet. A similar root depth was found at Phillipsburg, Kansas, and roots penetrated to 7 feet in Pierre clay at Ardmore. At Colorado Springs, taproots were 9 to 12 feet deep.

In summary this psoralea has a deep taproot with no provision for surface absorption and, in fact, seldom branches in the surface foot of soil. The laterals are often large and widely spreading as well as deeply penetrating. The root system as a whole is not well supplied with fine absorbing rootlets. This is a stable species little modified in root habit by varying conditions of the environment. Its presence is indicative of available moisture in the deeper soil.

HAIRY GOLDEN ASTER

The preceding root depth was exceeded by that of a composite, *Chrysopsis villosa.* This plant, widely distributed over the Great Plains, attained a height of only 12 inches. The strong, thick, woody taproot was extremely well branched in the surface 18 inches of soil. Several large branches attained depths of 7 to 8 feet and the main root was 13 feet deep.

SMALL SOAPWEED

Yucca glauca is a widely distributed species, often occurring in abundance on dry, sandy, gravelly or rocky slopes and forming extensive societies throughout many areas in the Great Plains. Its large size, long duration, and often its abundance combine to make it a prominent component of the vegetation. A number of plants were examined.

An excavation was made around 2 plants growing 2 feet apart. They had each developed a caudex (stem) 3 inches in diameter but neither of these reached a depth greater than 18 inches. At this depth they branched and ran off laterally in a direction either parallel with or ascending toward the soil surface. The plants were connected by a large rootstock, and another underground stem ran off at nearly right angles from the connecting one and reached the surface 3 feet beyond. It had given rise to several small plants. Another plant had a caudex 3 inches thick. This reached a depth of about 2 feet. Here it divided into many branches, each abruptly tipped with a bud.

These large underground stems are supplied profusely with roots. The roots, beginning at the soil surface, varied from 2 to 4 mm. in diameter and ran off horizontally to great distances on all sides of the plant. Some were traced outward 32 feet. They occupied the soil chiefly at a depth of 6 to 18 inches. They were reddish in color, nearly uniform in diameter for long distances, and very sparingly branched. The abundance of the roots was surprising. In a single square foot of a trench wall, at a depth of 18 inches, 54 roots were encountered. Some roots did occur, running horizontally, at depths of 4 to 5 feet; a maximum depth of 7 feet was recorded. Thus, the roots of a single plant absorb water and solutes over a very extensive area in direct competition with the grasses. The thick, fleshy cortex of the roots serves for water storage.

The root system of cut-leaf goldenweed is shown in figure 64.

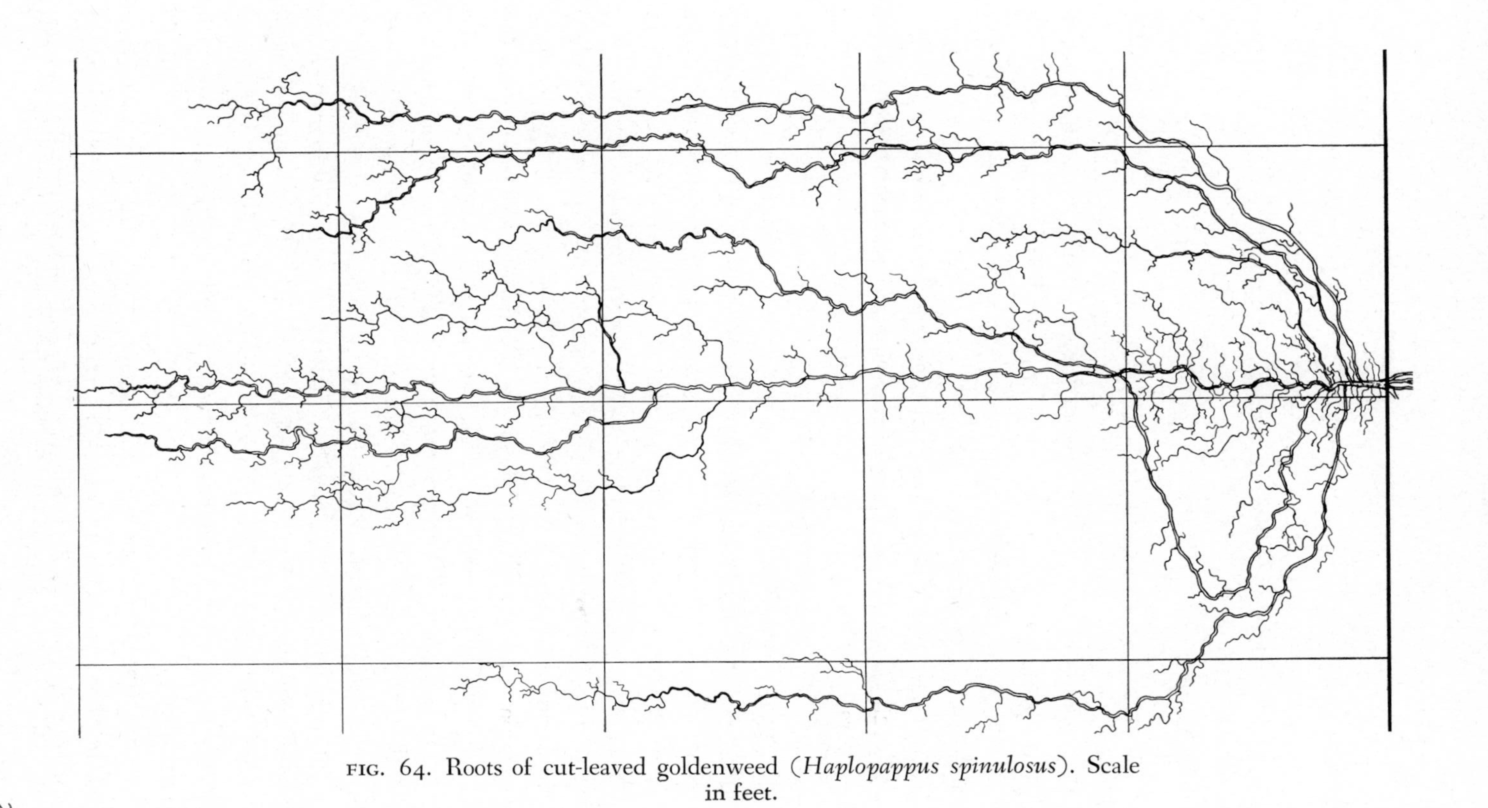

FIG. 64. Roots of cut-leaved goldenweed (*Haplopappus spinulosus*). Scale in feet.

CONCLUSIONS

Further study revealed that among 36 species of mixed-prairie plants on hard lands only 4, if 2 cacti are included, were rather superficially rooted; 16 species were of moderate depth (2 to 5 feet). Of this second group 3 were poorly equipped to carry on surface absorption. A third group of 16 species, including 3 grasses, had roots which extended well below the fifth foot of soil and many to a depth of 7 to 9 feet. Of this number, 7 were adapted for absorption in soils mostly below the surface foot or two only. Thus, 11 per cent of the 36 mixed-prairie species had little or no provision for surface absorption, and 61 per cent were both fairly deep-rooted and well adapted to absorb water even when the surface soil only was moist.

Just how does water penetrate so deeply into the soil under the rather light rainfall of the Great Plains? We have no substantial evidence of root penetration of plains plants into soil where water is nonavailable for growth. In many instances even the deepest roots were taken from moist soil. The answer seems to lie in soil disturbance; ground squirrels, gophers and badgers dig and burrow deep into the earth. Harvester ants channel and loosen the soil. Of scores of trenches dug in excavating roots of the prairie plants scarcely one was free from the work of recent or ancient soil excavation and refilling. Prairie dogs ranged nearly throughout the mixed prairie. They dig deeply, often to 12 or even 15 feet, and place enormous quantities of soil upon the land surface. Moreover, coarse, deep taproots upon their death and decay leave holes, curbed by soil compressed in their growth and expansion, which remain open, except perhaps at the top, a very long time. When prolonged periods of drought occur, as they did in the early 1890's and in the recent 1930's, very deep cracks and fissures 1 to 2.5 inches wide result from the shrinking of the soil. Such periods are followed by heavy rains, little water penetrating the nearly bared and dust covered parched soil. Large volumes of water sink through the cracks and, locally at least, thoroughly wet the deep soil. When the cracks are again closed, water is lost very slowly but permits deep root penetration.

Tortuous cracks in heavily grazed ranges at intervals of 5 to 10 feet were often bordered with a foot-wide strip of green vegetation following rains of 2 to 3 inches. This was the renewed growth from dormant grasses.

Between these green strips where the water had run off into the cracks the grass remained dormant.

ROOT DISTRIBUTION IN ROCKY SOIL

Root distribution in the usual loam soils and in sands (Chapter 11) has been described. Throughout the Great Plains a third type, stony or rocky soil, covers, in the aggregate, very large areas. A thorough study of the root habits of many species of plains plants growing in rock-filled soil has been made by Albertson (1937) near Hays, Kansas. The rock outcrops of the Fort Hays limestone on hillsides have been described. He also ascertained that these soils were much more permeable to water than either those of the level uplands clothed with short grasses or those of the lowland in the big bluestem community. Since each cubic foot of space was more than half filled with limestone, under the same rainfall the actual soil receives much more water per unit of surface than soils without rocks.

In the examination of the ecological relationships of plants underground, pickaxes and iron bars with sharpened ends were used to loosen the limestone layers. By this means only was it possible to examine the rock crevices and soil through which the roots penetrated. Vegetation characteristic of south-facing slopes is shown in figure 65. The roots of little bluestem and slender grama, though relatively fine, penetrated only to about 3 feet. Those of big bluestem, switchgrass and Indian grass usually extended 1 to 2 feet deeper. The fine roots of hairy grama, blue grama and buffalo grass were usually confined to the surface 18 inches. Thus, the roots of all these grasses were less extensive than usual.

Lead plant was the most important forb on this rocky soil. The course of its strong taproot illustrates beautifully how the roots followed the cracks, crevices, and pockets in the rocks and absorbed water and nutrients from the sandy-clay soil which they contained. It is of interest that root nodules occurred at all depths on the roots of this legume. Once water enters this soil, there is little loss except through transpiration. The maximum depth of 6 to 9 feet in this soil is not great compared with the 14 to 17 feet in depth attained by this species in loess.

The root system of few-flowered psoralea was usually modified by the underlying layers of limestone. It was often much branched in places where relatively solid layers of rock were encountered; elsewhere

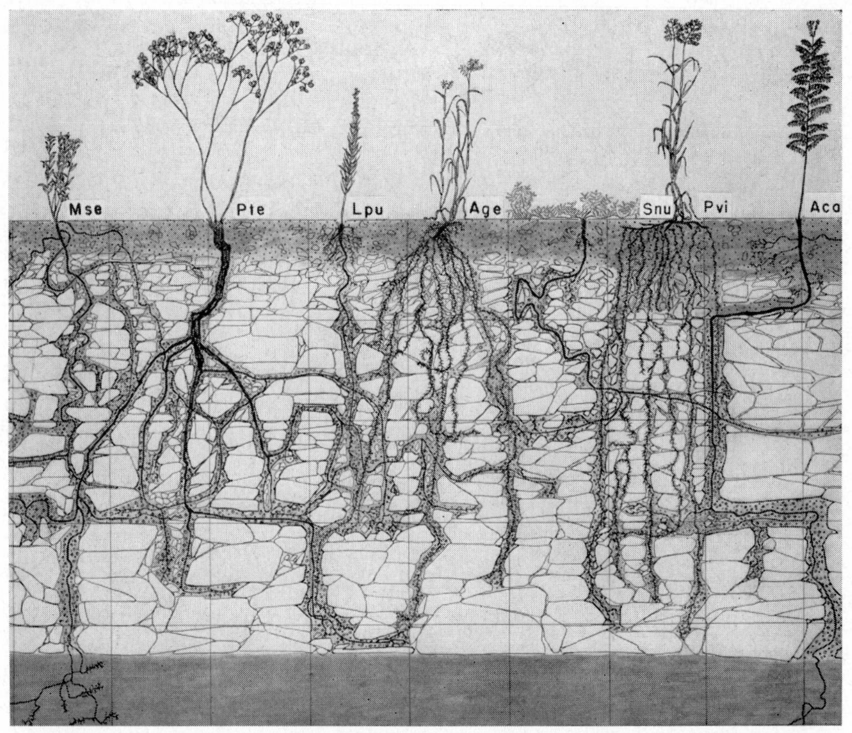

FIG. 65. Plants growing in shallow soil underlaid with limestone, showing root distribution in the crevices and pockets. From left to right are (Mse) tooth-leaved primrose (*Oenothera serrulata*), (Pte) few-flowered psoralea (*Psoralea tenuiflora*), (Lpu) blazing star (*Liatris punctata*), (Age) big bluestem (*Andropogon gerardi*), (Snu) sensitive brier (*Schrankia nuttallii*), (Pvi) switchgrass (*Panicum virgatum*) and (Aca) lead plant (*Amorpha canescens*). Shale occurs in the fifth foot.

the taproot was poorly divided and penetrated to a depth of 7 to 9 feet.

None of the roots of blazing star, purple coneflower, tooth-leaved primrose, or sensitive brier (*Schrankia nuttallii*) had a root extent greater than 3 feet. All are normally very deeply rooted plants. Despite the abbreviated root systems, these plants were plentiful and thriving. A decumbent milkweed (*Asclepiodora decumbens*) and Fremont's leather flower had widely spreading root systems confined to the first 2 feet of soil. Conversely, on north-facing slopes several species of plants extended their roots downward to 10 feet or more where crevices occurred. Prairie rose (*Rosa suffulta*) and licorice (*Glycyrrhiza lepidota*) were examples. In ordinary moist soils roots of these plants may penetrate 21 and 14 feet, respectively (Weaver, 1919). Thus, the soil environment has a profound influence upon root development.

CHAPTER 14

Grasslands of Colorado

THE HIGH PLAINS which occupy western Kansas and southern Nebraska do not extend entirely across Colorado to the mountains. A narrow belt of a piedmont lowland east of Pueblo and Colorado Springs rapidly widens northward to the Wyoming boundary until it extends eastward almost to the Nebraska-Colorado border. It is believed that the mantle of alluvial waste that formerly must have composed this portion of the High Plains has been eroded away. The South Platte and Arkansas River systems have removed the Tertiary materials and lowered the surface below the level of the High Plains eastward (Fig. 66). Along the Arkansas River the High Plains have been removed to the Kansas border, but north of the South Platte they extend westward through southern Wyoming (Cheyenne and northward) to the Laramie Mountains. Thus, the level High Plains and the much eroded Piedmont of lower elevation and lower rainfall share somewhat equally the Great Plains of Colorado east of the Rocky Mountains (*cf.* Fenneman, 1931; Atwood, 1940).

Studies in the two areas will be considered separately although the vegetation is not strikingly different. From the rather numerous investigations that have been made in the past half century, one can gain a good understanding of the vegetation without further description.

VEGETATION OF MESAS AND PIEDMONT

Shantz (1906) made a thorough study of the mesa region at the base of Pike's Peak northwest of Colorado Springs. The vegetation was typical of that of the Great Plains. A chief difference from that lying eastward was the absence of buffalo grass (*Buchloe dactyloides*). Blue grama (*Bouteloua gracilis*) was the chief dominant. Ringgrass (*Muhlenbergia gracillima* [1]), hairy grama (*Bouteloua hirsuta*) and red three-awn (*Aristida longiseta*) were abundant. Little bluestem (*Andropogon scoparius*) occurred on gravelly crests of hills and big bluestem (*A.*

[1] Scientific names are those used by Shantz.

FIG. 66. Greatly overgrazed range with mounds and bare soil due to harvester ants, near Arriba, Colorado. Three-awn grasses and remnants of short-grass vegetation prevail. (Lower) East Pawnee Butte near New Raymer in the piedmont area of northeastern Colorado. It reveals a long period of erosion. Short grasses prevail except in cultivated land along the road.

furcatus) in gravel. Other common grasses were squirreltail (*Sitanion elymoides*) tumblegrass (*Schedonnardus paniculatus*), Junegrass (*Koeleria cristata*), needle-and-thread (*Stipa comata*), New Mexico feathergrass (*S. neomexicana*) and western wheatgrass (*Agropyron occidentale*). Distribution of grasses and forbs was studied in relation to their local environments. The four seasonal aspects were discussed as well as the most important societies in each. A very large number of species occurred on the flat tableland, slopes, and lowlands. Structure of vegetation was illustrated by typical quadrats. A brief discussion of the chief societies of the Great Plains lying eastward was included.

Along the western border of the Great Plains where it meets the mountains there are numerous grassland communities. These are quite variable and mixed in character and consequently often not definite. Here climatic conditions undergo rapid transition, topography is considerably diversified, and soils are extremely variable. These fragments of prairie vegetation in the vicinity of Boulder, Colorado, have been described by Vestal (1914).

Near the mountains the short-grass disclimax was represented almost entirely by blue grama, buffalo grass occurring not at all or very sparingly. The western wheatgrass community was found typically in areas of deposition at the base of side slopes of the mesas in fine soil washed down from above. It occurred also in wind-blown drifts of soil. Its extent from the northern plains southward along the foothills was local.

The bunch-grass community was best developed on the outer ends of the higher mesas. It occurred elsewhere on moist slopes and higher mesa-tops and in small depressions where water was constantly available throughout the growing season. Chief grasses were little bluestem (*Andropogon scoparius*), Junegrass (*Koeleria cristata*), big bluestem (*Andropogon gerardi*), Indian grass (*Sorghastrum nutans*), mountain muhly (*Muhlenbergia montana*) and side-oats grama (*Bouteloua curtipendula*). Pure or nearly pure stands of big bluestem were also found in local areas of coarse soil or in fine-grained moist soil on the flood plain. Finally, a more or less typical prairie-grass community of Junegrass, pine bluegrass (*Poa scabrella*), green needlegrass, Kentucky bluegrass, western wheatgrass and slender wheatgrass was described. It occurred in rich black soil of fine texture and of high moisture content in spring and early summer. Such soil was regularly found on alluvial lower slopes of foothills and higher mesas. Vestal points out that such meadow-like zones border scrub oak communities farther south at Castle Rock, Perry Park near Larkspur, and Palmer Lake.

In his classification of the vegetation of Colorado, Shantz (1923, 1924) describes a rather narrow belt of the grama grass association, far more important northward, extending across the state from north to south just east of the mountains. The scarcity or complete absence of buffalo grass is worthy of notice. "Along the mountain front grama grass (*Bouteloua gracilis*) is often mixed with a great variety of plants which are more typical of the mountain grasslands. Among these may be mentioned mountain sage (*Artemisia frigida*), niggerwool (*Carex filifolia*), yarrow (*Achillea millefolium*), Eriogonums of various species, penstemons, wild roses, and lupines. These characterize an area in which the rainfall is greater than that of the adjacent grama-grass land. The soils are often not well developed but consist of loose granitic gravels." In southern Colorado near the mountains "conditions become so extreme as to temperature and drought, that grama grass gives way in part to [ringgrass] (*Muhlenbergia gracillima*) [*M. torreyi*]."

Eastward, over practically the whole state, the grama-buffalo grass community prevails. It is dominated by almost equal quantities of *Bouteloua gracilis* and *Buchloe dactyloides*. During years of more than normal rainfall prominent plants intermixed with the short grasses are *Stipa comata, Sporobolus cryptandrus,* and other mid grasses and characteristic forbs such as horseweed (*Conyza canadensis*) and gumweed (*Grindelia squarrosa*). With increased rainfall eastward or on lighter land, where moisture penetrates rapidly, *Aristida longiseta* and *Psoralea tenuiflora* are abundant.

Another type, sand grasses and sand sage, occupies scattered areas and is especially abundant in the northeastern portion of the state.

Hanson *et al.* (1931) studied a western wheatgrass type of vegetation near Fort Collins at an elevation of 5,100 feet. Average precipitation was 15 inches but had varied in 41 years from 7 to 27.5 inches. The area lay at the base of the foothills and on an alluvial clay soil. The vegetation was typical of much of the plains adjacent to and between the lower foothills in northern Colorado. Important grasses, in addition to wheatgrass, were blue grama, buffalo grass, species of *Stipa* (especially green needlegrass), red three-awn and tumblegrass. The chief forbs were silky sophora (*Sophora sericea*), scarlet gaura (*Gaura coccinea*), aster (*Aster hebecladus*), leafy musineon (*Musineon divaricatum*), red false mallow (*Sphaeralcea coccinea*), ragwort (*Senecio perplexus*), Drummond milk vetch (*Astragalus drummondi*), purple milk vetch (*A. hypoglottis*), few-flowered psoralea (*Psoralea tenuiflora*) and poverty sumpweed (*Iva axillaris*).

"Earliest growth [during 4 years] usually began about the middle of March. During May the season's growth was most rapid. In June the blooming of vegetation was at its height. In July drying began in several species and by the first of August many species had dried and disappeared. Ripening and drying continued throughout August and September and a few later species bloomed."

Although this was primarily a study of effects of different systems of grazing on the wheatgrass type, it involved an analysis of environmental factors, the composition of the vegetation, and much information on the life histories and habits of the most important species. All is essential information for proper range management.

In east-central Colorado, the mountain forest, consisting mainly of western yellow pine (*Pinus ponderosa*), extends eastward from the Rocky Mountains on the Platte-Arkansas divide. The main area is the Black Forest but scattered pines follow the rocky outcrops far eastward. Altitude varies from 6,500 to 7,600 feet and rainfall from 16 to 20 inches. Livingston (1952) found that "many stands of true prairie vegetation occur within the Black Forest and in the adjacent mixed prairie region at lower altitudes on the . . . divide." These communities are composed largely of species typical of true prairie, together with associated species from mixed prairie and mountain associations. Dominant species within or closely adjacent to the forests were prairie dropseed (*Sporobolus heterolepis*), needlegrass (*Stipa spartea*) and Kentucky bluegrass (*Poa pratensis*). Dominants at lower altitudes within the mixed prairie were prairie dropseed, little bluestem (*Andropogon scoparius*) and Indian grass (*Sorghastrum nutans*). Other true-prairie grasses found in some communities were big bluestem (*Andropogon gerardi*), switchgrass (*Panicum virgatum*) and sloughgrass (*Spartina pectinata*). Representative prairie forbs were stiff sunflower (*Helianthus rigidus*), stiff goldenrod (*Solidago rigida*), black-eyed Susan (*Rudbeckia hirta*) and prairie rose (*Rosa arkansana*).

These communities occurred only in sites where soil moisture conditions were unusually favorable because of topographic position or high water table. Livingston believes these are relics of true prairie left when this type of vegetation retreated eastward as a postglacial climate became drier.

Studies were made in eastern Weld county in northeastern Colorado and at stations in adjacent Wyoming and Nebraska by Albertson and Tomanek in 1954. These data are from areas ungrazed for a few years, the exact time not being ascertained (Fig. 67). At a station on loam soil on flat upland 69 per cent of the vegetation was composed of blue grama. Buffalo grass, rare on well drained uplands except in depressions, composed 9 and thread-leaved sedge 3 per cent. The mid grasses, needle-and-thread and western wheatgrass, were represented by 6 and 11 per cent, respectively. In disturbed places such as around ant hills, gopher mounds and prairie dog burrows, sand dropseed, squirreltail and red three-awn were common. Here Indian ricegrass (*Oryzopsis hymenoides*) and green needlegrass were also represented. An adjacent grazed area had few mid grasses.

On upland plains in sandy loam, 80 per cent blue grama, 5 per cent buffalo grass, and 13 per cent needle-and-thread were found. Western wheatgrass and sand dropseed were each represented by about 1 per cent.

On heavy bottom land soils, often used for hay meadows, western wheatgrass was the principal species with desert saltgrass (*Distichlis stricta*) and alkali sacaton (*Sporobolus airoides*). Conversely, on shallow, porous soils with very little surface loam overlying rocky or gravelly soil on ridges, the climax cover was little bluestem (often 50 to 60 per cent in abundance), side-oats grama, needle-and-thread and plains muhly. Formerly, such areas closely resembled true prairie. On lowland clay and clay loams along stream beds, western wheatgrass, green needlegrass and blue grama were all abundant. Thus, in this Colorado area many plant communities make up the vegetation.

At Carpenter, Wyoming, on ungrazed, upland, loam sites, blue grama (48 per cent), western wheatgrass (26) and needle-and-thread (24 per cent) almost composed the vegetation. Wheatgrass greatly decreased and needle-and-thread made a corresponding increase on sandy loam. On rocky breaks near Bushnell, Nebraska, mixed grasses prevailed. Little bluestem furnished 77 per cent of the cover, and side-oats grama, June-grass and needle-and-thread nearly all of the remainder (Fig. 54).

FIG. 67. (Upper) Upland site on sandy loam soil in northeastern Colorado. Chief grasses are blue grama with an overstory of needle-and-thread. (Lower) Relic mixed prairie of needle-and-thread and western wheatgrass with some blue grama outside the fence and ungrazed. The mid grasses have almost disappeared in the pasture. Photo near Carpenter, Wyoming.

STUDIES ON THE HIGH PLAINS

The natural vegetation of the Great Plains area was studied by Shantz (1911). The objective of this study was to ascertain what the various types or communities indicated in regard to the capabilities of the land for crop production. The most intensive research was conducted in two large counties in eastern Colorado (Washington and Yuma), but more general studies were made throughout the Great Plains region. The following data are from this work.

The most extensive type of vegetation indicating land of agricultural value was blue grama-buffalo grass. It occupied the greater part of the hard land. The little bluestem or bunch-grass type occurred in rather sandy soil where there was little loss of water and deep water penetration. A third or intermediate type on sandy loam was characterized by an abundance of red three-awn (*Aristida longiseta*) overtopping shorter grasses. This he designated as the wire-grass type.

"By indicating clearly the environmental conditions which prevail the native vegetation is of great value, not only in the classification of land, but also as an indicator of the kind of crop and methods of culture that are most likely to succeed under the given conditions. But differences in vegetation can be used to indicate changes in one factor of the environment only where all the other factors remain unchanged." In the High Plains, all three types of vegetation may be found repeatedly within a distance of a few miles. The aerial factors of light, temperature, wind, humidity and precipitation are nearly identical over these wide level stretches. Hence, Shantz correlated type of vegetation with soil moisture.

"Correlations with soil moisture are usually more easily established than with any other one factor, since it is through this factor that rainfall, evaporation, and the physical character of the soil chiefly affect the plant. Since plant growth is the ultimate measure of the suitability of the physical environment, the character, growth, and condition of the native vegetation are the best possible indicators favorable or unfavorable to crop production on land where crops have not yet been produced. The entire plant cover is a better indicator than the presence or condition of a single species, since in it we have a record which is as stable as the most stable species and as sensitive as the most exacting plant."

The areas occupied by the different types were mapped on blank township maps on a scale of 1 inch to the mile. Thus, the geographical distribution of each type was recorded. Exact records of the structure of the plant cover were made by means of chart quadrats. Since water is the chief limiting factor to plant growth in the Great Plains, very extensive soil samples were taken, and from these the amount of water available for growth was ascertained. Water penetrates slowly in part because of the high water-retaining power of the surface layers of fine sandy loam soils but also because of the vigorous absorption by the grasses. In eastern Colorado the average monthly rainfall is greatest during the period from April to August. "The increased heat in July and August makes it almost certain that drought will occur in these months."

Short-Grass Type

In the grama-buffalo grass type, the plant cover was uniform and velvet-like. In some places it covered practically the whole surface (90 per cent), but in others it was broken into alternating spaces of open ground and dense, mat-like cover, as little as 10 per cent of the soil surface being clothed. This corresponds to the closed mats and open mats of the short-grass type in Kansas. Pure grama grass often characterized the open mats, but where buffalo grass was intermixed the cover was nearly always denser. Here the vegetation was growing under a mean annual rainfall of only 17.4 inches, and it had long been closely grazed.

Perennial grasses, other than the two great dominants, were squirreltail (*Sitanion hystrix*), red three-awn (*Aristida longiseta*), tumblegrass (*Schedonnardus paniculatus*) and western wheatgrass (*Agropyron smithii*). However, Shantz made no attempt to give a complete list of plants. Grasses and forbs were all suppressed by grazing and were so inconspicuous that the grassland had an appearance of extreme monotony. Annual grasses and forbs in his list are found generally from the true prairie ecotone to the mountains. This annual vegetation becomes quite noticeable in early summer. It was composed chiefly of six-weeks fescue (*Festuca octoflora*),[1] false buffalo grass (*Munroa squarrosa*), Pursh's plantain (*Plantago purshii*), Whitlow grass (*Draba micrantha*), fetid marigold (*Dysodia papposa*), Russian thistle (*Salsola pestifer*), horseweed (*Leptilon canadense*) and lamb's quarters (*Chenopodium leptophyllum*). Often the bright green color of the landscape in June is caused by the luxuriant growth of six-weeks fescue. This short-lived grass quickly produces seed and ripens. During unusually dry years even short grass may fail to flower, but during exceptionally wet ones growth may continue almost without interruption. Height of these annuals varies from an inch

[1] Scientific names are those used by Shantz.

or two to six or more inches depending upon the current rainfall. All ripen some seed almost every year.

The list of the most abundant longer-lived forbs follows:

Many-spined cactus
Opuntia polyacantha
Brittle opuntia
Opuntia fragilis
Hedgehog cactus
Echinocereus viridiflorus
Ball cactus
Mammillaria vipipara
Red false mallow
Malvastrum coccineum
Gumweed
Grindelia squarrosa
Ground plum
Astragalus crassicarpus
Brown-plumed ptiloria
Ptiloria pauciflora
Scarlet gaura
Gaura coccinea
Fleabane
Erigeron canus
Crazyweed
Aragallus lambertii
Woolly loco
Astragalus mollissimus
Western wallflower
Erysimum asperum

Species of lesser importance were the following:

Fringed sage
Artemisia frigida
Broom snakeweed
Gutierrezia sarothrae
Few-flowered psoralea
Psoralea tenuiflora
Cut-leaved goldenweed
Sideranthus spinulosus
Hairy golden aster
Chrysopsis villosa
Umbrella plant
Eriogonum effusum
Blazing star
Liatris punctata

The preceding forbs are also common over much of the Great Plains area. (See figure 68.)

"On the Great Plains a pure short-grass cover indicates a condition of considerable runoff and of limited water penetration, the available moisture usually being confined during the greater part of the season to the first two feet of soil. . . . Short-grass vegetation is also an indicator of a rather short season favorable for growth. . . . The growing season is determined, not by the length of the period of suitable temperature, but by the length of the period when soil moisture is sufficient to maintain growth. Grama grass requires approximately sixty days for maturing and often fails to ripen its seed, largely because of insufficient water supply. Buffalo grass usually flowers and fruits early in the season, but when the early season is dry its fruiting may occur at any time during the summer when the water supply is sufficient. . . . The principal adaptation of these

FIG. 68. (Upper) Yellow-spined thistle (*Cirsium ochrocentrum*), and snow-on-the-mountain (*Euphorbia marginata*). (Lower) Purple poppymallow (*Callirrhoe involucrata*).

grasses to arid conditions seems to lie in their ability to dry out . . . and to revive quickly when water is again supplied . . . an enforced rest seems to do them no injury.

"The texture of the soil indicated by short-grass vegetation in this region is a loam, the type of land known locally as 'hard land.' . . . The open-mat type of vegetation indicates less favorable conditions for plant growth than the closed-mat type. Although it may occur in any part of the Great Plains, it is usually found much more commonly in regions with smaller or less evenly distributed rainfall, and especially on areas where runoff is very great. . . . Moreover the presence of an abundance of deeply rooted plants that require a long season for growth, such as *Psoralea tenuiflora,* indicates better conditions for crop production."

Wire-Grass Type

This community occurs on sandy loam soils into which almost all of the rainfall penetrates. Because of the lighter texture of the soil the water is distributed to a greater depth. This community is found in practically all areas where sand hills occur; it lies between the sandy areas and the hard lands. It was particularly abundant in Yuma and Washington counties in Colorado.

"The wire-grass association is much more varied in general appearance than the grama-buffalo grass association. The ground is covered by a short-grass mat which is usually not so dense as that of the typical grama-buffalo grass association. Overtopping this mat are numerous taller plants of many different species, among the more important of which are wire-grass and *Psoralea.* The wire-grass appears as low tufts . . . of a light silvery color." This community embraces a much greater number of species than the preceding one. Two of the most important were psoralea and the bush morning-glory. Both are tumbleweeds and leave no trace of their existence when the growth period is past.

Both the lower and upper layer of vegetation are conspicuous in this type of mixed prairie. A chief change in the understory is the almost complete absence of buffalo grass. The mat-like cover is composed largely of blue grama, but hairy grama often forms an important part. Chief species of taller plants are wire-grass (*Aristida longiseta*) and few-flowered psoralea. Most of accompanying plants are deeply rooted perennials and also require a rather long period for growth. Since this type is intermediate between the bunch-grass, to be described, and the grama-buffalo grass type, species from both types may occur here. Other common grasses were needle-and-thread (*Stipa comata*), sand dropseed (*Sporobolus cryptandrus*), needle-leaf sedge (*Carex stenophylla*) [*C. eleocharis*], tumblegrass (*Schedonnardus paniculatus*) and six-weeks fescue (*Festuca octoflora*).

Following is a list of important forbs:

Bush morning-glory
Ipomoea leptophylla
Red false mallow
Malvastrum coccineum
Prairie coneflower
Ratibida columnaris
Fine-leaf hymenopappus
Hymenopappus filifolius
Cut-leaved goldenweed
Sideranthus spinulosus
Hedgehog cactus
Echinocereus viridiflorus
Blazing star
Liatris punctata
Greenthread
Thelesperma gracile
Umbrella plant
Eriogonum effusum
Hairy golden aster
Chrysopsis villosa
Rusty lupine
Lupinus pusillus

"The wire-grass association indicates that there is a considerable amount of water in the deeper layers of the soil, owing to the lesser run-off and to the fact that the lighter soil permits deeper penetration. Conditions . . . are favorable for both shallow-rooted and deep-rooted plants and for a considerably longer period of growth than those indicated by the grama-buffalo grass association. . . . The presence of short grass, however, indicates a condition unfavorable to the greatest development of the taller, deep-rooted plants. If the water supply were increased the latter would undoubtedly entirely replace the short grass [by shading] and the vegetation would probably pass over into the bunch-grass [community]. . . . The conditions indicated by the wire-grass association are undoubtedly the most favorable for crop production of any found in eastern Colorado, since the soil is heavy enough not to blow badly and forms a stable substratum for all types of crops. At the same time it is pervious enough to enable a very high percentage of the rainfall to enter. . . . The greater part of the water lost by this soil is through transpiration by the plant cover."

Bunch-Grass Type

The little bluestem community in eastern Colorado is most extensive on sandy soil. There is practically no runoff, and evaporation from the soil surface is relatively low because of the rapid establishment of a surface mulch of dry soil following a rain. Little bluestem often forms a dense growth and composes nearly all of the vegetation. Usually the bunches are so scattered they may compose less than half of the cover. Even then, little bluestem with its reddish brown color characterizes the landscape. Vegetation is fairly dense and the soil is well covered. Thus, it is quite different from the more open bunch-grass type common on the less stable sand hills of Nebraska. In Colorado it produces large yields of hay.

Difference in the appearance of the vegetation also is due largely to variations in the amounts of little bluestem. Between the bunches numerous tall and mid grasses occur as well as mats of short grass. The soil is so well occupied and held so firmly that there is practically no soil blowing.

Among the more important species of grasses are sand bluestem (*Andropogon hallii*), sand reed (*Calamovilfa longifolia*), switchgrass (*Panicum virgatum*), red three-awn (*Aristida longiseta*), blue grama (*Bouteloua gracilis*) and hairy grama (*B. hirsuta*). Two very prominent forbs are *Psoralea tenuiflora* and *Artemisia filifolia*. All of the species of grasses and forbs listed in the wire-grass community also occur here. In addition many plants characteristic of the sand hills themselves may be found.

"Where bunch grass occurs we find a soil which contains moisture to a considerable depth. . . . All rainfall received by this type of land enters the soil . . . where the water supply is sufficient an almost pure, dense cover of bunch grass develops, but where the supply is less abundant the bunches are more scattered and there is a greater growth of short grass in the spaces between. The soil characterized by this association is not especially rich in plant food, but affords a better water supply than any other in the region."

Crop production on land characterized by different types of vegetation is of great economic importance. Shantz studied the behavior of crop plants on each type, precautions necessary in handling the sandy soils of bunch-grass land, soil blowing, and soil fertility.

Sand-Hills Mixed Type

The sand-hills mixed type showed great variation in botanical composition, as well as in general appearance. The most characteristic feature of the vegetation was the presence of large and sharply alternating communities of the coarse-stemmed sand reed (*Calamovilfa longifolia*) and sand bluestem (*Andropogon hallii*). Little bluestem often occurred but never in great abundance. Sand sage (*Artemisia filifolia*) was the third most noticeable plant. Other very important species were hairy grama, blue grama, red three-awn and few-flowered psoralea. The more open the vegetation the greater was the number of species represented. Grasses of secondary importance were switchgrass, Indian grass, side-oats grama, sand dropseed, needle-and-thread and big bluestem. The population of forbs was much the same as in the bunch-grass type of Nebraska sand hills although not so inclusive. Bush morning-glory and small soapweed were common. The soil is usually a purer sand than that characterized by the bunch-grass type, and the danger of soil blowing is greater here than in the bunch-grass land. Breaking or plowing occasionally results in establishing blow-out conditions.

"When well supplied with water short-grass land is the most productive under cultivation of any in eastern Colorado. During drought, however, crops suffer on this land sooner than on any other type. During exceptionally dry years bunch-grass land produces the best crops of any in eastern Colorado, but during wet years its production is surpassed by that of all others except the land characterized by the sand-hills mixed association. The soil under both of these types of vegetation is likely to blow badly. Wire-grass land represents a safe intermediate condition where in years of ample rainfall crop production compares not unfavorably with that on short-grass land and where, even during dry years, a fair crop can often be produced."

Thus, Shantz developed the method of indicator plant communities to a point where it showed clearly the possibilities of local soils and climates, as indicated by the vegetation, in terms of agricultural use. These ecological principles were later amplified and extended over western North America by Clements in his "Plant Indicators" (1920). Plants and plant communities as indicators have been fully discussed in Plant Ecology (Weaver and Clements, 1938) and by Sampson (1939).

SUCCESSION IN ABANDONED ROADS

Shantz (1917) has explained the destruction of the short-grass sod in wagon roads in eastern Colorado, their abandonment, and the plant succession leading to the grazing disclimax vegetation. Roads were formed by iron-tired vehicles driven over the short-grass sod in the same trail until the sod-mat was worn through and the soil exposed. The soil level was lowered to form 2 ruts 6 inches or more in depth, partly by packing and in part by wind erosion, during 3 or 4 years. The roads originally led directly from one point to another of the vast ranges; there were no fences to interfere. During rainy weather these roads became muddy and were often abandoned, the adjacent sod forming a more desirable place for travel. The high center of the old road was often used by one horse and the side of the road by the other, at least until the old road-center was also worn down. Always the new road ran parallel to the old one. By repetition of the process throughout a number of years, sometimes as many as 6 to 8 parallel roads were formed. Since a road once abandoned was seldom used again, the process of revegetation immediately began. As the country was settled fences were constructed. The age of the new vegetation on many of the roads could be ascertained with considerable accuracy, since it was possible to ascertain the time when the fences were built and traffic routed along section lines. The first of a single series of 13 roads leading into Akron, Colorado, from the east was formed in 1886, the last in 1914.

By means of transects across the roads and bisects to show the depth of soil removal, Shantz has clearly shown the coming in and later disappearance of new vegetation which composed the several stages in succession and the years required for the development of each stage. "The succession as outlined here applies with almost no modification south to the 'pan-handle' of Texas, and is typical, with minor modifications, for successions anywhere in the *Bouteloua-Buchloe* or *Bouteloua* associations from Texas to Montana.

1. Early weed stage: scattered plants of: [knotgrass] *Polygonum aviculare,* or [large bracted vervain] *Verbena bracteosa,* or [Russian thistle] *Salsola pestifer,* or [fetid marigold] *Dysodia papposa,* or [prostrate pigweed] *Amaranthus blitoides.*

2. Late weed stage: dense growth of plants of stage 1.

3. Short-lived grass stage: [tumblegrass] *Schedonnardus paniculatus* or [false buffalo grass] *Munroa squarrosa,* or [squirreltail] *Sitanion hystrix.*

4. Perennial stage: [broom snakeweed] *Gutierrezia sarothrae,* or [red

three-awn] *Aristida longiseta,* or [sleepy grass] *Stipa vaseyi,* or [fringed sage] *Artemisia frigida.*

5. Early short-grass stage: *Buchloe dactyloides,* or [ringgrass] *Muhlenbergia gracillima* [*torreyi*].

6. Late short-grass stage: *Bouteloua gracilis–Buchloe dactyloides,* or *Bouteloua gracilis.*"

The several stages occur on roads that have been abandoned for the following periods. Stage (1) 1 to 3 years, (2) 2 to 5 years, (3) 4 to 8 years, (4) 7 to 14 years, (5) 13 to 23 years, and (6) 20 to 50 years. "The stages of succession here outlined as they occur on abandoned roads do not differ essentially from those on fields which have been abandoned." (See figure 69.)

SUCCESSION ON ABANDONED LAND

Nearly 30 years later Costello (1944a) studied the natural vegetation on abandoned plowed land of northeastern Colorado. "The abandonment of cultivation on thousands of acres, beginning soon after settlement started in the Great Plains, has resulted in all stages of secondary succession from nearly bare fields to areas which have almost, if not entirely, returned to the original condition. Many of these areas should never have been plowed and their best use may still be had only when they have been returned to a productive cover of native forage plants." An early annual weed stage normally lasted 2 to 5 years; a late weed stage, mostly of annual and perennial forbs, controlled for 3 to 6 years; and the short-lived perennial grass stage of tumblegrass, foxtail barley, sand dropseed and squirreltail lasted from 4 to 10 years. The three-awn stage persisted for 10 to 20 years. The fully developed mixed prairie association, consisting of a mixture of short grasses, mid grasses, forbs, and shrubs, represented the climax or last stage in succession.

The re-establishment of mixed prairie vegetation on abandoned cultivated land has been studied in various parts of the Great Plains. Examples are the work of Booth (1941) and Smith (1940a) in Oklahoma, Savage and Runyon (1937) in the southern and central Great Plains, Tomanek, Albertson and Riegel (1955) in Kansas, Judd and Jackson (1939) in Nebraska, Tolstead (1941) in South Dakota, Whitman, Hanson and Loder (1943) in North Dakota, and Judd (1940) in Montana. In this semiarid climate with its periodic droughts, nature works slowly in replacing the climax vegetation. Twenty to 40 or more years may intervene between the early weed stage and the climax, especially (as nearly always happens) if the area is grazed. Indeed, heavy grazing holds the vegetation in a subsere stage almost indefinitely. Kinds of grasses originally present, intensity and duration of cultivation, and various other factors retard or accelerate rate of succession. Where cultivation has been light and rhizomes of western wheatgrass remain in the soil, only a few years are required for this species to become dominant.

The most widespread dominants of fallow fields are Russian thistle (*Salsola kali*), sunflowers (*Helianthus annuus* and *H. petiolaris*) and horseweed (*Conyza canadensis*). From the agronomic standpoint natural succession is important in returning abandoned cultivated lands to forage production. The yields of grass hay sometimes exceeds three-fourths ton per acre in moderately wet years only a few years after abandonment (Judd & Jackson, 1939; Tolstead, 1941).

WATER LOSSES

Water losses were ascertained from square-foot areas of buffalo grass and western wheatgrass in the mixed prairie at Burlington, Colorado, and from blue grama, buffalo grass and big bluestem at Phillipsburg, Kansas. By means of digging trenches around representative small areas of each grass and fitting a cylinder of heavy galvanized iron around each sample, unbroken columns of soil were tightly encased to a depth of 3 feet without destroying soil structure. The columns were cut off smoothly at this depth, and loosely fitting metal bottoms with upturned edges were sealed in place. After weighing, the samples were placed side by side in a row in a narrow trench cut in the undisturbed prairie sod. A sample with the soil bared of vegetation and a control with dead grass (killed by heat) were included. The enclosed soil columns weighed 251 to 285 pounds. Soil was packed about the cylinders and pieces of sod fitted around the tops. Thus, the soil columns were kept at normal soil temperatures, and the above-ground parts were at the same general level as the surrounding vegetation. Except when rain was actually falling and the plants were covered with long wooden roofs, aerial environment was normal during

FIG. 69. (Upper) Prairie larkspur (*Delphinium virescens*), large-flowered yellow flax (*Linum rigidum*) (center), and smooth white hymenopappus (*Hymenopappus corymbosus*). (Lower) Narrow-leaved milkweed (*Acerates angustifolia*) and narrow-leaved stenosiphon (*Stenosiphon linifolius*). Each of these plants is about 2.5 feet tall.

the 15 days of the experiment. Since the soil was dry at Burlington, measured amounts of water were added from time to time to keep the grasses from wilting.

At Burlington water loss was ascertained from July 5 to 20, and at Phillipsburg, 180 miles eastward, from June 18 to July 3. Here the soil had a good supply of moisture. At the Colorado station, approximate sunshine during the experiment was 71 per cent, average day temperature 80° F., and average day humidity 57 per cent. Similar data at the Kansas station were 75 per cent, 80.6° F., and 60 per cent, respectively. Losses were as follows:

Burlington, Colorado			Phillipsburg, Kansas		
Container	Species	Lbs. Loss	Container	Species	Lbs. Loss
1	Buffalo grass	12.5	1	Blue grama	14.6
2	Buffalo grass	11.2	2	Blue grama	16.2
3	Buffalo grass	12.7	3	Buffalo grass	14.3
4	Wheatgrass	18.7	4	Big bluestem	28.2
5	Wheatgrass	16.8	5	Big bluestem	27.1
6	Dead buffalo grass	5.0	6	Dead blue grama	4.4
7	Bare soil	7.0	7	Bare soil	7.2

Thus, the average daily loss of water per square foot of native vegetation at Burlington was 0.96 pound per day; at Phillipsburg it was 1.33 pounds (Weaver and Crist, 1924).

SAND HILLS

The sand areas of Colorado include many districts of a few square miles. Those in 6 northeastern counties of Colorado on both High Plains and Piedmont were studied by Ramaley (1939). This was 100 to 300 miles west of the Nebraska sand hills and under a rainfall which usually varied between 10 and 18 inches. The dunes were often only 30 feet high. The heaviest winds were from the northwest; they produced blowouts and caused extensive sand movement. The upland vegetation was sparse, with much bare ground, and species were few in number. Only about one-third of the sand-hills flora consisted of true sand-dwellers; two-thirds belonged regularly to plains and prairies. The vegetation lacked many of the species which extend west only as far as the Nebraska sand hills, and they had few or no western forms coming eastward from the Rocky Mountains.

Ramaley traced the xerosere from loose sand and blowouts, through a sand-hill mixed and a sand-sage community to the sand prairie type. The chief dominant in each community was, in sequence, Indian ricegrass (*Oryzopsis hymenoides*), sandhill muhly (*Muhlenbergia pungens*), sand sage (*Artemisia filifolia*) and, finally, needle-and-thread (*Stipa comata*), sand bluestem (*Andropogon hallii*) and sand reed (*Calamovilfa longifolia*). Since ponds were temporary and streams were small, few and intermittent, the hydrosere was poorly represented. Grass meadows of wheatgrasses (*Agropyron*), big squirreltail (*Hordeum jubatum*) and switchgrass (*Panicum virgatum*) occupied level areas of valley floors and supplied most of the native hay of the sand hills. Descriptions of the seasonal aspects were given and a statement that in predrought years these sand hills were a lovely land of flowers; since then, except in early spring, they have seemed little more than a desert waste.

FORAGE TYPES AND RANGE CONDITION

The major forage types and their important species have been described by Costello (1944b) for the Great Plains area in Colorado and Wyoming. He gives the following present-day picture of the vegetation. The types are the short-grass, dry meadow, sand sagebrush, sagebrush, and weed.

Blue grama is the dominant species in the short-grass type. Buffalo grass commonly alternates with blue grama or is intermingled with it in varying proportions. On ranges which have been conservatively used for a number of years various mid grasses such as red three-awn, western wheatgrass, needle-and-thread and sand dropseed tend to become abundant. June-grass and thread-leaf sedge, locally abundant in some areas, provide early spring forage. Blue grama alone produced 71 per cent of the forage in eastern Colorado and buffalo grass 18 per cent. "Clipping studies and extensive grazing intensity tests on the Central Plains Experimental Range near Nunn, Colorado, indicate that maximum forage production on short-grass ranges is maintained when not more than 45 to 50 per cent of the total seasonal weight production of these grasses is utilized each year."

After 4 years of study of growth characteristics of blue grama in northeastern Colorado, Turner and Klipple (1952) conclude: "Blue grama responds quickly to favorable and unfavorable growing conditions. The volume of herbage produced varies widely from year to year, depending largely upon the amount and distribution of rainfall. Chances for reliable prediction of the size of the crop are small. The herbage crop can be produced in a few weeks when growing conditions are favorable. . . . The ability of blue grama to make prompt, full use of favorable growing conditions is an important factor contributing to its dominance in the native vegetation of the central Great Plains."

The dry meadow forage type occurs in alkaline swales, on the borders of streams and frequently as one of the concentric zones of vegetation bordering intermittent ponds. Desert saltgrass (*Distichlis stricta*) and alkali sacaton (*Sporobolus airoides*) are the dominant species, often furnishing 60 to 90 per cent of the forage in a typical meadow. They have a high winter-grazing capacity. Western wheatgrass (*Agropyron smithii*) is a secondary species often of local abundance where subsoil moisture is plentiful. *Buchloe dactyloides* is often present but produced only 4 to 5 per cent of the forage. Foxtail barley (*Hordeum jubatum*), Baltic rush (*Juncus balticus*) and needle-leaf sedge (*Carex eleocharis*) are other species of common occurrence.

The sand sagebrush type, confined to sandy soils, is characterized by an abundance of *Artemisia filifolia*. Small soapweed (*Yucca glauca*) is also a conspicuous species. The sagebrush produced only about 8 per cent of the forage and blue grama 57 per cent. Needle-and-thread, red three-awn, and sand dropseed in addition to sand reed (*Calamovilfa longifolia*) and sand bluestem (*Andropogon hallii*) usually occur if the range has been only moderately grazed for a number of years. Additional species are certain sand-hill grasses and forbs such as sandhill muhly (*Muhlenbergia pungens*) and prairie sunflower (*Helianthus petiolaris*). This type with low grazing capacity is largely the degenerated bunch-grass (little bluestem) community or the sand-hills mixed association described by Shantz nearly half a century earlier.

Big sage (*Artemisia tridentata*) gives a shrubby aspect to the sagebrush type, although the major forage species is blue grama. This type is very abundant in Wyoming. Grasses which occur in this type, especially along streams and valleys, are mid grasses. Chief species are western wheatgrass, needle-and-thread, plains bluegrass and Junegrass. Costello states: "there is a tendency for these secondary grasses, together with thread-leaf sedge and bearded bluebunch wheatgrass to be abundant on moderately used ranges but rare or absent on areas that have been subjected to continuous heavy grazing. In seasons with moderate to heavy rainfall these grasses tend to obscure the understory of blue grama." Big sagebrush and other shrubby sages invade the short-grass type under continuous heavy grazing. This not only changes the forage type and decreases the amount of grass but also results in a marked reduction in grazing capacity.

Weed types occur over thousands of areas of varying size, formerly under cultivation but now abandoned or used for grazing. These are in all stages of plant succession from bare ground to practically complete stands of blue grama.

A classification of condition of short-grass ranges in the central Great Plains has been made by Costello and Turner (1944). Ranges in excellent condition are at their highest productive capacity for both forage and livestock. "Excellent short-grass range is characterized by an almost continuous turf of blue grama and buffalo grass in which taller grasses, such as bluestem [western] wheatgrass, needle-and-thread, and red three-awn are commonly present. The tall grasses are particularly evident on such ranges in eastern Wyoming, northeastern Colorado, and western Nebraska, but less abundant on those in western Kansas. . . . Over wide areas of eastern Wyoming, plains bluegrass [*Poa arida*], thread-leaf sedge, bluebunch wheatgrass [*Agropyron spicatum*], and needle-and-thread are present on excellent range.

"The weed [forb] population consists mainly of perennial species of fair or average palatability. . . . Annual weeds are rare and inconspicuous. The shrubs sometimes present are usually good browse; particularly common are winterfat, found on the better sites, and fourwing saltbush, largely restricted to alkaline flats. Fringed sage occurs in fair abundance in some localities. Plains pricklypear is never abundant.

"Under careful management, excellent ranges can be maintained. A considerable residue of the abundant plant materials should remain unused on the ground at the end of the growing season."

Such ranges, which closely approach the climax condition, can still be found, as well as many good ranges. The great majority have deteriorated into the fair and poor condition class.

Thus, the vast area of grassland which formerly covered both High Plains and Piedmont of Colorado has been greatly changed by destructive grazing and by plowing. The two-layered prairie with its hosts of non-grasslike herbs has either been plowed or nearly all reduced to a short-grass sod in which blue grama alone often furnishes the bulk of present day forage and in which the palatable forbs have been largely replaced by weeds. Improving depleted ranges and maintaining those still in good condition are extremely important economic problems.

Overstocking of grasslands results in too high a percentage of total yield being used for sheer maintainance of livestock rather than for the production of meat and milk. When this happens profits are reduced, sometimes to nil. For example, heavy stocking has been shown to decrease the weaning weight of calves as much as 33 pounds per animal compared to moderate or light stocking. Moreover, at 18 months of age they still suffered the set-back in weight imposed by too heavy range stocking during the suckling period (Woolfolk and Knapp, 1949). Undoubtedly the injury to the range was of even longer duration. Continued overgrazing will result in scarcely half the potential production.

CHAPTER 15

Vegetation of Oklahoma

THE GRASSLANDS of the panhandle of Oklahoma are practically identical with those of Kansas. The mixed prairie, which occupies the western one-fourth of the state, differs chiefly in a greater abundance of silver beard-grass (*Andropogon saccharoides*) and the occurrence of many forbs found sparingly or not at all in Kansas. This great prairie begins about 60 miles east of the Texas-Oklahoma border along the Red River on the south and 100 miles or more east of the eastern boundary of the state's panhandle on the north. From the transitional area with true prairie in the Redbed Plains, it extends westward across the wide belt of Gypsum Hills and then over the High Plains northwestward (Fig. 70).

In the area of transition, the appearance of short grasses occurs first on thinner soils of exposed areas. With increasing aridity westward, most grasses of true prairie become less vigorous, but the short grasses increase in abundance to replace them. Thus, the true prairie without a short-grass understory gradually changes to one in which mid grasses are regularly intermixed with shorter ones. "Outstanding exceptions to the general rule are areas of [mid and] tall grasses many miles in extent which cover the sandy tracts that lie in a more or less northwest to southeast direction, especially north of the sand-choked rivers [Canadian, Cimarron, South Fork of Arkansas] from whose dry beds the sand has been blown" (Bruner, 1931). Over the area generally, many grasses and forbs which flourish in the true prairie become dwarfed and then disappear as the aridity increases westward. Rainfall is about 30 inches on the eastern border of Oklahoma mixed prairie but only 20 in the panhandle, but evaporation is high. This decrease of species is replaced in part by drought-resistant western species of both grasses and forbs.

VEGETATION OF THE HARD LANDS

An extensive study of mixed prairie was made by Bruner (1931) during several years preceding the great drought of 1933–40. In addition to thousands of square miles of grazed lands, he found areas protected from grazing and fires for long periods of time. Hay meadows and the right-of-way along railroads were assumed to have a flora which most nearly represented natural conditions. The following species were domi-

FIG. 70. (Upper) Mixed prairie on the Gypsum Hills in the west-central portion of Oklahoma. (Lower) View in mixed prairie near Cheyenne in western Oklahoma, showing deciduous trees along the ravines and red cedars on the rocky outcrops. Photos by Bruner. (Reproduced by courtesy of Ecological Monographs)

nant: *Andropogon scoparius, A. saccharoides, Agropyron smithii, Koeleria cristata, Buchloe dactyloides, Bouteloua gracilis, B. curtipendula* and *B. hirsuta.* The following data are from Bruner's studies.

The prairie consists of an upper layer of rather sparsely distributed mid grasses and a lower one of short grasses, or of alternating areas of mid and short grasses. The layers are well represented in areas where western wheatgrass and side-oats grama are associated with buffalo grass, blue grama and hairy grama. More commonly, however, little bluestem or silver beardgrass is associated with the short grasses. Both of these mid-grass dominants are bunch formers but the short grasses sod over the intervening spaces more or less completely. All degrees of intermixing occur in zones and in alternating dominance of species.

Little bluestem occurs as bunches more or less thickly scattered in a short-grass sod. The bunches are 6 to 12 or more inches wide and reach a height of 18 to 20 inches. Dead flower stalks from the previous year's growth remain in the luxuriant green mats of the following spring. In late summer and autumn both flower stalks and foliage take on a reddish-brown color. "*Andropogon saccharoides* is quite common in the southern part of the area where it forms clumps and in other respects is very much like the little bluestem. The white cotton-like bristles of the inflorescence make it easily distinguishable in the flowering stage. In habit it is less erect than *A. scoparius* and this tendency toward spreading helps in its identification during the vegetative stages."

Junegrass occurred commonly but it was never found to dominate an area. Western wheatgrass became less abundant than in the northern plains, and the bluestems assumed the most important role among the mid grasses. Side-oats grama, however, probably reached its maximum development here. It frequently formed almost pure stands, which yielded 200 to 250 grams of forage per square meter. Pure stands were probably the result of local conditions since this species was more commonly found in association with blue grama or little bluestem. Hairy grama has a limited distribution since it is largely confined to dry, sandy soils. It was abundant wherever the soil was too sandy for the other grasses to thrive.

"*Bouteloua gracilis* is the most important single dominant. Its spread has been encouraged by grazing until it now extensively occurs throughout the area, frequently almost to the exclusion of other grasses. . . . It occurs as a codominant with all of the other dominants of the association.

. . . The most frequent grouping is formed with *Andropogon scoparius* and *Bouteloua racemosa* [*B. curtipendula*], accompanied by *Andropogon saccharoides* in the south. Occasionally it is associated with *Agropyron,* especially in the northeast.

"As a result of continued overgrazing many pastures almost entirely consist of the short grasses. . . . The vegetation in protected areas along lanes and highways presents indubitable evidence that the present condition of the grassland has been brought about by long continued grazing. *Andropogon scoparius* and other tall grasses are found in places where neither grazing nor mowing interferes with their development, but in grazed areas just across the fence hardly a spear of tall grass is to be found." Throughout the panhandle and the hard lands in the western tier of counties of Oklahoma, the great grazing disclimax of western Kansas extends southward into Texas. Although the closed mat type of short grass prevails on thin soils, because of underlying rocks or gravel, the open-mat cover and bare areas are frequent and often extensive in the aggregate. The extreme southwestern portion is strongly modified by the invasion from the southwest of certain shrubs or small trees. Among these are mesquite (*Prosopis juliflora*) and a large, thorny shrub, lotebush (*Condalia obtusifolia*), frequently 6 to 8 feet high. Over the disclimax portion blue grama, buffalo grass, hairy grama, and side-oats grama prevail.

Bruner described this disclimax in 1931 as follows. "The region as a whole is characterized by the dense sod of the short grasses which form a carpet-like mat of foliage that is interrupted but little by trees, shrubs, or tall grasses, even in the moister parts. The tough, fibrous roots and rhizomes bind the soil and protect it from water erosion just as the mat-like cover of leaves retards the erosive effects of torrential rains and wind." How different is this dustbowl landscape today!

An extensive list of non-grasslike species of each of the seasonal aspects is presented. In the western part, however, forbs occurred sparingly. Examples of abundant species found here, which do not occur or are not abundant in the Kansas plains, are pearlwort (*Sagina decumbens*), rushpea (*Hoffmanseggia falcaria*) and short-podded primrose (*Oenothera brachycarpa*). They blossom early. Prairie acacia (*Acacia angustissima*) and ball cactus (*Neomammillaria vivipara*) blossom later in spring. The summer aspect is marked in part by Carleton's four-o'clock (*Mirabilis carletoni*), tree cactus (*Opuntia arborescens*) and gaillardia (*Gaillardia fastigiata*). Among autumnal bloomers are cut-leaved gerardia (*Gerardia densiflora*), stiff-haired sunflower (*Helianthus hirsutus*), and willow-leaved sunflower (*H. salicifolius*). About 25 per cent of the more abundant species are of southern extraction. Their presence usually affects but little the composition and density of the grassland types. (See figure 71.)

The effects of overgrazing and erosion in the eastern border of mixed prairie on both plants and animals (chiefly insects but also some birds and mammals) were studied by Smith (1940). He lists the relative abundance of 53 species of prairie plants in normal prairie and properly grazed prairie and three stages of overgrazing and erosion. This is supplemented by a list of decreasing, increasing, and invading species under moderate grazing and under conditions of overgrazing and erosion. Conditions produced by overgrazing caused the dropping out of many species [of insects] but enabled grasshoppers to increase enormously in abundance.

Several studies on the effects of overgrazing upon biotic communities have been made in Oklahoma prairie (Phillips, 1935). Carpenter (1940) presented a considerable amount of information on mixed prairie in his study of "The Grassland Biome" and a list of references on studies in grassland by both botanists and zoologists.

VEGETATION ON SAND AND SANDY SOILS

A postclimax prairie, similar in many ways to that of the Nebraska sand hills, occurs as numerous large belts and islands in the climax grassland of western Oklahoma. Deposits of sand form extensive areas along the streams, and large isolated tracts of sand masses also occur. Many such sandy areas are 8 to 16 miles in width and 50 to 150 miles long. These nearly all lie north or northeast of the Arkansas, Cimarron, and Canadian Rivers and other streams which flow mostly southeastward. "The greater portion of the substratum is, of course, in a fairly stable condition, but along the streams small dunes are still in the process of formation and a few rather large active dunes occur" (Bruner, 1931). Shifting sand dunes are found in only a few places in western Oklahoma; those near Waynoka are most extensive. In times of high water the flood plains as well as the stream beds receive extensive deposits of sand. The winds sweep down the river channels and carry a constant stream of sand which wears away the banks of the rivers and drifts the sand into fresh dunes on the flood plains.

During storms great quantities of sand and dust are carried many miles. Often layers of sand cover thinly a more fertile substratum into which deeply rooted plants may penetrate (Bruner, 1931).

It is estimated that this sandy type of soil covers approximately 15 million acres in Oklahoma and Kansas. Topography of these areas varies greatly from steep dunes with blowouts through hummocky and undulating to nearly level land. Originally the sand hills were covered with tall, mid and some short grasses mostly of the same species as those described farther northward. Vegetation was of the open type in comparison with that of the hard lands. Water penetrates readily and deeply. There is little or no runoff and any excess rainfall becomes part of the ground water. Moreover, the surface sand dries quickly and forms a mulch which greatly decreases further water loss by evaporation.

Most of these sandy soils are not well adapted to crop production, but the native vegetation furnishes excellent grazing. The original stands of sand-hill vegetation have been badly depleted and the most palatable grasses and forbs are now found rather sparingly. Certain short grasses have increased greatly, and various weedy species of both grasses and forbs have become extremely abundant. Sand sage has increased enormously (Fig. 72). The more or less spherical crowns of this shrub have developed a cover 3 to 4 feet high.

A present-day description of the vegetation reveals that most plant life on the sandy soils is usually overtopped and dominated by a fairly uniform stand of sand sage (*Artemisia filifolia*). Short grasses generally form an understory on fairly heavy soil, and mid and tall grasses occur in greatest abundance on dunes and in other sandy areas.

Where blowouts occur and where sand is least stable the cover is indeed sparse and often limited to blowout grass (*Redfieldia flexuosa*) and a taller, more robust and different species of sand reed than is found northward, called *Calamovilfa gigantea.*

Sand bluestem (*Andropogon hallii*) is widely scattered over the hills and in places still forms local dense stands. When fully developed this tall grass exceeds sand sage in height and may be found growing up through the crowns of the protecting sage. Little bluestem (*A. scoparius*) is often

FIG. 71. (Upper) Fremont's leather flower (*Clematis fremontii*) in fruit, and sensitive brier (*Schrankia nuttallii*). (Lower) Engelmann daisy (*Engelmannia pinnatifida*) and Baldwin's ironweed (*Vernonia baldwini*).

not so widely distributed as sand bluestem but it persists in fairly dense communities in depressions on the hillsides and on more compacted level sand. Sand lovegrass (*Eragrostis trichodes*) has usually been nearly grazed out. Although not abundant it is widely scattered, especially on lower hill-sides and stabilized places.

FIG. 72. Sand hills in western Oklahoma after many years of heavy grazing. Chief shrubs are sand sage (*Artemisia filifolia*) and, on the slope, skunkbush sumac (*Rhus trilobata*). The most abundant grasses are blue grama and sand dropseed.

Hairy grama (*Bouteloua hirsuta*) occurs in greatest amounts on sandy knolls and on the sides and lower slopes of dunes. Blue grama (*B. gracilis*) and buffalo grass (*Buchloe dactyloides*) are generally limited to finer-textured soils of level land and ravines. Here the total ground cover is much higher than that found elsewhere. Both switchgrass (*Panicum virgatum*) and Indian grass (*Sorghastrum nutans*), which are generally limited to moist localities, occur here and often form an incomplete upper story to the shorter grasses of the lowlands.

Sand dropseed (*Sporobolus cryptandrus*) occurs rather uniformly over the entire area. It has profited greatly by the disturbance of grazing and also by drought. It is most abundant in those places which have been very heavily grazed. It is least common in the better cover of the more compacted and finer-grained soils of level lands.

Species of less abundance are purple three-awn (*Aristida purpurea*), Texas bluegrass (*Poa arachnifera*), sand paspalum (*Paspalum strami-*

neum) and purple sandgrass (*Triplasis purpurea*), but there are many others. McIlvain *et al.* (1950) state that more than 50 species of grasses are found in these sandy lands and approximately 200 species of forbs and woody plants.

The following abbreviated list of species is representative of the sand sage type:

Narrow leaved four-o'clock
Mirabilis linearis
Sand sage
Artemisia filifolia
Annual eriogonum
Eriogonum annuum
Evolvulus
Evolvulus nuttallianus
Biennial gaura
Gaura biennis
Bush morning-glory
Ipomoea leptophylla
Narrow-leaved puccoon
Lithospermum linearifolium
Stickleaf
Mentzelia nuda
Plains lemon monarda
Monarda pectinata
Tooth-leaved primrose
Oenothera serrulata
Buckley's beardtongue
Pentstemon buckleyi
Chickasaw plum
Prunus angustifolia

The following occur largely on level or lowland areas:

Western ragweed
Ambrosia psilostachya
White prickly poppy
Argemone intermedia
Skunkbush sumac
Rhus trilobata
Pitcher's blue sage
Salvia pitcheri
Large-bracted spiderwort
Tradescantia bracteata
Small soapweed
Yucca glauca

Much excellent work on the proper management of these grasslands of sandy soils has been done at the U.S. Southern Great Plains Field Station at Woodward since its establishment in 1937. The following informative excerpt is from the 19-year summary of range improvement studies (McIlvain *et al.*, 1955). "Proper use represents a stocking rate, grazing system, and class of livestock which will produce the greatest total volume of forage, and livestock gain, on a continuous basis. Forage plants survive by manufacturing food in green leaves. This plant food is necessary to produce more leafage and vigorous roots which will enable the plants to provide forage and withstand drouth periods. Therefore, green leaves cannot be grazed off completely at any time without serious injury to the plant. It has been stated that no more than 50 percent of total annual forage can be utilized by livestock without plant injury. This is undoubtedly true on hardland grazed yearlong or on any range grazed during summer only. However, the 10-year investigations at Woodward indicate that three-fourths of the total forage on sandy land in the Southern Plains can be utilized on a year-long basis without injury to the vegetation."

Extensive brush control studies have been conducted at Woodward. It has been found that three-fourths of sand sage can be killed by a single proper treatment of 2, 4-D. "Subsequent forage and beef production can be increased from 50 to 75 per cent if grazing is deferred or is extremely light for two successive summers after the sage is controlled. Chemical control is cheaper, faster, and usually more effective than mechanical control" (McIlvain *et al.*, 1954).

Savage and Costello (1948) pointed out that "much of the sandier types of range land are seriously infected with sand sagebrush and considerable quantities of skunkbush and sand-hill plum. The Miles series of sandy soils along the breaks of the High Plains in Oklahoma, Texas, and New Mexico is heavily infested with shinnery oak. Soapweed occurs thickly on many of the shallow sands, particularly in the northern and western parts of the [Southern Great Plains] region. Mesquite brush offers serious competition to grasses in Texas and New Mexico."

Oklahoma is a transitional area from North to South. Through it one enters a grassland empire of vast extent, different in many ways from the regions described. Throughout, however, are so many of the dominant grasses and important forbs already discussed that this vegetation will readily be recognized as a southward extension of mixed prairie.

CHAPTER 16

Mixed Prairie in Texas

By B. W. Allred
Soil Conservation Service

A large region of Mixed Prairie extends far southward from the Oklahoma panhandle almost to the Rio Grande. Its width in most places is 250 miles, and its length approximately 500 miles. The eastern boundary is True Prairie. On the south it gives way to the Coastal Prairie Association, and on the southwest to Desert Plains Grassland (Fig. 73). About five-sixths of this grassland is on the Great Plains, the remainder occurs eastward in the Central Lowland. The soils are mostly Reddish Chestnut although areas of sand and rough breaks occur in the central area and along the edge of the caprock in the Canadian River Valley. The Shinnery Oak Savannah lies almost entirely upon Rendzina soils.

PHYSIOGRAPHY AND CLIMATE

Most of the Mixed Prairie grows on a great tableland of outwash material that originated from the Rocky Mountains during the Tertiary period. This extends from near these mountains to the caprock escarpment of the eastern High Plains and southward, including the eastern two-thirds of the Edwards Plateau, a limestone area of Cretaceous age. The eastern part continues from the caprock on the eastern edge of the Llano Estacado to the western boundary of True Prairie. The Basement rocks here are the redbeds of the Permian system.

A long finger of the Rocky Mountain Foothill Community extends eastward along the Colorado-New Mexico boundary on the backbone of a rugged headland, a basaltic lava flow of the Pliocene period. This is called the Mesa de Maya and its easternmost terminus is Black Mesa in the western Oklahoma panhandle.

Another geological feature that has a modifying effect on vegetation is the numerous and often extensive post-Ice Age sand masses which originally supported excellent stands of postclimax mid and tall grasses.

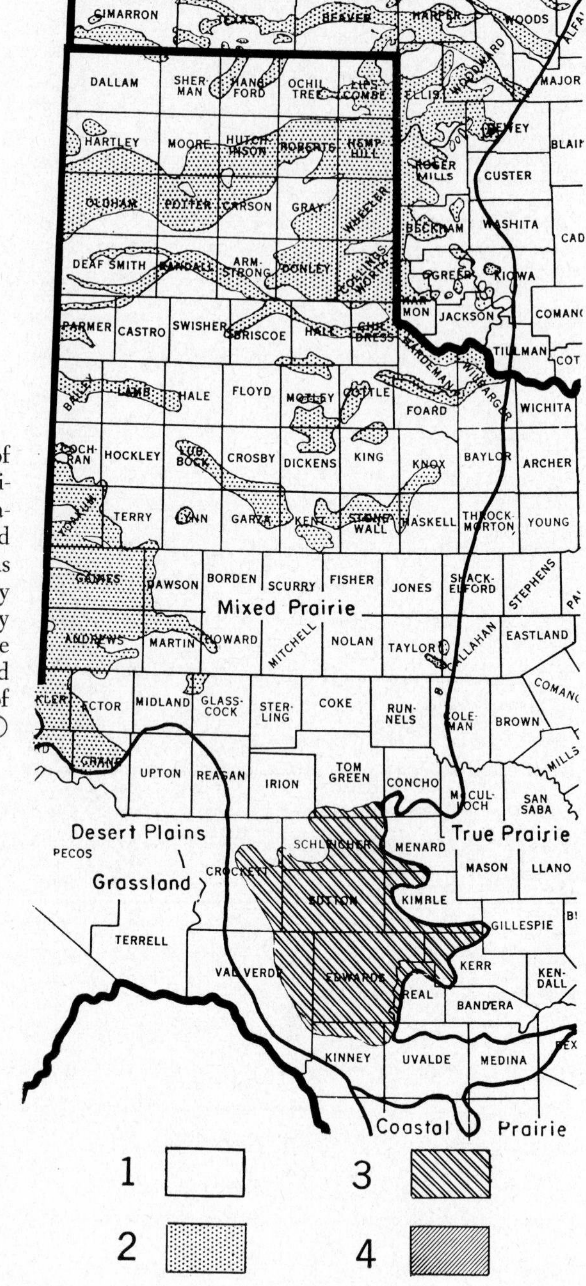

FIG. 73. Distribution of Mixed Prairie communities in Texas and Oklahoma: 1, Climax Mixed Prairie; 2, High Plains Bluestem; 3, Shinnery Oak Savannah; 4, Rocky Mountain Foothills. Note the surrounding grassland associations. (Courtesy of Soil Conservation Service)

These are most prevalent in the west-central and northern areas (Fig. 73).

Annual precipitation varies from 12 to 24 inches. Yearly evaporation from a free water surface is from 60 to 80 inches. Winters are warm enough for cool-season plants to grow in the southern part, but it is so cold on the northern edge that they may remain dormant 2 to 4 months in winter.

GRAZING PRACTICES

Livestock are kept on the range all year and yearlong grazing is practiced on all but the flat, treeless areas of the Llano Estacado where animals are fed in artificial or natural shelters during winter. Vegetation is dormant in the northern four-fifths of the Mixed Prairie during late fall, winter, and early spring, and at such times animals are fed protein and sometimes home-grown roughages to supplement range forage when it is deficient in protein and carotene. Supplements are usually fed out on the ranges when natural shelter is adequate. Best winter protection is afforded in postclimax communities where topographic features provide more natural protection than on ranges of the more level Mixed Prairie climax areas.

The Shinnery Oak Savannah and adjoining Mixed Prairie lie within a favorable temperature belt where many grasses and forbs remain green in winter. Large numbers of ranchers buy lambs in the fall, winter them on green range forage, and sell to packers in the early spring. Beef cattle and sheep and sometimes goats are grazed together on ranches in the southeastern and southern part of the Mixed Prairie. Beef cow and calf enterprises are common elsewhere. Wheat-growing is a widespread operation in the northern two-thirds of the area. Grazing of winter wheat is practiced during years favorable to its growth and many wheat-growers carry a cattle fattening operation as part of their agricultural program.

MIXED PRAIRIE CLIMAX

The Mixed Prairie Climax is by far the largest of the five communities to be described. The others, all postclimax communities, are, in order of their importance, High Plains Bluestem, Shinnery Oak Savannah, Post Oak Savannah, and Rocky Mountain Foothills. They have resulted from soil and physiographic influences that have modified plant patterns within the general Mixed Prairie climatic belt.

Climax Mixed Prairie vegetation is produced on normal upland soils of medium to heavy texture (Fig. 74). There are several climax grass dominants that are found throughout. The mid grasses are side-oats grama (*Bouteloua curtipendula*), silver beardgrass (*Andropogon saccharoides*), sand dropseed (*Sporobolus cryptandrus*) and purple three-awn (*Aristida purpurea*). The first two are so well liked by livestock that they decrease under grazing. Conversely, the last two become more abundant under grazing and are designated as increasers. Important short grasses are blue grama (*Bouteloua gracilis*), buffalo grass (*Buchloe dactyloides*) and hairy grama (*Bouteloua hirsuta*). Generally these short grasses are increasers and buffalo grass and blue grama occur as an extensive disclimax where grazing has subdued the mid grasses. However, blue grama is a decreaser on a few dry, hard-land sites. It is more prominent in the climax than buffalo grass and less common in the disclimax because cattle eat it in preference to buffalo grass; hence blue grama decreases and buffalo grass increases in density. Purple three-awn is a cool-season grass; the others are warm-season species.

Distinguishing forbs which prevail throughout the Mixed Prairie are slimleaf scurfpea (*Psoralea linearifolia*),[1] few-flowered psoralea (*Psoralea tenuiflora*), purple prairie clover (*Petalostemum purpureum*), scarlet globemallow (*Sphaeralcea coccinea*), wavy-leaf thistle (*Cirsium undulatum*), Virginia spiderwort (*Tradescantia virginiana*), Dakota verbena (*Verbena bipinnatifida*), and blazing star (*Liatris punctata*).

There are a number of climax grasses that grow in limited areas of the southern Mixed Prairie which are often quite important. Among the cool-season decreasers are western wheatgrass (*Agropyron smithii*), which grows only about as far south as Lubbock, (Lubbock County) Texas. From there southward plains bristlegrass (*Setaria macrostachya*) becomes more important. Needle-and-thread grows farther south than western wheatgrass. It is finally replaced by Texas wintergrass (*Stipa leucotricha*) in areas of Permian redbeds and Edwards Plateau to the east and south, and to the west and south by New Mexico feathergrass (*Stipa neomexicana*).

FIG. 74. (Upper) Short-grass disclimax in Texas Mixed Prairie. About 80 per cent of the cover is blue grama; buffalo grass is next in abundance. Mid grasses have practically disappeared and mesquite (*Prosopis*) has begun to invade. (Lower) View of range in southwestern Texas. Tobosa grass (*Hilaria mutica*) is the mid grass; buffalo grass is shown in the foreground. The grass cover is increasing under good grazing practices. (Photos by Soil Conservation Service)

[1] Plant names in this chapter are in part from Wolff and Rechenthin (1954), A Guide to Plant Names, Soil Conservation Service.

Some warm-season grasses that decrease under grazing are galleta (*Hilaria jamesii*), cane bluestem (*Andropogon barbinodis*) and cottontop (*Trichachne californica*). Galleta is found largely on the High Plains on a line north of Lubbock. Cane bluestem is one of the superior bluestems found largely in the south half of the southern Mixed Prairie. It resembles silver beardgrass and is often mistaken for it, since intergrades of the two species are common. Cottontop (*Trichachne californica*) is most common south of Amarillo (Potter County) and Childress (Childress County), Texas. Vine-mesquite (*Panicum obtusum*) also becomes a decreaser in the southern half of the area. It thrives, however, as an invader on postclimax sites in the lower part of the northern Great Plains.

A number of grasses which are increasers also occur but in only part of the southern Mixed Prairie. The important ones are black grama (*Bouteloua eriopoda*), tobosa grass (*Hilaria mutica*), and curly mesquite (*Hilaria belangeri*). They become increasingly more common southward from Amarillo and Childress. Fall witchgrass (*Leptoloma cognatum*) is found on all but hard-land sites on the southern High Plains.

The most prevalent species of invading grasses and forbs follow:

Perennial Grasses

Red three-awn (*Aristida longiseta*)
Hairy tridens (*Tridens pilosus*)
Ear muhly (*Muhlenbergia arenacea*)
Sand muhly (*Muhlenbergia arenicola*)
Tumblegrass (*Schedonnardus paniculatus*)
Red grama (*Bouteloua trifida*)

Annual Grasses

Sixweeks fescue (*Festuca octoflora*)
Little barley (*Hordeum pusillum*)
Mat sandbur (*Cenchrus pauciflorus*)
False buffalo grass (*Munroa squarrosa*)
India lovegrass (*Eragrostis pilosa*)

Perennial Forbs

Broom snakeweed (*Gutierrezia sarothrae*)
Western ragweed (*Ambrosia psilostachya*)
Many-spined opuntia (*Opuntia polyacantha*)
Prairie coneflower (*Ratibida columnifera*)
Riddell groundsel (*Senecio riddellii*)

Annual Forbs

Russian thistle (*Salsola kali*)
Texas croton (*Croton texensis*)
Common sunflower (*Helianthus annuus*)
Horseweed (*Conyza canadensis*)
Buffalobur (*Solanum rostratum*)
Snow-on-the-mountain (*Euphorbia marginata*)
Annual umbrella plant (*Eriogonum annuum*)

Annual Forbs (Continued)

Peppergrass (*Lepidium* spp.)
Deervetch (*Lotus americanus*)

Southwestern carrot (*Daucus pusillus*)
Alfileria (*Erodium cicutarium*)

Shrubs and Trees

Mesquite (*Prosopis juliflora*)
Small soapweed (*Yucca glauca*)

A number of desert shrubs overlap into Mixed Prairie on the broad ecotone where it joins the Desert Plains Grassland on the south. Some of the most important are acacias, nolinas, agaves, opuntias, condalias, crotons, sotols (*Dasylirion*), creosote bush (*Larrea tridentata*), mimosas, and yuccas.

Two of the most controversial grasses are curly mesquite and tobosa grass (Allred, 1950). Curly mesquite, a mat-forming grass resembling buffalo grass, has been overrated, but the mid grass, tobosa grass, has generally been underrated. They are increasers that are not very abundant in the climax but have prospered with the advent of grazing and reduction of decreasers. Curly mesquite has increased on ranges where better grasses which have been grazed out have left open ground for it to colonize by seedlings and aggressive stolons. The stolons root at the nodes and establish new plants. It is not very palatable to grazing animals and in addition becomes dormant during drought earlier than buffalo grass and other better grasses. Hence, it survives where the stand of preferred grasses becomes thin as the plants die. Compared to other good grasses that the range will support, forage yields and production of litter by curly mesquite are low. Curly mesquite taken from ranges after three years without grazing yielded at the rate of only 3,100 pounds of forage per acre. There were also only 889 pounds of litter. This contrasts poorly with production of forage and litter of side-oats grama which was 6,700 and 4,100 pounds per acre, respectively.

Tobosa grass is a superior soil conserving plant. The yield is high, old stems and leaves are tough, and litter decays slowly. Almost pure stands occupy hard-land flats and valleys in the Southwest where they characterize the landscape. Although the densest stands usually are found on heavy clay soils, the plant has a greater tolerance for various soils than is generally recognized. Tobosa grass is not as palatable as side-oats grama and blue grama, two excellent grazing species with which it grows; hence it increases when they are grazed out. The fact that tobosa grass in flats and valleys is often left ungrazed while upland grama grass ranges are overused presents to stockmen a critical problem in range management. They are beginning to fence large tobosa flats and graze them in summer when the forage is palatable and nutritious and are reserving the surrounding upland, grama grass ranges for winter. In one experiment, calves from cows kept all summer on tobosa flats weighed slightly more than calves from cows grazed during summer on upland grama ranges. The tobosa flats had a considerably higher grazing capacity than an equal area of upland.

Cane bluestem (*Andropogon barbinodis*), green sprangletop (*Leptochloa dubia*) and plains lovegrass (*Eragrostis intermedia*) are native grasses that have been selected by the Soil Conservation Service for revegetating arid southwestern ranges. They are very palatable and productive. Probably the most promising is the robust cane bluestem, one of the feathery bluestems, which reproduces rapidly under proper grazing.

Mesquite (*Prosopis*) is the most obvious woody invader over most of the Mixed Prairie. The open tablelands of the Llano Estacado are freer of this pest than any other area but even there the plants are invading. There are over 55 million acres of mesquite in Texas and much of this area lies within the Mixed Prairie. This invasion has taken place since the introduction of domestic livestock and is a result of the decline in range condition. As the taller grasses disappear under heavy use they are replaced by short grasses and weeds that are unable to prevent mesquite invasion. Once established, the plants are too deeply rooted to be suppressed by competition with grasses. Mechanical or chemical methods of control must be used.

Tree-dozing, brush-cutting, cabling, and deep plowing have all given good results when correctly used. Original costs range from 5 to 15 dollars per acre for tree-dozing, 4 to 5 dollars for brush-cutting, 1 to 4 dollars for cabling, and 10 to 20 dollars per acre for deep plowing. Benefits are short-lived unless followed by control of sprouts and seedlings. On the better range sites, both seedlings and sprouts usually return quickly. A good stand of vigorous climax grasses, however, will help hold them back. Sprout-control with rolling types of brush-cutting maintainers costs from 25 cents to a dollar per acre per year.

Of the chemical controls, kerosene and hormone sprays have been most widely used. Costs of kerosene treatment range from 7 to 16 dollars per acre. In many places 90 per cent of the treated trees have died but poorer results are more common. Sand sage (*Artemisia filifolia*) can be killed with 2,4-D at a cost of 2 dollars per acre. Successful trials of this chemical and 2, 4, 5-T are underway on mesquite and other brush.

HIGH PLAINS BLUESTEM COMMUNITY

Widely scattered over the Texas Mixed Prairie are areas of coarse sand and canyon breaks that provide a better than average habitat for grass, largely because of decreased runoff. Here tall grasses similar to those found in the True Prairie occur. Grasses that formerly made up the major portion of the cover are Indian grass (*Sorghastrum nutans*), little bluestem (*Andropogon scoparius*), switchgrass (*Panicum virgatum*), sand bluestem (*Andropogon hallii*), sand lovegrass (*Eragrostis trichodes*), big sand reed (*Calamovilfa gigantea*), side-oats grama (*Bouteloua curtipendula*) and Canada wild-rye (*Elymus canadensis*). All have high forage value and are so palatable that they decrease under heavy grazing. Wild-rye is the only cool-season species.

Grasses that increase under grazing include hairy grama, blue grama, and black grama, hooded windmill grass (*Chloris cucullata*), sand drop-seed, purple three-awn, fringeleaf paspalum (*Paspalum ciliatifolium*) and sand paspalum (*Paspalum stramineum*). Purple three-awn is a cool-season grass and the two paspalums begin growth earlier in spring than the blue-stems and gramas.

Two species of shrubs originally formed an open savannah with the climax grasses of this community, but with the advent of heavy grazing and reduction of the stand of grasses both have increased in density. They are Havard oak (*Quercus havardi*) and sand sage (*Artemisia filifolia*). The oak often develops into dense mottes (clumps of trees in prairie) that exclude all other plants. Stands of sand sage seldom become so thick that all of the grasses and forbs are excluded.

The important perennial forbs are Virginia tephrosia (*Tephrosia virginiana*), white prairie clover (*Petalostemum candidum*), bush morning-glory (*Ipomoea leptophylla*), and Virginia spiderwort (*Tradescantia virginiana*).

Important grasses that invade under grazing are mat sandbur (*Cenchrus pauciflorus*), the perennial, red lovegrass (*Eragrostis oxylepis*) and six-weeks fescue (*Festuca octoflora*).

Chief invading forbs are the perennial broom snakeweed (*Gutierrezia sarothrae*) and various weedy species of shorter life span. Most common are horseweed (*Conyza canadensis*), common sunflower (*Helianthus annuus*), annual umbrella plant (*Eriogonum annuum*), deervetch (*Lotus americanus*) evening primrose (*Oenothera*) and red sorrel (*Rumex acetosella*).

Invading trees and shrubs include small soapweed (*Yucca glauca*), mesquite (*Prosopis*) and skunkbrush sumac (*Rhus trilobata*).

SHINNERY OAK SAVANNAH

The Shinnery Oak Savannah is a postclimax community found at the southern end of the Mixed Prairie (Fig. 75). Most of it occurs in Schleicher, Sutton, and Edwards counties. Here the fractured Cretaceous limestone beds provide better than usual sites for the dominant grasses of Mixed Prairie and several additional important grasses have been added. Also, several species of low-growing oak, known locally as shinnery, originally formed an open savannah with grasses, but now vast areas have become dense, scrub-oak thickets.

Decreaser grasses of this community are side-oats grama, cane bluestem, silverbeard bluestem, pinhole bluestem (*Andropogon perforatus*), little bluestem (*A. scoparius*), green sprangletop (*Leptochloa dubia*), vine mesquite (*Panicum obtusum*), Neally grama (*Bouteloua uniflora*), Canada wild-rye, Texas wintergrass (*Stipa leucotricha*), white tridens (*Tridens albescens*), Texas cupgrass (*Eriochloa sericea*) and plains lovegrass (*Eragrostis intermedia*).

Climax grasses that increase under heavy grazing are purple three-awn, buffalo grass, curly mesquite, fall witchgrass (*Leptoloma cognatum*), slim tridens (*Tridens muticus*) and hairy grama.

Certain perennial forbs of high grazing value that are not commonly found in the rest of the mixed prairie occur here. They are awnless bush sunflower (*Simsia calva*), shorthorn zexmenia (*Zexmenia brevifolia*), Engelmann daisy (*Engelmannia pinnatifida*), trailing ratany (*Krameria secundiflora*) and Pitcher's salvia (*Salvia pitcheri*). Black dalea (*Dalea frutescens*) is an important, palatable, shrubby legume in this community.

Chief species that invade the Shinnery Oak Savannah as a result of grazing follow.

Perennial Grasses

Hairy tridens (*Tridens pilosus*)
Ear muhly (*Muhlenbergia arenacea*)
Texas grama (*Bouteloua rigidiseta*)
Burro grass (*Scleropogon brevifolius*)
Red grama (*Bouteloua trifida*)
Sand muhly (*Muhlenbergia arenicola*)
Tumblegrass (*Schedonnardus paniculatus*)

Annual Grasses

Rescue grass (*Bromus catharticus*)
Little barley (*Hordeum pusillum*)

Perennial Forbs

Croton (*Croton* spp.)
Prairie coneflower (*Ratibida columnifera*)
Broom snakeweed (*Gutierrezia sarothrae*)
Milkweeds (*Asclepias* spp.)
Mealycup sage (*Salvia farinacea*)

Annual Forbs

Broom weed (*Gutierrezia dracunculoides*)
Small head sneezeweed (*Helenium microcephalum*)
Croton (*Croton* spp.)
Bitterweed actinea (*Actinea odorata*)
Hairy caltrop (*Kallstroemia hirsutissima*)
Ragweed parthenium (*Parthenium hysterophorus*)

Shrubs and Trees

Englemann pricklypear (*Opuntia engelmanni*)
Tasajillo (*Opuntia leptocaulis*)
Agrito (*Mahonia trifolioata*)
Pinchot juniper (*Juniperus pinchoti*)
Ashe juniper (*Juniperus ashei*)
Mesquite (*Prosopis* spp.)

POST OAK SAVANNAH

This Post Oak Savannah is the westerly extension of the Post Oak Savannah known as the Oklahoma and Texas Cross Timbers, described by Dyksterhuis (1948) in his excellent monograph. This savannah grows on sand outliers where conditions of soil moisture are sufficiently improved over the climatic normal so that trees and shrubs, particularly oaks, form savannah with the grassland dominants of the True Prairie (Fig. 75).

Original grass dominants of this community are little bluestem, big bluestem, Indian grass, switchgrass, side-oats grama and purpletop (*Tridens flavus*). Post oak (*Quercus stellata*) and blackjack oak (*Quercus marilandica*) are the distinguishing trees although many other trees and shrubs are common. Rainfall is lower in the Post Oak Savannah of Mixed Prairie than in True Prairie eastward. Consequently the trees are more dwarfed and the cover of grasses less dense.

Since the introduction of domestic livestock 100 years ago the grasses have been greatly reduced by grazing and savannahs have become either thickets or denser scrub forests. These scrub oak sites are potentially very productive of forage, once the oak trees are killed and grasses re-established.

FIG. 75. (Upper) View of Shinnery Oak Savannah. Texas wintergrass (*Stipa leucotricha*) at mature-seed stage obscures an understory of buffalo grass and curly mesquite. Scrub live oak in the background is a natural part of this community, but mesquite (*Prosopis*), many now large trees, has invaded. (Lower) View in Post Oak Savannah community. Hand cutting of the trees reduces shade, protects the grass, and increases moisture and nutrients for bluestems and other climax grasses. (Photos by Soil Conservation Service)

Much progress is being made toward converting areas of post oak and blackjack oak to productive grasslands. They can be reclaimed profitably because brush-controlled ranges produce 5 to 10 times more grass than brushy thickets.

Use of chemical sprays that control the growth of oak trees is proving to be a revolutionary method of clearing the land. Within 2 or 3 years following treatment many of these ranges develop good stands of native grasses that, when grazed by cattle, produce as much as 70 pounds of beef per acre per year.

Chemicals that are showing greatest promise for controlling weedy bushes and trees in the oak savannahs are the hormones, known as 2, 4, 5-T and 2, 4-D. Good results are being obtained from use of 50-50 mixtures plus a standard amount of diesel oil. Costs per acre vary from 7.5 to 14 dollars, depending on whether 1 or 2 applications are required. Follow-up operations cost from 3.5 to 5 dollars per acre.

The following lists indicate the behavior of various climax grasses under heavy grazing.

Decreasers	Increasers
Little bluestem	Side-oats grama
Indian grass	Hairy grama
Big bluestem	Blue grama
Sand bluestem	Scribner's panicum (*Panicum scribnerianum*)
Switchgrass	Purpletop (*Tridens flavus*)
Sand lovegrass	Purple lovegrass (*Eragrostis spectabilis*)
Mississippi dropseed (*Sporobolus macrus*)	

There is an abundance of forbs, many of which are grazed with the grasses. They furnish a considerably varied diet. Some of the better forbs are Shapely milkpea (*Galactea regularis*), trailing lespedeza (*Lespedeza procumbens*), slender lespedeza (*L. virginica*), narrow-leaved dayflower (*Commelina angustifolia*), Virginia spiderwort (*Tradescantia virginiana*), Virginia tephrosia (*Tephrosia virginiana*), many-flowered posoralea (*Psoralea tenuiflora*) and heath aster (*Aster ericoides*).

The most important grasses that invade are listed.

Perennials	Annuals
Tumble lovegrass (*Eragrostis sessilispica*)	Six-weeks fescue (*Festuca octoflora*)
Red lovegrass (*Eragrostis oxylepis*)	Mat sandbur (*Cenchrus pauciflorus*)
	Prairie three-awn (*Aristida oligantha*)

Perennials (Continued)

Silver beardgrass (*Andropogon saccharoides*)
Fringeleaf paspalum (*Paspalum ciliatifolium*)
Red three-awn (*Aristida longiseta*)
Windmill grass (*Chloris verticillata*)

The five most abundant invading perennial forbs are Carolina horsenettle (*Solanum carolinense*), western ragweed (*Ambrosia psilostachya*), slender verbena (*Verbena halei*), Arkansas dozedaisy (*Aphanostephus skirrhobasis*) and hairy pinweed (*Lechea villosa*).

The following are invading annual forbs:

Common sunflower (*Helianthus annuus*)
Showy partridgepea (*Chamaecrista fasciculata*)
Spotted beebalm (*Monarda punctata*)
Camphorweed (*Heterotheca subaxillaris*)
Lanceleaf gaillardia (*Gaillardia lanceolata*)
Rough buttonweed (*Diodia teres*)
Deervetch (*Lotus americanus*)
Buffalobur (*Solanum rostratum*)
Horseweed (*Conyza canadensis*)
Annual umbrella plant (*Eriogonum annuum*)

Under original conditions woody vegetation grew sparsely among the grasses. Post oak was the most prominent species and blackjack oak was second in abundance. Small amounts of coralberry (*Symphoricarpos orbiculatus*), smooth sumac (*Rhus glabra*), and hawthorns (*Crataegus* spp.) were present. These and many other woody species have increased in abundance since the introduction of grazing.

ROCKY MOUNTAIN FOOTHILL COMMUNITY

The Mesa de Maya, an igneous rock highland, rises 500 to 3,000 feet above the base of the Great Plains along the boundary between Colorado and New Mexico. Increased elevation, bringing with it higher rainfall and cooler temperatures, creates a habitat that produces a mountain-foothill type of savannah. Rainfall is highest near the Rocky Mountains and least on the Black Mountain terminus in northwestern Oklahoma.

On south-facing slopes the important grasses are little bluestem, side-oats grama, hairy grama and galleta. Black grama also grows on the dry shallow soils on top of Black Mesa. North-facing slopes and mountain tops support good stands of western wheatgrass, plains bluegrass (*Poa arida*), and some small cool-season species of *Carex*. Crazyweed (*Oxytropis lambertii*) occurs in small amounts in the climax but where grazing has reduced the grasses it has taken over large areas on this mesa.

Original trees and shrubs of the savannah were western yellow pine (*Pinus ponderosa*), one-seed juniper (*Juniperus monosperma*), gambel oak (*Quercus gambeli*), true mountain-mahogany (*Cercocarpus montanus*) and pinyon pine (*Pinus edulis*). Generally trees and shrubs have thickened as grasses were reduced by grazing.

EFFECTS OF GRAZING AND DROUGHT ON CLIMAX VEGETATION

There are several thousand acres of southern Mixed-Prairie ranges in or near the climax condition. The owners of such ranges have been careful stewards of their soil and grass. Unfortunately most of the Mixed Prairie is far below climax condition and several million acres have few or no climax plants remaining. Plant cover is made up primarily of increasers and invaders. Woody invaders, especially, are increasing in many areas faster than man is able to subdue them.

This great grassland is still (1955) in a serious drought that has been prolonged in places 4 to 7 years. The drought has added further damage to a weakened plant cover. Recent examination revealed that all range land, whether grazed or not, suffered some losses. Droughty ranges provided too little moisture to permit all of the plants to live and reproduce. Ranges that had many climax grasses before the drought are recovering with enough living grass to restock them with desirable species. Considerable grass and forbs of good forage value survived in localities covered with brush where animals have been unable to graze. Areas without brush lost proportionately more grass than brush-covered ranges, except where light grazing was practiced. An exception occurred on sandy, shinnery-oak ranges near Cheyenne (Roger Mills County), Oklahoma. Ranges that have had moderate grazing are recovering more rapidly than those on which heavy grazing had been practiced. Moderately grazed ranges are recovering almost as rapidly as those in similar condition which had not been grazed for several years.

Vegetation on rocky ranges survived better than that on hard land. The better and more deeply rooted grasses endured drought longer on rocky ranges because moisture conditions were more favorable. Moreover, grazing is usually heavier on hard lands because they are smoother and the forage is more easily grazed by livestock. The taller grasses are grazed out first and are replaced by buffalo grass and curly mesquite, both of which are killed by severe drought. Runoff is greatest from poorly covered hard lands and the water does not penetrate very deeply into hard-land soils. Hence, evaporation is high and little water is available for plant growth under such conditions.

All plants survived better on well managed ranges than on fair or poor ones. Generally the taller and more deeply rooted grasses, the first to go out under heavy use, survived the best. However these decreasers survived and produced normally under correct grazing use. Losses by death even among this group of grasses varied from 5 to 30 per cent. Examples of these best grasses are side-oats grama, several species of bluestem, green sprangletop (*Leptochloa dubia*) and vine-mesquite (*Panicum obtusum*).

Grasses in the group of increasers suffered more from drought than the decreasers. Drought losses in this group ranged from 25 to 90 per cent. Among these species are tobosa grass (*Hilaria mutica*) buffalo grass, curly mesquite, purple three-awn and hairy grama. Where grazing was sufficiently heavy to thin the stand of these grasses they were replaced by invaders. These are plants often with shallower root systems. Losses among them during the drought ranged from 35 to 95 per cent. Some of these invaders are red grama (*Bouteloua trifida*), red lovegrass (*Eragrostis oxylepis*), hairy tridens (*Tridens pilosus*), red three-awn (*Aristida longiseta*), burro grass (*Scleropogon brevifolius*) and annual weeds.

Examination of seedlings in areas where drought was broken indicated that those of taller grasses were still scarce. Generally there were fewer of the taller grasses left to produce seed. Exceptions were cane bluestem (*Andropogon barbinodis*) and silverbeard bluestem (*A. saccharoides*), both of which produce an abundance of seeds which are carried some distance by the wind. The seeds germinate readily and the seedlings are hardy.

Buffalo grass and curly mesquite were spreading rapidly by means of stolons, the vine-like, prostrate stems that aid their migration. Some seed of both grasses had also produced new plants. Three-awns were making a rapid recovery by seedlings; as many as 5 to 50 young plants per square foot were found on some rocky sites. The short rootstocks of tobosa grass were rapidly thickening the stand. Where rains had occurred repeatedly, an abundance of weedy grasses and forbs had appeared. Among these were red grama, burrograss, red lovegrass, hairy tridens, purple three-awn and many annual weeds, including the poisonous bitterweed actinea (*Actinea odorata*).

Before the drought it was estimated that 10 to 12 million acres of range land needed seeding in order to restore their productivity. The present drought probably has added another 3 to 4 million acres to that unfortunate condition. The loss of plant cover during the recent drought has been the heaviest known by the white man. This is true not only for Mixed Prairie but also for the Desert Plains Grassland. More than half of the drought area was in this latter, drier association.

Drought experiences of southwestern ranchers show clearly that ranches on which sound conservation had been practiced suffered less hardship than those without conservation. On the former loss of grass was comparatively much less, livestock lived better, and the income was considerably greater.

Range production varies from year to year depending upon available moisture for growth of forage. Good ranch managers vary the stocking rates annually to keep livestock and forage in proper balance so that both may thrive. Average safe stocking rates, based on past experience, have been ascertained for ranges in various conditions and these findings are shown as acres per cow, year-long grazing, under the several range conditions.

Plant Community	Range Condition			
	Excellent	Good	Fair	Poor
Mixed Prairie Climax	16–23	25–30	35–40	55 +
High Plains Bluestem	14–16	18–22	25–30	35 +
Shinnery Oak Savannah	18–20	24–26	35–40	55 +
Post Oak Savannah	18–22	28–32	50–60	70 +
Rocky Mountain Foothills	28–32	38–42	50–60	65 +

Clearly, the amount and value of the forage, aside from drought, are largely a matter of proper range management, which includes due regard to soil and water conservation.

The following references are of especial value in a study of Texas Mixed Prairie: Allred and Nixon, 1955; Bray, 1906; Rechenthin, 1949; Whitfield and Jones, 1951; and Young, 1953.

CHAPTER 17

Mixed Prairie in New Mexico

By ARNOLD HEERWAGEN
Range Conservationist [1]

THE MIXED PRAIRIE association occupies an estimated 35 to 40 per cent of the total land area of New Mexico. It occurs principally on comparatively level to rolling dissected plains, plateaus, and broad river valleys at elevations ranging from approximately 4,500 to 7,000 feet.

The major portion of this extensive grassland is located in the eastern half of the state, lying generally to the east of the Sangre de Cristo Mountains in the lower Canadian River Valley and to the east of the Mescalero Escarpment of the Pecos River Valley (Fig. 76). Another extensive portion of this grassland extends along the base of the foothills of the eastern front of the Sacramento Mountains, northward and westward across the plains and plateaus of the central portion of the state between the Pecos and Rio Grande River Valleys. This includes the Estancia Valley, lying immediately east of the Sandia and Manzano Mountains.

The major concentration of Mixed Prairie in the western portion of the state is located in the northwestern corner of the San Juan drainage. However, there are interrupted areas of this plant association found on the high plains, mid-elevation plateaus, and river valleys in the west central portion of the state to the north of the Gila River drainage extending to the Arizona state line. The largest single area of Mixed Prairie in this portion of the state occurs on the St. Augustine Plains which extend generally westward from Magdalena, New Mexico.

These grasslands provide year-long grazing principally for cattle and to a lesser degree for sheep. Portions of this area, particularly those adjacent to the major river valleys, have been subject to grazing use by domestic livestock since the time of the early Spanish settlements. Because of the prevailing semiarid climate, a comparatively small percentage of these grasslands has ever been subjected to cultivation.

[1] Southern Plains States, Soil Conservation Service.

At the present time dry farming operations are concentrated principally in the extreme eastern portion of the state and to a limited acreage in the Estancia Valley. Only a very small acreage of Mixed Prairie has been developed for irrigated farming operations.

CONTACTS WITH OTHER ASSOCIATIONS

Mixed Prairie in eastern New Mexico is an extension of this association from the High Plains of eastern Colorado and the Texas and Oklahoma panhandles. Its major contact within the state is with the Pinyon-Juniper Woodland Association of interspersed foothills and mountains and with the Desert Plains Grassland to the south. To a limited extent, direct contact is made with the lowest extension of the Montane Forest, principally at interrupted points along the eastern front of the Sangre de Cristo and Sacramento Mountains.

In the lower Pecos River Valley contact between Mixed Prairie and Desert Plains Grassland consists of a relatively wide ecotone made possible by a comparatively uniform topography. In the central and lower Rio Grande Valley this ecotone is comparatively narrow or non-existent in as much as the Desert Plains Grassland of the valley floor directly contacts Pinyon-Juniper Woodland as a result of abrupt topographic changes produced by mountains rising abruptly from the valley floor. Principal contact in the west central and northwestern portion of the state is with the Pinyon-Juniper Woodland of interspersed mountain ranges.

PHYSIOGRAPHIC CHARACTERISTICS AND SOILS

Mixed Prairie lying to the east of the Sangre de Cristo and Sacramento Mountains is in the Great Plains Province. In this province, grasslands north of the Canadian Escarpment occur on a trenched peneplane surmounted by dissected lava-capped plateaus and buttes. In the mid-Pecos River Valley it occurs on late mature to old plains, but grasslands immediately east of the Mescalero Escarpment are on a portion of the High Plains characterized by broad inter-valley remnants of smooth fluviatile plains. Mixed Prairie in the northwestern portion of the state is in the Colorado Plateau Province, consisting principally of young plateaus. Remaining Mixed Prairie of the central portion of the state is in the Basin and Range Province, characterized by block plateaus and broad valleys.

Geological materials underlying these grasslands are predominantly

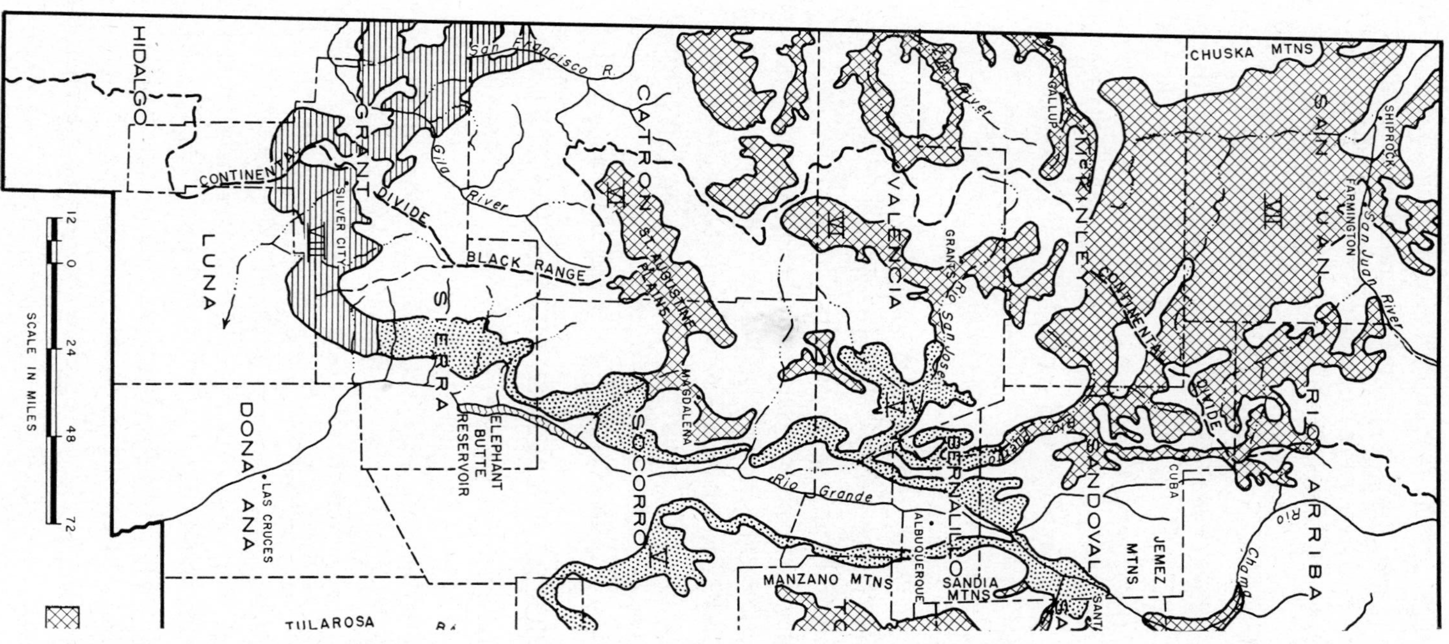

FIG. 76. Mixed Prairie of New Mexico: 1, area characterized by southwestern mixed prairie dominants; 2, mixed prairie dominants associated with some species of Desert Plains Grassland; 3, a portion of Desert Plains Grassland containing important elements of the Mixed Prairie. (Compiled from Soil Conservation field surveys and revised by Arnold Heerwagen, 1955.)

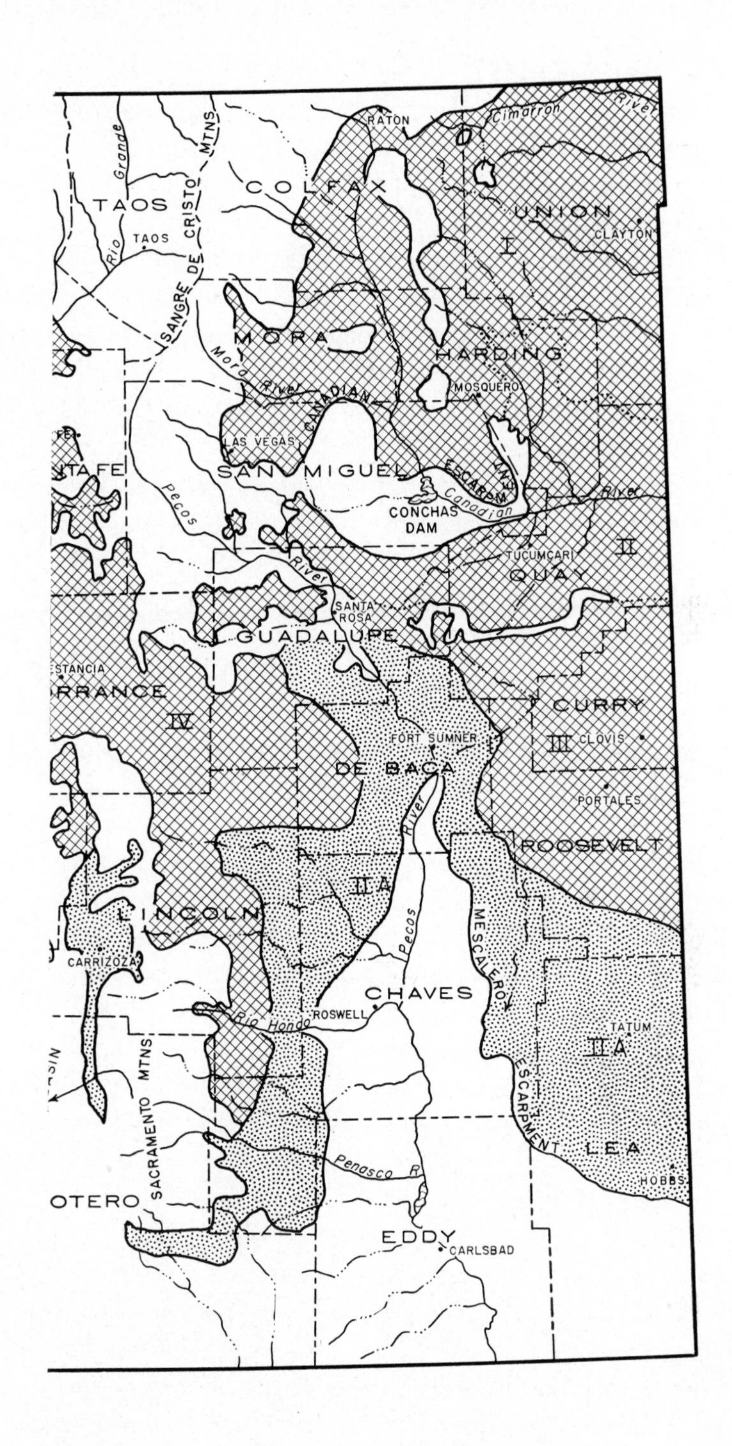

RATON
Cimarron River
COLFAX
UNION
CLAYTON
I
TAOS
TAOS
Rio Grande
SANGRE DE CRISTO MTNS
MORA
Mora River
HARDING
MOSQUERO
CANADIAN ESCARPMENT
LAS VEGAS
SAN MIGUEL
Canadian River
CONCHAS DAM
II
TUCUMCARI
QUAY
Pecos River
SANTA ROSA
GUADALUPE
ESTANCIA
IV
CURRY
III
CLOVIS
FORT SUMNER
DE BACA
PORTALES
ROOSEVELT
II A
LINCOLN
Pecos
MESCALERO ESCARPMENT
CARRIZOZA
CHAVES
ROSWELL
Rio Hondo
TATUM
II A
SACRAMENTO MTNS
LEA
HOBBS
Penasco R
OTERO
EDDY
CARLSBAD
1
2
3

sedimentary depositions of sandstone, limestone, and shale, dating to the Cretaceous period. In many places, soils have been derived from reworked mountain outwash materials overlying these deposits.

Because of the widely divergent topography and variations in climate and parent materials, soils of the Mixed Prairie in New Mexico are highly variable. For the most part they are included in the Brown Soils group. However, there is a representation of the Reddish Chestnut Soils and Reddish Brown Soils, particularly along the eastern border of the state, in the lower Canadian River Valley, and east of the Mescalero Escarpment. Undifferentiated shallow soils are scattered throughout as are deep sands, particularly adjacent to major drainage ways.

Volcanic outcrops are scattered throughout the Mixed Prairie, resulting in soils derived from basalt materials. Frequently the latter are characterized by profiles containing rock and boulders. Soils of the predominant rolling upland topography are generally of moderate depth and are characterized by lime accumulations in the subsoil.

Textures vary from fine sandy loam to silty clay loam. There are, however, substantial areas where soils have been derived from shale materials. These are characterized by finer textured soils, principally with silty clay loam or silty clay surface soils underlain by clay loam or massive clay subsoils.

Postclimax plant communities are scattered throughout the Mixed Prairie, principally on deep sandy soils and on soils characterized by rock-filled profiles or underlain by fractured rock strata. Preclimax plant communities are restricted primarily to limited areas where consolidated rock or indurated caliche is overlain by a mantle of thin soil. Characteristic plant communities are to be found on the flood plains adjacent to major drainage ways. Such communities are subject to distinctive variation, depending upon the degree of flooding and the presence or absence of high water tables and varying amounts of salinity or alkalinity. Thus, there is a great diversity of plant and community habitats.

CLIMATE

The Mixed Prairie of New Mexico has a semiarid climate. Annual precipitation varies from approximately 8 inches in portions of the San Juan Basin in the northwestern portion of the state to 18 inches along portions of the Oklahoma and Texas state boundaries. Precipitation during the growing season (April 1 to September 30) varies from approximately 76 per cent of the annual total in the eastern portion of the state to 61 per cent in the northwestern portion. July, August and September are the wettest months. Except for occasional storms, the winter period is characteristically dry and open. Dry spring seasons are common, and moisture supplies are further depleted in this period by frequent winds.

Evaporation records are limited. A 10-year record at Portales in Roosevelt County averages approximately 91 inches annually. Six-year records at Conchas Dam in San Miguel County average 98 inches. A large percentage of the rain in the growing season falls as brisk, scattered showers. Short-period drought during the growing season is common, and protracted periods of major drought are a matter of record.

VEGETATION OF LOAMY TEXTURED UPLAND SOILS

The predominant type of Mixed Prairie is that occurring on rolling upland topography characterized by moderately deep to deep, loamy textured soils with lime accumulation in the subsoil. Texture of the A horizon varies from very fine sandy loam to silt loam and that of the B horizon varies from loam to clay loam. Under these conditions blue grama (*Bouteloua gracilis*) is the outstanding dominant species throughout the state. It characteristically comprises from 50 to 75 per cent of the vegetation (Fig. 77). The principal associated species vary somewhat with geographic locality. Buffalo grass (*Buchloe dactyloides*) is the most important associated species in the area adjacent to the Oklahoma and Texas state lines where annual precipitation is from 16 to 18 inches and elevations are generally below 5,500 feet. It gradually decreases in abundance in areas of lower rainfall or higher elevation, but in such localities it is to be found principally in small isolated patches in swales and under certain deteriorated flood plain conditions.

Western wheatgrass (*Agropyron smithii*) is important principally in the area to the north of the Canadian Escarpment and in the Mixed Prairie of the north and northwestern portion of the state. South of the Canadian Escarpment and in the west-central portion of the state, it is found principally in swales and flood plains receiving extra moisture supplies. In its northern area it is of greater abundance on the finer textured shale-derived soils than on the loamy textured uplands. Its importance as an associate of blue grama is most pronounced in a relatively narrow belt

FIG. 77. (Upper) Upland Mixed Prairie on plains in east-central New Mexico on a light-textured loam. The dominant is blue grama, with limited amounts of side-oats grama and sand dropseed. Small soapweed is scattered throughout. (Lower) A similar prairie that has deteriorated under heavy grazing. Blue grama has been largely replaced by a mixed stand of secondary grasses and half-shrubs including sand dropseed, purple three-awn, broom snakeweed and fringed sage. (Photos by Soil Conservation Service)

of Mixed Prairie adjacent to the foothills and mountains in an arc extending from Las Vegas north and eastward to Raton and Clayton. In this locality it frequently makes up from 10 to 20 per cent of the plant cover on loamy textured uplands.

The most widely spread associated species of blue grama is galleta (*Hilaria jamesii*). It is found in association with blue grama throughout the Mixed Prairie in New Mexico. The relative amount of galleta on loamy textured upland soils increases from east to west and reaches its maximum abundance in the extreme northwestern portion of the state in the San Juan drainage. Here it may comprise from 30 to 40 per cent of the plant cover. In the extreme eastern portion of the state, on the other hand, galleta usually makes up less than 15 per cent of the cover on pastures receiving moderate use. With the possible exception of the extreme northwestern portion of the state, galleta tends to increase under moderately heavy to heavy grazing because of the marked grazing preference for blue grama as compared to galleta. At present this species composes 30 to 50 per cent of the plant cover in some pastures in the eastern half of the state (Fig. 77).

Secondary grasses that normally occur in very limited amounts on relatively undisturbed loamy textured upland soils include hairy grama (*Bouteloua hirsuta*), ringgrass (*Muhlenbergia torreyi*), sand dropseed (*Sporobolus cryptandrus*), species of three-awn (*Aristida*), squirreltail (*Sitanion hystrix*) and wolftail (*Lycurus phleoides*). Although not abundant under climax conditions, these species, especially three-awn, sand dropseed and ringgrass, may increase markedly under heavy grazing. Side-oats grama (*Bouteloua curtipendula*), little bluestem (*Andropogon scoparius*) and New Mexico feathergrass (*Stipa neomexicana*) although abundant under certain postclimax situations are rare on loamy textured upland soils.

Forbs generally make up less than 10 per cent of the total plant cover. The most common and widely distributed species include scarlet globemallow (*Sphaeralcea coccinea*), scurfpea (*Psoralea tenuiflora*), scarlet gaura (*Gaura coccinea*), cut-leaved goldenweed (*Haplopappus spinulosus*), plains zinnia (*Zinnia grandiflora*), gumweed (*Grindelia squarrosa*) and prairie coneflower (*Ratibida columnifera*), as well as certain species of ragwort or groundsel (*Senecio*) and greenthread (*Thelesperma*).

Shrubby species are almost entirely absent under climax conditions. Two half-shrubs that increase markedly with heavy grazing are broom snakeweed (*Gutierrezia sarothrae*) and fringed sage (*Artemisia frigida*). Occasionally isolated plants or small patches of winterfat (*Eurotia lanata*) and rabbitbrush (*Chrysothamnus* spp.) may be found (Fig. 77).

VEGETATION OF FINE TEXTURED UPLAND SOILS

The dominant plant cover resembles that of the loamy textured uplands in many respects but shows some significant variations. Fine textured soils in this portion of the Mixed Prairie are principally derived from shale parent materials. The A horizon varies in texture from silty clay to silty clay loam. The B horizon may be of the same texture or may be clay. Although blue grama is the outstanding dominant species, three associated species assume more importance under these conditions as compared to loamy textured uplands. These associated dominants include western wheatgrass, galleta and alkali sacaton (*Sporobolus airoides*). Where the salt content of the soil increases moderately, alkali sacaton may assume dominance in localized areas. Generally, however, blue grama constitutes at least half of the total plant cover.

As in the loamy upland soils, western wheatgrass is of most importance in the northern third of the state, and particularly adjacent to foothills and mountains and in the swales scattered throughout the grassland. As compared to the loamy upland soils, galleta is somewhat more abundant, particularly in the northwestern portion of the state where it may assume equal dominance with blue grama. Grasses of secondary importance include three-awn in limited amounts, ringgrass, and, in the northeastern portion of the state, plains muhly (*Muhlenbergia cuspidata*).

Although most species of forbs common to the loamy upland soils also occur here, there are certain forbs that are especially characteristic. These include silky sophora (*Sophora sericea*), two-grooved loco (*Astragalus bisulcatus*), Drummond milk vetch (*Astragalus drummondi*) and short-rayed coneflower (*Ratibida tagetes*). Rabbitbrush (*Chrysothamnus*) is also more abundant here than on the loamy textured uplands. Other shrubby species of limited occurrence include winterfat (*Eurotia lanata*), groundsel tree (*Baccharis wrightii*) and scattered individuals of fourwing saltbush (*Atriplex canescens*). Broom snakeweed (*Gutierrezia sarothrae*) may increase markedly with range deterioration. A significant difference between the Mixed Prairie of New Mexico and that of northern plains states, is the relative scarcity of cool-season grasses and sedges. The only cool-season species of consequence are western wheatgrass, New Mexico feathergrass and needle-and-thread. The latter two species occur principally under postclimax conditions. Prairie Junegrass and species of *Poa* and *Carex* although relatively common at higher elevations in the Montane Forest of northern New Mexico are rare in the Mixed Prairie.

INVASION BY WOODLAND AND SHRUBS

Invasion of the Mixed Prairie of New Mexico by woodland and larger brush species, though not uncommon, is relatively minor as compared to the extensive invasions of mesquite and creosote bush in the Desert Plains Grassland and of sagebrush in the Palouse Prairie.

The most common invasion is by Pinyon-Juniper Woodland. Such invasion occurs where Mixed Prairie meets the Pinyon-Juniper Woodland of the foothills of major mountain ranges and where these species occur as a postclimax savannah on rocky outcrops and mesa escarpments within the grassland proper. By far the most prevalent invasion is by two species of juniper (*Juniperus scopulorum* and *J. monosperma*). By comparison, the invasion of pinyon pine (*Pinus edulis*) is comparatively rare. Seeds of juniper are ingested by birds and apparently germinate readily following the digestive process. Seedlings become established in degenerated grasslands adjacent to and at some distance from the parent stands. Conversely, seeds of the pinyon are destroyed by the digestive process. They are also readily consumed by rodents. Evidence of invasion of juniper from woodlands and postclimax savannahs is apparent in all sections of the state.

Big sagebrush (*Artemisia tridentata*) has invaded a limited area of Mixed Prairie in the San Juan drainage. Except for the upper Rio Grande Valley in the vicinity of Taos and portions of the Jemez Mountain system, big sagebrush is limited principally to the higher elevations along the Continental Divide south of Farmington and in the vicinity of Gallup. In the area south of Farmington it has invaded the grasslands principally adjacent to the foothills and lower elevations of the Continental Divide north and west of Cuba, New Mexico.

Various species of rabbitbrush (*Chrysothamnus*) are believed to be minor constituents of the climax on the fine textured upland soils of the Mixed Prairie, particularly in the northwestern corner of New Mexico.

Mesquite (*Prosopis juliflora*) has invaded Mixed Prairie in portions of the Canadian River Valley in the vicinity of Tucumcari northwestward to the Canadian River Escarpment and in the upper Pecos River Valley in the vicinity of Santa Rosa. To date, it has not established the dense stands characteristic of portions of the Desert Plains Grassland.

VEGETATION IN TRANSITIONAL AREAS

Mixed Prairie joins the Desert Plains Grassland by means of relatively broad ecotones in those areas where no abrupt changes in topography are involved. The largest ecotone of this nature is found adjacent to the Pecos River Valley generally south of Fort Sumner but extending northward at lower elevations to the Canadian River Escarpment north of Santa Rosa. This broad ecotone rims the Desert Plains Grassland of the lowest elevations of the Pecos River Valley southward from Santa Rosa to the Carlsbad vicinity, extending across the Mescalero Escarpment north and east of Roswell and southeastward to Texas. To the west it occurs between the Desert Plains Grassland of the valley floor and the southern extension of the Mixed Prairie along the Sacramento Mountain foothills.

Along the eastern rim of the Tularosa Basin and along the rim of the Rio Grande Valley south of Albuquerque, New Mexico, the ecotone consists of a narrow interrupted band between the Desert Plains Grassland of the valley floor and the Pinyon-Juniper Woodlands of the mountain masses which characteristically rise abruptly from the valley floor. The ecotone supports plant species typical of both the Mixed Prairie and the Desert Plains Grassland. For most of this area, however, the dominant is blue grama with galleta as the principal associate. Consequently, the area is more representative of Mixed Prairie than of Desert Plains Grassland. The most common component of the Desert Plains Grassland in this ecotone is black grama (*Bouteloua eriopoda*) which in some localities may comprise from 20 to 35 per cent of the total vegetation. Tobosa grass (*Hilaria mutica*) is not uncommon, particularly in swales and flood plains adjacent to Desert Plains Grassland.

Burro grass (*Scleropogon brevifolius*) may become abundant in swales and floodplains following degeneration. Bush muhly (*Muhlenbergia porteri*) though uncommon on the loamy textured uplands may be locally important on sandy soils and on rocky outcrops. Two mid-grass components of the Mixed Prairie, side-oats grama and New Mexico feathergrass, are common on rocky soils and on shallow soils underlain by fractured limestone or caliche. Mesquite occurs along drainage ways and has invaded some of the sandier soils. Creosote bush is limited only to those areas immediately adjacent to the Desert Plains Grassland, principally on rocky outcrops or ridge tops with shallow soils.

In addition to the ecotones, certain portions of the Mixed Prairie contain significant elements of Desert Grassland species. Particularly is this true of the lower Canadian River Valley in the Tucumcari vicinity, in the Rio Grande Valley, north, northeast, and northwest of Albuquerque, and in the area immediately to the north of the Tularosa Basin. Although dominance is definitely that of Mixed Prairie species, principally blue grama and galleta, black grama (*Bouteloua eriopoda*) in particular plays an important secondary role. Not uncommonly it may make up from 10 to 20 per cent of the total plant cover on loamy-textured upland and in rocky soils. Tobosa grass (*Hilaria mutica*) intergrades with galleta as a minor conponent of climax plant cover, particularly in swales and flood plains. Burro grass (*Scleropogon brevifolius*) may become locally abundant following degeneration.

POSTCLIMAX PLANT COMMUNITIES

The moderately deep to deep loamy, silty, and clay-textured upland soils in the Mixed Prairie are dominated by short grasses with comparatively minor mid grass components. But both tall- and mid-grass species assume a dominant role in various postclimax situations. From an acreage standpoint the most common postclimax plant community is that found on sand hills and sandy plains. Also of importance is the postclimax community occurring on soils having fractured rock substrata or relatively deep soil profiles containing interspersed rocks or boulders.

Deep dune-type sands occur principally on the leeward side of major drainageways in the Mixed Prairie of New Mexico. Extensive areas of deep sand in eastern New Mexico occur in portions of Union, Harding and Quay Counties in the northeastern corner of the state and in scattered localities east of the Mescalero Escarpment in the southeastern portion (Fig. 78).

Deep sands in these localities are dominated by sand bluestem (*Andropogon hallii*), little bluestem (*Andropogon scoparius*) and side-oats grama (*Bouteloua curtipendula*). A wide variety of secondary grasses includes

FIG. 78. (Upper) Typical sand-hill postclimax in northeastern (Union County) New Mexico. Dominants are sand bluestem, little bluestem and side-oats grama. Other species are Indian grass and sand sage. (Lower) Postclimax rocky site in northeastern New Mexico. Boulders of basalt on and in the soil concentrate the soil water. Dominants are big bluestem, little bluestem, side-oats grama, switch grass and Indian grass. (Photos by Soil Conservation Service)

lovegrasses (*Eragrostis oxylepis, E. intermedia, E. curtipedicellata* and *E. spectabilis*), ear muhly (*Muhlenbergia arenacea*), Indian grass (*Sorghastrum nutans*), switchgrass (*Panicum virgatum*), Hall's panicum (*Panicum hallii*), sand paspalum (*Paspalum stramineum*) and plains bristlegrass (*Setaria macrostachya*). Under stabilized and relatively undisturbed conditions, hairy grama (*Bouteloua hirsuta*) and blue grama comprise less than 10 per cent of the total vegetation. Sand reed (*Calamovilfa longifolia*), a common sandy land dominant northward, is rare in New Mexico. However, giant sand reed (*Calamovilfa gigantea*) is relatively abundant on deep loose sands east of the Mescalero Escarpment, as is also giant dropseed (*Sporobolus giganteus*).

Blowout grass (*Redfieldia flexuosa*) is an uncommon pioneer on blowouts. Sandhill muhly (*Muhlenbergia pungens*), though common on depleted sandy land in the northwestern part of the state, is not abundant in the eastern half. Various species of three-awn (*Aristida*), sand dropseed (*Sporobolus cryptandrus*) and mesa dropseed (*Sporobolus flexuosus*) are minor components of the climax but may assume temporary dominance following deterioration. Black grama (*Bouteloua eriopoda*), bush muhly (*Muhlenbergia porteri*) and cottontop (*Trichachne californica*) occur in small quantities in the southern limits of this postclimax community.

Sand sage (*Artemisia filifolia*) is a minor climax species in the eastern half of the state but may assume dominance with deterioration. Shin oak (*Quercus havardi*) occupies a similar place on sandy lands east of the Mescalero Escarpment. Shrubs and shrub-like plants of secondary importance include sand cherry (*Prunus besseyi*), queens delight (*Stillingia sylvatica*), small soapweed (*Yucca glauca*) and, more rarely, lead plant (*Amorpha canescens*).

Forbs are relatively abundant. The more common species include scurfpea or few-flowered psoralea (*Psoralea tenuiflora*), lance-leaved psoralea (*P. lanceolata*), purple prairie clover (*Petalostemum purpureum*), white prairie clover (*P. candidum*), umbrella plant (*Eriogonum* spp.), evening primrose (*Gaura* spp.), bush morning-glory (*Ipomoea leptophylla*), clammy weed (*Polanisia trachysperma*) and heliotrope (*Heliotropium convolvulaceum*).

Bluestems gradually become less abundant from east to west. In the extreme driest sections of the northwestern corner of New Mexico, various species of dropseed, including *Sporobolus giganteus, S. cryptandrus, S.*

flexuosus, S. interruptus and *S. contractus,* assume dominance on deep sand. Indian ricegrass (*Oryzopsis hymenoides*) is an important associated species. Principal shrubs include sand sage (*Artemisia filifolia*) and four-wing saltbush (*Atriplex canescens*). A shrubby mint (*Poliomintha incana*) is locally abundant in portions of the San Juan drainage.

On sandy plains having somewhat finer textured sandy soils or coarser textured sands underlain by finer textured subsoils or other less permeable substrata, plant communities containing elements of both the deep sands and the loamy textured uplands are to be found. Dominant grasses include a mixture of sand bluestem, little bluestem, side-oats grama, hairy grama and blue grama. Secondary grasses include most of the species found in deep sands but in lesser amounts. As compared to the deep sands where blue grama and hairy grama are minor climax components, they may comprise up to 30 or 40 per cent of the climax plant cover in this type of range land.

On moderately deep to deep soils with scattered rocks or boulders in the soil profile or on soils underlain at relatively shallow depths by fractured rock strata, postclimax communities consisting of a mixture of tall and mid grasses develop throughout the Mixed Prairie area. This situation is not to be confused with the preclimax plant communities that develop on truly shallow soils underlain at shallow depths by consolidated rock strata or indurated caliche or with exposed rock surfaces such as lava flows. In the former soils the rocks interspersed in the soil matrix serve to concentrate soil moisture supplies, thereby permitting the development of a more mesic plant cover than the adjacent upland rock-free soils.

Typical of such postclimax communities is that developed on the basalt boulder areas in the northeastern corner of New Mexico. Here the predominantly silty clay loam soil profiles may contain irregularly shaped basalt or andesite rocks on the soil surface and interspersed throughout the soil profile (Fig. 78). Under these conditions dominant species include big bluestem, little bluestem and side-oats grama. Switchgrass and Indian grass are important secondary species. Additional secondary grasses include blue grama, hairy grama, wolftail (*Lycurus phleoides*), spike muhly (*Muhlenbergia wrightii*), green muhly (*Muhlenbergia racemosa*), tall dropseed (*Sporobolus asper*) and New Mexico feathergrass (*Stipa neomexicana*). Shrubs are not abundant but include scattered individuals or clumps of lead plant (*Amorpha canescens*), skunkbush sumac (*Rhus trilobata*), rose (*Rosa*), currant (*Ribes*) and western thimbleberry (*Rubus parviflorus*). Associated forbs include purple prairie clover (*Petalostemum purpureum*), white prairie clover (*P. candidum*), scurfpea (*Psoralea tenuiflora*), silver-leaf psoralea (*P. argophylla*), vetch (*Vicia americana*), James dalea (*Dalea jamesii*), ground plum (*Astragalus crassicarpus*), Missouri milk vetch (*A. missouriensis*), Short's vetch (*A. shortianus*), crazyweed (*Oxytropis lambertii*), hairy golden aster (*Chrysopsis villosa*), phlox (*Phlox* spp.), goldenrod (*Solidago* spp.) and cudweed sage (*Artemisia ludoviciana*). With deterioration, tall and mid grasses are replaced by blue grama and hairy grama. Purple three-awn (*Aristida purpurea*), fringed sage (*Artemisia frigida*), broom snakeweed (*Gutierrezia sarothrae*) and thread-leaf groundsel (*Senecio longilobus*) may become abundant with severe deterioration.

OTHER COMMUNITIES

Preclimax communities characterized by short grasses and mat-like half-shrubs are scattered as small patches throughout the Mixed Prairie. They occur on truly shallow or immature soils where thin soil mantles are underlain by impermeable materials such as consolidated rock strata or indurated caliche. Dominant grasses are hairy grama and blue grama. Associated grass species include wolftail (*Lycurus phleoides*), purple three-awn (*Aristida purpurea*), Fendler three-awn (*A. fendleriana*), hairy tridens (*Tridens pilosus*) and sand dropseed (*Sporobolus cryptandrus*). Various forbs, half-shrubs and cushion plants occur. Frequently interspersed in such areas wherever moisture supplies are enhanced by rock crevices or fractures are localized postclimax stands of grasses dominated by little bluestem, side-oats grama and New Mexico feathergrass. The latter species dominate shallow soils underlain by permeable limy materials in the eastern half of the state.

Flood plains of the Mixed Prairie in New Mexico have distinct plant communities the nature of which is dependent principally upon the relative amount of run-in water received and upon various degrees of alkalinity and salinity. The deep alluvial soils vary from loam to clay in texture but may have interspersed sand layers or surface outwash. Alkalinity and salinity varies from slight to severe. Areas having an effective high water table are rare.

Alkali sacaton (*Sporobolus airoides*) is the dominant species on the vast majority of these flood plains. Common associated species in areas where alkalinity or salinity is not prohibitive, include western wheatgrass and vine mesquite (*Panicum obtusum*). Secondary species that may increase materially with deterioration include creeping muhly (*Muhlenbergia repens*), blue grama, buffalo grass, galleta, three-awn and ringgrass (*Muhlenbergia torreyi*). The limited population of forbs includes two-grooved loco (*Astragalus bisulcatus*), Drummond milk vetch (*A. drummondi*), silky sophora (*Sophora sericea*), vetch (*Vicia americana*), peavine (*Lathyrus eucosmus*), short-rayed coneflower (*Ratibida tagetes*) and red false mallow (*Sphaeralcea coccinea*). Shrubs may be lacking although in some situations there may be scattered individuals or moderate stands of fourwing saltbush (*Atriplex canescens*) or black greasewood (*Sarcobatus vermiculatus*).

Flood plains in the northern portion of the state may be dominated by western wheatgrass in areas where alkalinity or salinity are not prohibitive. Sacaton (*Sporobolus wrightii*) occasionally dominates similar situations in the southern portion of the state, particularly on flood plains adjacent to major drainages.

Flood plains in the Canadian River valley in Quay County, although dominated by alkali sacaton in relatively undisturbed situations, may as a result of deterioration be dominated by galleta and, to a more limited extent, by tobosa (*Hilaria mutica*). Here also mesquite has invaded flood plains, lending a savannah aspect to some pastures.

Flood plains having high salt concentrations in the upper horizons of the soil profile are dominated by mixtures of alkali sacaton (*Sporobolus airoides*) and desert saltgrass (*Distichlis stricta*). Secondary grasses include scratchgrass (*Muhlenbergia asperifolia*) and Nuttall alkaligrass (*Puccinellia airoides*). Torrey seepweed (*Suaeda torreyana*) and pickleweed (*Allenrolfea occidentalis*) occur on the most alkaline spots. Black greasewood (*Sarcobatus vermiculatus*) is a common shrub component.

CHAPTER 18

The Northern Great Plains

A LARGE portion of the Great Plains extends northward from the Pine Ridge Escarpment (approximately the Nebraska-South Dakota boundary) far into Canada. It reaches from the Central Lowlands on the east to the Rocky Mountains on the west. This vast area is commonly called the Northern Great Plains and includes somewhat more than the western half of North and South Dakota, the northeast one-fourth of Wyoming, and approximately the eastern two-thirds of Montana. Only a relatively small portion (mostly eastward) is cultivated; the major part produces the nutritious native forage characteristic of mixed prairie. This portion of the Great Plains Province is the Missouri Plateau (Fig. 79).

THE MISSOURI PLATEAU

Except for the Sweetgrass Hills and Bearpaw and Little Rocky Mountains, mostly flat glacial plains lie north of the Missouri River. Here during late glacial times the hills were abraided and the valleys filled. Through a portion of these plains flows the Milk River in northern Montana, but the nearly level or rolling land extends far into Canada. Here there is little natural protection for grazing animals in winter. Although the western limit of the ice of the great glacier was nearly along the present course of the Missouri River, east of this river in the Missouri Coteau the land is hilly (Willard, 1903). Rough lands predominate in the unglaciated section of the Missouri Plateau. It has not been leveled by glacial deposits and is very different from the High Plains in that it has been deeply eroded. Natural shelter for livestock is afforded by the rough terrain; brush and some trees may occur along streams. Although spring wheat and other crops occupy rather large areas of the glacial plains, only a small part of the rough lands have known the plow. Much of the land is grazed by cattle and (formerly) by horses, but sheep also use a large part of it. As pointed out by Woolfolk (1949), the ranges are grazed for long periods each year. Sheep, especially, graze the range continuously for 9 to 11

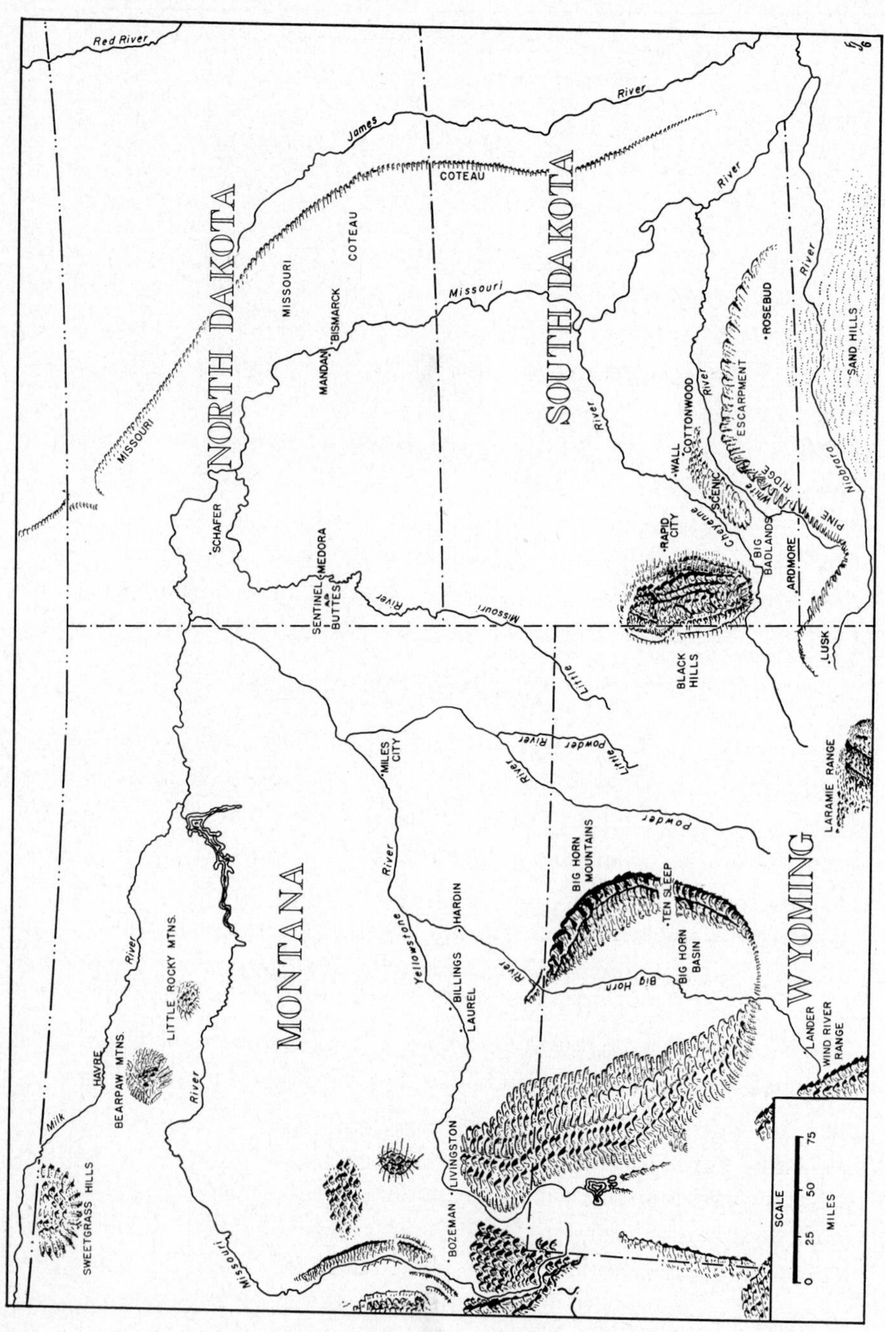

FIG. 79. Outline map of the Northern Great Plains showing locations where special studies of Mixed Prairie have been made.

months and even year-long in areas where forage is available and weather is not too severe. Although some winters are mild, some ranges are normally snow-bound for several months and "severe blizzards and ice-covered ranges have repeatedly brought financial ruin to hundreds of ranchers who were not well prepared" (Hurtt, 1950). The amount of precipitation during April and May exerts a great influence upon the production of forage. A normal rainfall during the early season practically insures a reasonable growth of native forage, even though the later rainfall is below normal. Production of hay is, in general, not great, but the cured herbage has relatively good forage value. These grasslands have now been grazed for more than three-quarters of a century; the first herds of cattle were driven northward from Texas when its vast ranges became overstocked. This is the northern portion of the world's most productive grasslands.

In addition to the Black Hills of South Dakota and Wyoming, there occur small, isolated mountain groups scattered over the western portion of the plateau. All of them are a result of the same forces which made the Rocky Mountains. Some are uplifts similar to the Black Hills, others are of volcanic origin. The steep slopes of these elevated areas (above 4,500 feet eastward and 500 feet higher in the west), like many high ridges, are covered with western yellow pine or other forest trees and shrubs. Various features of the Great Plains have been mentioned. Many of these occur on the Missouri Plateau. Those most common and covering the greatest areas are rolling topography, moderately steep hills, wide flood plains and terraces with level or gently rolling topography, and rough topography with precipitous slopes and sharply cut canyons called badlands. Badlands are rough areas in which constant erosion maintains a soil surface which is either sparsely vegetated or bare.

The Big Badlands lie southeast of the Black Hills between the White and Cheyenne Rivers (Fig. 79). Only the steep slopes are without plant cover. The flat tops or tablelands are clothed with prairie vegetation as are also many of the flat or somewhat rounded bottoms (Fig. 80). Badlands along the Little Missouri River in North Dakota form a belt 5 to 25 miles wide and nearly 200 miles in length. Here the slopes usually retain a cover of grass, as do those of many smaller badland areas which occur along portions of numerous rivers. All are a part of this great domain of grasses.

FIG. 80. (Upper) Mixed prairie on Sheep Mountain Table in western South Dakota. Vegetation is scarcely disturbed because of lack of water for livestock. (Lower) Badlands of South Dakota. Barren slopes occur in the foreground and the nearly level clay flats with a cover of grassland (dark) are several hundred feet below.

The rough and broken topography affords various plant habitats on dry ridges, xeric southern slopes, moist north hillsides and ravines, plateaus, buttes and canyons. These have furnished refuges for scattered remnants of older vegetational climaxes which have advanced and retreated with climatic pulsations during recent geological time. Species of true prairie occur in places still favorable to them, even to the western mountain border. Representative grasses and forbs of the Palouse Prairie of the far Northwest extend as far eastward as western North Dakota and the Black Hills. Over considerable portions of the plains, long continued overuse has reduced both vigor and density of the most palatable species of grasses and forbs so greatly that invasion of sagebrush (*Artemisia*), rabbitbrush (*Chrysothamnus*), and saltbush (*Atriplex*) has occurred. Their original migration from the Great Basin probably took place during a warm dry period following glacial retreat. Studies of the vegetation in various parts of the Northern Great Plains will now be described.

MIXED PRAIRIE OF NORTH DAKOTA

A half century ago when most of the Dakota grasslands were unbroken, three general types of vegetation were distinguishable. The first, true prairie, occupied and was largely confined to the valley of the Red River, an area (in North Dakota) approximately 40 to 50 miles wide. The central grassland type lay westward. It occupied the Drift Plain and extended westward approximately to the edge of that part of the Missouri Plateau designated as the Missouri Coteau. Thus, the central grassland was very much wider along the Canadian border than it was in the central and southern part of the state (Fig. 79). A third part, the western grassland type, covered the remainder of the state westward and southward.

"As one goes from east to west across the Central grassland the taller grasses [such as big bluestem and needlegrass] gradually drop out and the medium and short grasses become more important. Needle-and-thread, feather bunchgrass [green needle grass], western wheatgrass, slender wheatgrass [*Agropyron trachycaulum*], blue grama, prairie Junegrass, and Kentucky bluegrass are the dominant species throughout most of this grassland type.

"As we go toward the southwestern corner of the State across this western grassland type the rainfall decreases and the shorter grasses largely replace the taller [mid-grass] species. . . . In the Western grassland type blue grama, needle-and-thread, western wheatgrass, niggerwool (a sedge), prairie Junegrass, little bluestem, and western [Sandberg] bluegrass [*Poa secunda*] are the principal species. The first four species make up the major part of the vegetation in the typical development of this Western grassland type" (Whitman *et al.*, 1941).

Sandberg bluegrass (*Poa secunda*) is a common, perennial, and well-known bunch grass of the northern mixed prairie. The plants are commonly a foot tall and the bunches are often several inches in diameter. Like the sedges, it is a drought evader. It begins growth in spring, as soon as frost is out of the soil, when moisture is available, matures by June, and then soon dries and remains dormant during the dry part of the summer. It is an important range grass in Colorado and northward as well as in the Dakotas. It produces much seed and in this way increased its area during the great drought when later-maturing grasses decreased.

Where special soil, moisture, or topographical situations prevail, Whitman points out that distinct and characteristic types of grassland vegetation are developed. The drier ridges and knolls in the central grasslands support a vegetation essentially similar to that of normal prairie westward. Loose sandy soils and sand hills present many species common to similar areas in Nebraska, as previously described. In distinctly wet areas, such as sloughs and ditches, over the state and over the Missouri Plateau as a whole, one finds cordgrass (*Spartina pectinata*), reed canary grass (*Phalaris arundinacea*), etc. Saline soils support desert saltgrass, plains bluegrass (*Poa arida*), Nuttall alkaligrass (*Puccinellia airoides*) and other salt-tolerant species. Even in the western portion of the state, big bluestem, needlegrass, prairie dropseed and other species of both grasses and forbs of true prairie occur in moist, non-saline depressions.

STUDIES AT MANDAN

A fine tract of mixed prairie, a square mile in area, was set aside for study and experiment at Mandan just south of central North Dakota near Bismark. The land is nearly level over most of the area but partly rolling. The soil is a silty clay loam, and the precipitation averages 17.4 inches. Observations began in 1913 on the cover of climax vegetation, which had previously been mowed for hay, and continued until 1941 (Sarvis, 1920, 1923, 1941). This abstract is from his studies.

The object of the experiments was to study the influence of different systems and intensities of grazing upon the various species of plants that made up the vegetation. This involved careful consideration of both the composition and density of the plant cover. The land used is not materially different from that over vast areas in western North Dakota; although not so rough or rolling as that ordinarily used for grazing, it was well adapted for experimental purposes because of the uniformity of the soil, contour, and vegetation.

The vegetation, which makes 75 per cent of its growth during May and June, was remarkably uniform throughout the area. The dominant species of grasses and sedges were blue grama (*Bouteloua gracilis*), needle-and-thread (*Stipa comata*), thread-leaf sedge (*Carex filifolia*), and sun sedge (*C. heliophila*). These are listed in the order of their abundance as determined by their basal area in numerous quadrats. The order of the primary species was determined by count, and that of the secondary species was estimated. Scientific names are those of Sarvis with current names in brackets.

Primary Grasses

Junegrass
Koeleria cristata
Western wheatgrass
Agropyron smithii
Little bluestem
Andropogon scoparius
Green needlegrass
Stipa viridula
Red three-awn
Aristida longiseta
Needlegrass
Stipa spartea

Secondary Grasses

Plains muhly
Muhlenbergia cuspidata
Sand reed
Calamovilfa longifolia
Side-oats grama
Bouteloua curtipendula
Slender wheatgrass
Agropyron trachycaulum
Agropyron caninum
Agropyron tenerum

Primary Forbs

Prairie sage
Artemisia [*ludoviciana*] *gnaphalodes*
Gray goldenrod
Solidago [*nemoralis*] *pulcherrima*
Green sage
Artemisia [*dracunculus*] *dracunculoides*
Silver-leaf psoralea
Psoralea argophylla

Secondary Forbs

Blazing star
Lacinaria [*Liatris*] *punctata*
Bastard toad-flax
Comandra pallida
Many-flowered aster
Aster [*ericoides*] *multiflorus*
Purple prairie clover
Petalostemon purpureum
White prairie clover
Petalostemon candidum

Primary Forbs (Continued)

Fringed sage
Artemisia frigida
Purple coneflower
Echinacea angustifolia
Milkwort
Polygala alba
Prairie coneflower
Ratibida [columnifera] columnaris

Secondary Forbs (Continued)

Large-flowered blue lettuce
Lactuca pulchella
American vetch
Vicia [americana] sparsifolia
(See figure 81.)

Field determinations showed that blue grama and two sedges composed most of the ground layer, and needle-and-thread and silver-leaf psoralea the upper one. The basal cover of vegetation was 60 per cent. Blue grama composed approximately 20 per cent and needle-and-thread 10 per cent. The grasses of this region made up about 50 per cent of the dry weight of all species of plants; 90 per cent of them were palatable and afforded excellent grazing for cattle. "The composition of the native vegetation growing in the pastures . . . does not differ from that found over much of western North Dakota and adjacent portions of Montana, Wyoming, and South Dakota. The density of the vegetation [near Mandan] is somewhat higher than in some other parts of the region" (Sarvis, 1941). Of the 250 species of plants on this Northern Great Plains Field Station prairie, less than a dozen species played an important role in grazing. In 1917, for example, blue grama produced 40 to 50 per cent of the season's forage, needle-and-thread 15 to 20 per cent, and the two sedges combined somewhat less than 10 per cent.

Experiments were conducted with four pastures, of 100, 70, 50 and 30 acres, respectively, under a system of continuous grazing. Ten steers were placed in each pasture. In the 100-acre pasture only 51 per cent of the forage was removed, but 98 per cent was utilized in the 30 acre pasture. In order to avoid injury to the vegetation under a system of continuous grazing, 15 to 25 per cent of the cover must remain at the end of the grazing season. Grazing at the rate of 1 steer per 7 acres provided approximately the area of land required to produce the maximum gains per head under this system of summer grazing.

Needle-and-thread was severely damaged by the drought. Western wheatgrass, which occurred rather extensively on lower ground and was scattered over the prairie, increased greatly to become the dominant mid-

FIG. 81. (Upper) Winterfat (*Eurotia lanata*) and a legume, silky sophora (*Sophora sericea*). (Lower) A wild onion (*Allium drummondi*) and purple coneflower (*Echinacea pallida*).

grass species. Great increases of this early-growing, drought-evading grass have been recorded over thousands of square miles elsewhere (Weaver, 1942, 1943).

Grasses of lesser importance localized on certain soil types, along ravines, or in other spots suitable to their development and not yet mentioned in this square mile of prairie are listed in approximate order of abundance. The last occurred in only two or three patches.

Six-weeks fescue
Festuca octoflora
Desert saltgrass
Distichlis stricta
Canby bluegrass
Poa canbyi
Sandberg bluegrass
Poa secunda
Plains bluegrass
Poa arida
Big bluestem
Andropogon [*gerardi*] *furcatus*
Slender wheatgrass
Agropyron trachycaulum
Bearded wheatgrass
Agropyron subsecundum
Buffalo grass
Buchloe dactyloides

STUDIES NEAR SENTINEL BUTTE

Characteristics of major grassland types in western North Dakota were studied by Hanson and Whitman (1938) in the vicinity of Sentinel Butte and Medora. This is an unglaciated section of the Northern Great Plains. Because of erosion by wind and water and burning lignite veins, there is great heterogeneity in the topography. This presents very diverse habitats for vegetation, such as tops of plateaus, slopes, terraces, valleys, buttes and low hills. This is in the general region of Dark Brown soils. The average precipitation is about 15 inches, but rainfall ranges from 6 to 23 inches. About 40 per cent falls in May and June.

Thirty-six test areas, 2 to 20 acres in size and uniform in topography and vegetation, were selected. Usually they were located in winter-grazed pastures, in lightly grazed pastures, or in land adjoining cropped fields. Thus, they were free from the effects of harmful grazing, mowing, and trampling. Botanical analyses of the vegetation were made, soil profiles were described in the field, and soil samples analyzed in the laboratory. The 36 areas were then classified into 9 major vegetational types. In the following abbreviated outline of each type, the data recorded in sequence include name of type, dominant species, secondary dominants (if any), number of species and proportion of forbs, topography, kind of soil and development of profile.

1. Grama-needlegrass-sedge
Bouteloua gracilis, Stipa comata, Carex filifolia
Carex [*eleocharis*] *stenophylla, Agropyron smithii, Koeleria cristata*
Thirty-three to 53 species per sample, about three-fourths were forbs

Upland plateaus and gentle upland slopes, largely soil from residual material; profile well developed

2. Western wheatgrass-grama-sedge
   Bouteloua gracilis, Agropyron smithii, Carex filifolia
   Number of species low, 20 to 29; about three-fourths forbs
   Fairly long, gradual slopes; valley-fill deposits
   Usually clay loams, 30 per cent or more of clay and less than 40 per cent sand; profile moderately well developed
3. Little bluestem
   Andropogon scoparius
   About 50 species of which two-thirds were forbs
   Soil varied from sandy loam to silty clay; profile not well developed
4. Sandgrass
   Calamovilfa longifolia
   Carex filifolia, C. eleocharis, C. pennsylvanica, Bouteloua gracilis, Stipa comata and *Koeleria cristata*
   Moderately high number of species (35–42), about two-thirds forbs
   Sandy ridges and hills, soil apparently residual in origin; profile not well developed
5. Sagebrush
   Artemisia cana
   Agropyron smithii, Bouteloua gracilis, Stipa viridula
   Total species variable (23 to 50); 75 to 80 per cent forbs
   Flats along streams and in valleys
   Soil texture variable, mostly clay loam and clay, soil alkaline throughout; profile usually not well developed
6. Saltgrass—western wheatgrass
   Distichlis stricta, Agropyron smithii, Bouteloua gracilis
   Moderate number of species (28 to 36); three-fourths or more forbs
   Moderately low stream terraces subject to occasional flooding
   Usually silt loam; mildly alkaline; profile poorly developed
7. Saltgrass—alkali meadow grass
   Distichlis stricta, Puccinellia [*airoides*] *nuttalliana*
   Number of species low, about 80 per cent forbs
   Low stream terraces and depressions, drainage poor
   Soils loam to clay; very high salt content; profile poorly developed
8. Big bluestem
   Andropogon furcatus [*gerardi*], *A. scoparius, Sporobolus heterolepis*
   High total number of species (41 to 63); 3/4 to 4/5 forbs
   Lower parts of slopes receiving moisture in addition to direct precipitation
   Loam to sandy loam, usually 40 to 55 per cent sand; profile well developed
9. Buffalo grass (*Buchloe dactyloides*), not abundant, found in small patches on lower portions of some slopes, in small draws and depressions in some valleys, mostly on clay

Some of the findings in this study follow. In the Little Missouri country, it appears that the grama-needlegrass-sedge type on upland plateaus and gentle slopes is nearer stabilization with climatic conditions than any of the other types studied. It has had the longest time in which to reach stabilization. In years of favorable rainfall, the cover is fairly dense.

The western wheatgrass-grama-sedge type appears to be a successional stage on slopes developing in the direction of the preceding type. Since the slopes are subject to runoff, erosion, and deposition, development of both vegetation and soil is retarded. Vegetation is often sparse, especially in drought years, because these slopes tend to become deficient in soil moisture sooner than areas that are more level and contain more sand.

Little bluestem type occurs on slopes where snow drifts in and on northerly aspects of fairly steep slopes. This type is widespread. It seems to be a successional stage following erosion on many slopes. The type is of great ecological importance because it stabilizes areas subject to heavy runoff and erosion, holds drifting snow, and hastens soil development because of the numerous roots to 3.5 feet in depth and large volume of herbage.

Sandgrass type is a successional stage on sandy areas. It is apparently developing into the grama-needlegrass-sage type.

The sagebrush type, with its numerous grasses, seems to be a successional type on terraces where soil moisture is usually available in the subsoil throughout the season. As the stream erodes a deeper channel and the terrace becomes drier, type 2 or 1 may replace the sagebrush type.

The saltgrass-western wheatgrass and saltgrass-alkali meadowgrass types belong in a halosere on poorly drained or solonetz soils. The small areas of big bluestem are minute outliers of true prairie. Additional moisture to normal rainfall is received by runoff from slopes above and possibly from melting snowdrifts and seepage. Buffalo grass communities occur in secondary seres following cultivation, overgrazing, and salinization.

OTHER STUDIES

The vegetation on several sites in western North Dakota was studied by Albertson in 1954. Big Mountain Plateau, 5 miles northeast of Medora, lies within the South Unit of Theodore Roosevelt National Memorial Park. Away from the breaks, the topography was slightly rolling to nearly level. Vegetation of the sandy loam had been grazed only lightly (Fig. 82). The upper layer of vegetation was composed mostly of needle-and-

FIG. 82. (Upper) Big Mountain Plateau in background in South Roosevelt Memorial Park, North Dakota. The slopes are clothed with excellent stands of little bluestem (*Andropogon scoparius*), needle-and-thread (*Stipa comata*) and western wheatgrass (*Agropyron smithii*). (Lower) Looking westward in same general area shown above. Upland in foreground is covered with prairie vegetation; north-facing slope (extreme right) is clothed with grasses and junipers; dry south-facing slopes (center) are almost bare.

thread, green needlegrass, and western wheatgrass. Blue grama was the most abundant species in the lower layer but thread-leaf sedge was also abundant. Where the vegetation had been repeatedly grazed in spots, these two species formed most of the plant cover. Over the area as a whole the basal cover was 29 per cent.

The most abundant species of non-grasses were linear-leaved sage (*Artemisia dracunculus*), fringed sage (*A. frigida*), red false mallow (*Sphaeralcea coccinea*), many-flowered aster (*Aster ericoides*) and blazing star (*Liatris punctata*). Others of considerable abundance were cudweed sage (*Artemisia ludoviciana*), stiff sunflower (*Helianthus rigidus*), cut-leaved goldenweed (*Haplopappus spinulosus*), and velvety goldenrod (*Solidago mollis*). Others found only infrequently included purple cone-flower (*Echinacea angustifolia*), purple prairie clover (*Petalostemum purpureum*), silver-leaf psoralea (*Psoralea argophylla*), and broom snakeweed (*Gutierrezia sarothrae*).

A second study was made in the North Unit of the same park a few miles southwest of Schafer. Here the topography was quite rolling and a large variety of grasses and forbs occurred. A basal cover of about 30 per cent was composed of blue grama, needle-and-thread, Junegrass, and plains muhly (*Muhlenbergia cuspidata*). Prairie sand reed (*Calamovilfa longifolia*), little bluestem, big bluestem, western wheatgrass, and thread-leaf sedge were also present in variable amounts. Forbs were much the same as those in the South Unit, with silver-leaf psoralea, linear-leaved sage and hairy golden aster ranking highest in abundance.

The steep walls of the plateau were bare or only sparsely clothed with vegetation. The plant cover often discontinued at the top of the wall only to begin again in the broad valley at its bottom. Where foothills occurred, the south-facing slopes were clothed with an open cover of grasses and forbs. The north-facing slopes presented a different environment and a different type of vegetation. Here an understory of grasses developed beneath an open canopy of pine, junipers, and other evergreen trees.

An interesting account of the vegetation on scoria and clay buttes in western North Dakota is given by Whitman and Hanson (1939). They have also studied the "scabby spots" or "slick-spots" (solodized solonetz complexes) which produce the pitted nature of the landscape of western North Dakota and which also occur widely over the plains, extending into

Canada. In the aggregate they occur on thousands of acres. The stages in the revegetation of the bare pits have been described (Hanson and Whitman, 1937).

Changes in native vegetation on grazed ranges in western North Dakota were determined by Whitman, Hanson and Peterson (1943) over a 10-year period beginning in 1932. During the first half of this period there was considerable deterioration, mostly as a result of drought but partly because of heavy grazing. Blue grama was reduced in density about 64 per cent and needle-and-thread about 53 per cent. Western wheatgrass was reduced in abundance 67 per cent and Junegrass 33 per cent. Little bluestem decreased in abundance 74 per cent and sand reed 33 per cent. Thread-leaf sedge maintained its area and needle-leaf sedge increased in abundance.

Western wheatgrass, which at first occurred only in occasional, scattered bunches, increased so extensively that it composed 1 to 2 per cent of the cover of upland ranges. Density of the range grassland, about 30 per cent in 1933, was reduced to 13 per cent in 1936.

After 1936, the vegetation showed continued improvement. Cessation of drought and removal of large numbers of livestock from the region were the causes of the improvement. Recovery of the grassland vegetation was comparatively rapid. Drought injury was not so severe in western North Dakota as it was in Montana and in the central and southern Great Plains. Average grazing capacity of the western North Dakota range is about 26 acres per animal unit.

CHAPTER 19

Grasslands of South Dakota

GRASSLAND is of vital importance to the welfare of the Dakotas. The range area of South Dakota includes approximately 30 million acres, about 75 per cent of which is being grazed (Johnson *et al.*, 1951). West of the Missouri River in South Dakota, 80 per cent of the area is grassland, and 14 counties just east of this river have an average of more than 50 per cent of the land in grass (Franzke and Hume, 1942).

GENERAL DESCRIPTION

"While short-grasses were originally present in the eastern part of the state, species of this group were dominants only in the 'mixed prairie' of central and western South Dakota. Short-grasses make up the greatest area of the grass vegetation over a large portion of the 'mixed prairie' where overgrazing long prevailed and where rainfall and evaporation are less favorable to the growth of mid-grasses. . . . Mid grasses have been dominants, along with short-grasses, in the 'mixed prairie' of central and western South Dakota. . . . Too close grazing here has favored the short-grasses at the expense of the taller growing species. . . . When grazing pressure is relieved and normal or excess rainfall exists, mid-grasses are able to compete with the short-grasses on even terms, and may even completely dominate them. Localized heavy grazing, together with the dry cycle of the last decade, has favored the short-grasses to the extent that they are found as dominants on many ranges and pastures throughout South Dakota excepting the extreme southeastern corner" (Franzke and Hume, 1942).

An excellent description of the early conditions for grazing in the Northern Great Plains in western South Dakota, northwestern Nebraska, eastern Wyoming, eastern Montana and western North Dakota is given by Black *et al.* (1937). "During the early years of the settlement of this region, range management was relatively simple. Settlement was not dense enough to limit the amount of range available, and cattle were moved about according to their needs. In the spring they were taken to upland pastures away from the principal water courses. This was done for two reasons: (1) owing partly to the carry-over of cured grasses, pasture was available on them earlier than on lowlands; and (2) water was usually present on these uplands in the spring, but was not available later in the season. The cattle were moved from one place to another as the feed became too short for profitable grazing. Lowlands and the uplands which were near watercourses were kept for winter pasture and for use when no water was available on the uplands away from watercourses. Lowland meadows were used for producing hay for winter use."

BLACK HILLS AREA

The grassland climax in and adjacent to the Black Hills was studied in fourteen separate areas by Hayward (1928). The mid-grass dominants were *Koeleria cristata, Stipa comata, Agropyron smithii* and *A. spicatum* (bluebunch wheatgrass). Junegrass was the most abundant; *Stipa viridula* (green needlegrass) was occasionally found with *Stipa comata; Agropyron* was much less common than either *Koeleria* or *Stipa.* In the short-grass layer *Buchloe dactyloides* was most abundant with *Bouteloua gracilis* ranking second. *Carex eleocharis* and *C. filifolia* occurred in most of the areas examined.

Tall grasses were represented by *Andropogon gerardi* and *Calamovilfa longifolia.* Other mid grasses of mixed prairie were *Andropogon scoparius, Aristida longiseta, A. fendleriana,* and *Sitanion hystrix.* Grassland seemed able to maintain itself against invasion of chaparral or woodland only where the rainfall did not exceed 18 inches.

In greatly overgrazed areas south and west of the Black Hills grasses of mixed prairie had largely been replaced by invading sage and other species common to the Great Basin. Conspicuous and often abundant shrubs were big sage (*Artemisia tridentata*), sand sage (*A. filifolia*), silver sage (*A. cana*) and fringed sage (*A. frigida*). Here rabbitbrush (*Chrysothamnus graveolens*) and broom snakeweed (*Gutierrezia sarothrae*) furnished abundant evidence of overstocking. Black greasewood (*Sarcobatus vermiculatus*) occurred in saline soil. Similar disclimax areas occurred in adjacent northwest Nebraska and especially in east-central Wyoming.

North of the Black Hills, especially in South Dakota but also in Montana, western wheatgrass with its understory of blue grama and buffalo grass is characterized by an abundance of silvery saltweed (*Atriplex argentea*) and various kinds of sages.

SAND HILLS AND BRULE CLAY

The northern border of the Nebraska Sand Hills not only extends north of the Niobrara River but also occurs in the southern half of four bordering counties in South Dakota. The sand-hill communities in the vicinity of Rosebud, South Dakota (Todd County), about 100 miles west of the Missouri River, and two types of mixed prairie were studied by Tolstead (1941). The distribution of communities on upland was determined by the efficiency of the absorption of the summer rainfall by the several types of soil. Local areas of dune sand were covered with postclimax grasses and forbs, like those described in the Nebraska Sand Hills. Climax communities of fine sandy loam soils (from Tertiary limy sandstones) were dominated by needle-and-thread, thread-leaved sedge, and blue grama. Western wheatgrass, buffalo grass, purple three-awn, sand dropseed and tumblegrass were all less abundant. Silt loam soils derived from Brule clay covered the level land, low rolling hills and narrow valleys stretching far northward from Rosebud. They presented an area of the western wheatgrass-buffalo grass-blue grama type to be described. These grasses were accompanied by needle-leaf sedge. Here needle-and-thread and thread-leaf sedge were secondary species. Western wheatgrass also dominated in well watered, broad, shallow ravines. Little bluestem occurred on lower moist slopes of north hillsides, and side-oats grama was common on rough, stony land.

Extreme drought (1935 to 1937) reduced the basal cover in the *Stipa-Carex-Bouteloua* community 55 per cent and that of the *Agropyron-Buchloe-Bouteloua* type 73 per cent. (See figure 83.)

BUFFALO GRASS AND WESTERN WHEATGRASS

Buffalo grass is of greatest abundance in an area including several counties east and south of the Black Hills. It is an important dominant west of the Missouri River, except in the two large northwestern counties, and also occurs as a chief species eastward. Blue grama occurs throughout and is usually the most important grass of the understory.

Western wheatgrass is one of the general dominants everywhere but is especially abundant over a broad area nearly half the width of the state and extending from the Black Hills to the Missouri River, especially on heavy soils. Shantz (1924) described it as follows: "This grassland is characterized by an even sod of grama and buffalo grasses and a scattered growth of western wheatgrass (*Agropyron smithii*). During favorable years, when the wheatgrass fruits abundantly, prairie hay is cut from this type. It presents a more luxuriant appearance than pure short-grass and produces a heavier crop of forage. As a rule it contains few non-grasslike plants, and often occurs as a practically pure cover. This type is distributed over the unusually heavy gumbo soils derived from Fort Pierre shales in South Dakota."

Moisture from the 15- to 20-inch rainfall penetrates only slowly in the clay soil, as is shown by lime accumulations, usually in the second foot. Most grasses thrive less well here than on loam soils. Usually available soil moisture is exhausted by the wheatgrass and short grasses by mid or late summer and a period of dormancy ensues.

Because homesteaders fenced much of the land, the open range became inadequate. Grasses were closely grazed over the entire region and great injury resulted to the vegetation. To meet the need for reliable information on the effects of different methods of grazing of the native vegetation, several Dry Land Field Experiment Stations were established in the Northern Great Plains, one at Ardmore in southwestern South Dakota. These stations have furnished valuable information on the various types of native vegetation, their forage value, best season for use, and their behavior under grazing.

USE OF GRASSES FOR HAY

Blue grama, western wheatgrass, and buffalo grass are all abundant in South Dakota. They are examples of grasses which cure well when overtaken by cold or drought. They retain much of their nutrient properties and furnish excellent winter pasture. The pioneers mowed the grasses in late summer or fall for hay to be used only when the range was covered with snow. Western wheatgrass hay is very nutritious. Experiments at Ardmore, South Dakota, have shown that a ration of 15 pounds of this hay was as satisfactory as a similar quantity of alfalfa hay for wintering yearling steers (Black and Mathews, 1930). It has recently been ascertained by Moxon *et al.* (1951) that hay cut in autumn contained only 50 to 70 per cent as much protein as hay mowed in mid-July. Early

FIG. 83. (Upper) Plains milkweed (*Asclepias pumila*) in fruit, and (lower) prickly poppy (*Argemone intermedia*) with large white flowers.

cutting also yielded more dry matter and more protein per acre than hay cut late. When the hay was raked into windrows and compared with the standing grass samples, it was found that, in general, the crude protein and phosphorus content of the windrowed hay remained unchanged, but it declined in the samples from unmowed grass. Average yields of early-cut hay had over 400 pounds more dry matter and about 50 pounds more protein per acre than late-cut hay.

Western wheatgrass makes its best growth in lowlands; on flat lands that are occasionally flooded extensively, nearly pure stands are produced. Good stands occur also on upland in heavy soil; but more usually it has an understory of short grasses, although forbs are less abundant in areas with wheatgrass than in most other types. This is not due to shading but to an early use of the available water by this rapidly growing cool-season grass (Weaver, 1942).

Western wheatgrass is much less preferred by livestock than the short grasses; it can not withstand early and close clipping or grazing, as do buffalo grass and blue grama. It is readily eaten by livestock when other grasses are scarce. When mowed it furnishes the greatest yields of hay. Conversely, the short grasses yield much hay only on wet years, but they are highly preferred for grazing by cattle and are harmed only when excessively grazed.

In the heavily grazed pastures about Ardmore, and over extensive areas elsewhere, the preceding grasses and plains bluegrass (*Poa arida*) often furnish 85 to 90 per cent of the forage (Black *et al.*, 1937). The original mid grasses—needle-and-thread, Junegrass, green needlegrass, squirreltail, and others—have nearly disappeared, as have also most of the edible forbs.

VEGETATION IN THE BADLANDS

A study of relic grasslands on an isolated mesa on Medicine Butte in South Dakota was made by Larson and Whitman (1942). This butte, with slopes so steep that livestock could not gain access to its top, is located on the eastern edge of the Badlands about 85 miles southeast of Rapid City (Fig. 79). The vegetation of this area, about 6 acres in extent, was examined and compared with that on two larger adjacent tablelands of similar elevation, about 3,000 feet. The three areas presented the following conditions: "An area in the mixed prairie association which apparently had never been grazed by livestock nor subject to any use by

man. . . . One had moderate intermittent use recently and probably was used slightly in the past. The other has had continuous use for 40 years and undoubtedly was subjected to varying degrees of grazing prior to that time either by livestock or wild animals."

Dominants of the protected mesa were western wheatgrass, needle-leaf sedge (*Carex eleocharis*), penn sedge, blue grama, thread-leaf sedge and needle-and-thread. The following occurred in smaller amounts: side-oats grama, green needlegrass, red three-awn, little bluestem, and big bluestem. The short grasses and sedges composed 60 per cent of the cover and the mid grasses 40 per cent. Forbs and woody plants were unimportant.

The dominant species of the mesa vegetation used intermittently were much the same as those on the protected area. There were differences in relative amounts of species, and distribution was less uniform. Western wheatgrass and blue grama were dominants of about equal importance. Sedges were next in abundance, and needle-and-thread ranked nearly as high. Short grasses and sedges composed about 45 per cent of the cover and the taller grasses about 50 per cent. Forbs and woody plants were of appreciable importance. Yield of forage was more than a ton per acre and almost equal to that of the protected mesa. It was only about three-fourths as great on the area under continuous use.

The vegetation used continuously was of the short-grass type. Western wheatgrass and needle-and-thread made up only about 5 per cent of the cover but blue grama and the sedges 90 per cent. No bluestems were found. Forbs and woody plants composed only a minor part of the vegetation.

Vegetation on three widely separated upland sites in the National Badlands Monument were studied by Albertson and Tomanek in 1954. The first was 15 miles southeast of Wall. On the level upland a vegetal mulch 2 to 3 inches thick indicated that the cover had not been removed for a long time. A basal cover of 39 per cent was found. The species composing the cover and their percentage composition were as follows: needle-and-thread 28, western wheatgrass 3, and green needlegrass 7 per cent. Thread-leaf sedge furnished 9 per cent, buffalo grass 21, and blue grama, 32. Thus, the short-grass life form composed 62 and mid grasses 38 per cent (Fig. 84).

On gentle slopes the same species occurred but the composition of the vegetation was different and the basal cover was only 21 per cent. Here

FIG. 84. (Upper) Ungrazed mixed prairie in climax condition. Prominent bunches in foreground are well-developed thread-leaf sedge (*Carex filifolia*) but the general understory is blue grama and buffalo grass. Western wheatgrass is the chief mid grass. (Lower) General view of mixed prairie near Hot Springs, South Dakota. Western wheatgrass (*Agropyron smithii*) and green needlegrass (*Stipa viridula*) are chief species in the foreground. A nearly pure stand of little bluestem occurs on northwest-facing slopes.

western wheatgrass was most abundant (62 per cent). Needle-and-thread furnished only 6 per cent, and green needlegrass about 1, making a total cover of 69 per cent mid grasses. Thread-leaf sedge (14 per cent), buffalo grass (10), and blue grama (7) composed the 31 per cent furnished by the understory.

On Sheep Mountain, about 12 miles southwest of Scenic, a fifty-acre tract had been ungrazed or very lightly grazed for years. This slightly rolling upland sloped gently southeastward. Basal cover was 25 per cent and percentage composition of the vegetation was as follows:

Species	%	Species	%
Needle-and-thread	26	Blue grama	36
Western wheatgrass	19	Thread-leaf sedge	5
Sand dropseed	2	Buffalo grass	2
Little bluestem	2	Penn sedge	5
Purple three-awn	1	Other species	2
Total	50		50

Thus, the vegetation here and on the first level upland described did not vary greatly. The preceding localities, like the following, were on mellow silt loam soil. Moreover, forbs were the same in both places. Most abundant species were fringed sage (*Artemisia frigida*), red false mallow (*Sphaeralcea coccinea*), cut-leaved goldenweed (*Haplopappus spinulosus*), false boneset (*Kuhnia eupatorioides*) and plains milkweed (*Asclepias pumila*). The following were of less abundance but common: cudweed sage (*Artemisia ludoviciana*), many-flowered aster (*Aster ericoides*), scarlet gaura (*Gaura coccinea*), many-spined cactus (*Opuntia polyacantha*), silver-leaf psoralea (*Psoralea argophylla*), prairie turnip (*P. esculenta*), large-bracted psoralea (*P. cuspidata*) and low milk vetch (*Astragalus lotiflorus*).

On a rolling upland 10 miles southwest of Wall, vegetation had been grazed closely for so long a time that it had undergone great change. This short-grass disclimax had a basal cover of 46 per cent. Buffalo grass and blue grama composed 63 and 32 per cent of the cover, respectively. There was about 4 per cent western wheatgrass, no needle-and-thread and mere traces of a few other species. Vegetal mulch was almost absent and only a few of the preceding forbs occurred.

Experiments at Cottonwood in west-central South Dakota at the Cottonwood Range Field Station have demonstrated clearly the serious effect that over-utilization has on subsequent foliage production and consequently on livestock as well (Johnson *et al.* 1951). "It was shown that continued heavy grazing reduced range condition from 70 per cent in 1942 to 50 per cent in 1949. Under moderate grazing, range condition remained about the same, whereas under light grazing an improvement took place with an increase in range condition from 73 per cent in 1942 to 82 per cent in 1949."

During years of average rainfall (14.7 inches) on the dense, slowly permeable, silty clay loam to heavy clay soils, it has been ascertained that 15 to 16 acres of range land are required to support a cow and calf for the seven months grazing period. This is a smaller area than is necessary westward under decreased rainfall.

The total annual foliage utilization under heavy, moderate, and light intensities of grazing (as determined by clipped plots) averaged 63, 46, and 37 per cent, respectively, over a period of nine years. Average amount of air-dry foliage produced per year from 1942 to 1950 was 1,262 pounds per acre in heavily grazed pastures, 1,571 pounds in pastures moderately grazed, but 2,046 pounds in pastures lightly grazed.

"An annual removal of only 40 to 55 per cent [by weight] of the available foliage was the maximum utilization rate under which the range vegetation could be maintained." Thus was developed the slogan "Graze half and leave half, and the half grazed becomes larger and larger." The preceding data are from Johnson *et al.* (1951).

Results from these and other highly valuable experiments if used widely may yet save the mixed prairie from extreme deterioration. It is becoming generally known that grassland in good or excellent condition can produce more forage year after year at less cost than ranges in fair or poor condition. A survey was made of representative commercial cattle ranches in the Great Plains section of Colorado and New Mexico to determine the influence of range condition on production of market livestock (McCorkle and Heerwagen, 1951). The measure used for ranch production was the total weight of livestock marketed. The ranches averaging good condition marketed an average of 14.3 pounds of cattle per acre; those averaging fair condition 11.2 pounds; and those averaging poor condition only 8.9 pounds. Moreover, "the better condition ranches have improved to such an extent that the forage production is increased. These ranches are stocked on the basis of forage production, not to maintain a fixed rate of stocking."

OTHER GRASSLANDS

Aside from the grasslands discussed—Black Hills, Sand Hills, Badlands, and wheatgrass and buffalo grass areas on heavy clay soils—the main area of mixed prairie is found elsewhere throughout the State, extending nearly to the James River eastward. It is variable but not complex in composition. More than 90 per cent of the native grassland forage is composed of less than a dozen grasses and sedges. The most abundant are blue grama, western wheatgrass, buffalo grass, needle-and-thread, thread-leaf sedge, Sandberg bluegrass, and sun sedge (*Carex heliophila*). Other species of less abundance, in part due to overgrazing, are side-oats grama, Junegrass, green needlegrass and little bluestem. Numerous minor species occur. The list does not include tall, postclimax prairie grasses:

Kentucky bluegrass	Sand dropseed
Canby bluegrass	Needle-leaf sedge
Plains bluegrass	Penn sedge
Canada bluegrass	Various wheatgrasses
Plains muhly	Six-weeks fescue

All of the preceding species are also found in North Dakota. They occur in many groupings according to local environmental conditions, stages in succession and past and present usage. In wet places and saline areas the vegetation is almost identical with that found in similar habitats in North Dakota. Forbs in mowed prairie and in excellent and good ranges normally make up less than 15 per cent of the total composition of these grasslands.

CHAPTER 20

Grasslands of Montana and Wyoming

Over this great area, except for small groups of isolated mountain ranges, mixed prairie prevails. Long periods of overgrazing have reduced nearly all of the vegetation to a disclimax type.

VEGETATION AND ENVIRONMENT

Blue grama is the chief short grass throughout; buffalo grass occurs sparingly and only, in any abundance, south of the Yellowstone River. It is of secondary importance in Montana except in one southeastern county (Carter) and nowhere attains the dominance shown in eastern Colorado and Kansas. Southward in Wyoming it is present, but of secondary or minor importance except in the eastern part of the state (Wenger, 1943). The place of this grass in the understory is taken by various low-growing sedges and by certain bluegrasses. As in the Dakotas, the many groupings of cool- and warm-season grasses give Montana and Wyoming a reputation for high quality forage. Many areas have been so abused by long periods of overgrazing that they have been invaded by various sages (*Artemisia*), shadscale (*Atriplex*), rabbitbrush (*Chrysothamnus*), and other shrubs characteristic of the Great Basin southwestward (Clements and Clements, 1939).

In the sagebrush type an understory of blue grama is nearly always present except in the most heavily used places, but the overtopping shrubs, especially big sagebrush, determine the aspects or general physiognomy. Costello (1944b) listed the important grasses of the big sagebrush type in east-central Wyoming "where it dovetails with the short-grass type . . . or in many instances assumes the nature of a gradual transition, with the short-grasses prevailing as an understory beneath the sagebrush." Chief species were blue grama, western wheatgrass, needle-and-thread and plains bluegrass (*Poa arida*). Other species were thread-leaf sedge, June-grass, and bluebunch wheatgrass.

In both Montana and Wyoming big sage is the most conspicuous plant and gives character to the landscape over hundreds of square miles (Fig. 85). The most extensive areas occur on heavy clay soils. It is an invader which spreads according to the degree in which the native grasses are killed by grazing. This has resulted in greatly decreasing the grazing capacity. Sagebrush itself provides little forage except in winter when heavy snows occasionally cover the grass. Along the Little Powder River

FIG. 85. Big sage (*Artemisia tridentata*) with the understory of grasses practically all grazed out. Photo by U.S. Forest Service.

in northeastern Wyoming and adjacent Montana, for example, Allred (1941a) describes the big sage. "*Artemisia tridentata* forms a great savannah with the grasses. It is disclimax but has gained precedence on some of the ranges when the grasses became depleted through overuse by livestock. It also thrives on flood plains and on soils with favorable moisture values, such as north hillsides. It is sometimes dominant in plant communities found in moderately salty, lowland basins. In these sites low in soil moisture it survives by developing a low scrub form . . . *Artemisia cana* grows on the better watered flood plains and drainages."

These species and many others have become more abundant because of continued extremely close use of the better grasses and shrubs by livestock and rodents.

"The experimental area, near Lander, is typical of much of the sagebrush-grassland in Wyoming between the elevation of 5,500 and 7,500 feet (Fig. 79). The general aspect is dominated by sagebrush with an all-age stand which averages 25 to 30 plants per 100 square feet. Other shrubby species include occasional plants of small rabbitbrush (*Chrysothamnus* sp.) and spineless horsebrush (*Tetradymia canescens* var. *inermis*). There is a fair to good herbaceous understory of thickspike wheatgrass (*Agropyron dasystachyum*) and streambank wheatgrass (*A. riparium*) with lesser amounts of bluebunch wheatgrass (*A. spicatum*), Cusick bluegrass (*Poa cusickii*), Sandberg bluegrass (*P. secunda*), and needle-and-thread (*Stipa comata*). Forbs are infrequent and produce little palatable forage" (Hull *et al.*, 1952).

"While the Great Plains area in Colorado extends eastward from the foothills of the Rocky Mountains, in Wyoming it extends eastward from the broad transition zone between sagebrush and short-grass which passes in a north-south direction through the east-central portion of the state" (Costello, 1944b). In Montana the western boundary is again the Rocky Mountains. As mapped by Shantz (1924) this is the blue grama region with large inclusions of western wheatgrass and sagebrush.

"This grassland occupies a soil which is very shallow, ranging in depth from 8 to 18 inches to the layer of carbonate accumulation, below which is a permanently dry subsoil. The soil moisture available during normal years is equivalent to form 1.5 to 2.5 inches in rainfall, the supply being replenished by occasional rains during the period of plant growth" (Shantz, 1923). The soils, which belong to the Northern Dark Brown and Northern Brown Zonal groups, have developed in a semiarid climate under a somewhat sparse vegetation; though shallow and light colored they are relatively rich in nutrients. With adequate moisture they produce highly nutritious vegetation. Although the growing season is short, 80 to perhaps 120 days, it is not low temperatures but lack of available water that causes the cessation of growth; the growing season is generally terminated by drought. Precipitation is only about 17 inches in grasslands of Wyoming and the eastern portion of Montana but 22 inches in the prairies at higher altitudes westward in Montana. However, it is only about 7 to 11 inches in the driest areas. The climate is cool and the rate of evaporation is low.

The most important species of the Montana-northeastern Wyoming area are, at present, blue grama, western wheatgrass, needle-and-thread, thread-leaf sedge, green needlegrass, sandberg bluegrass, and bluebunch wheatgrass. Junegrass, sand dropseed, little bluestem, plains muhly, buffalo grass, various dryland sedges, and several bluegrasses are also of considerable importance. As we shall see, there are many others. Important browse species are big sage (*Artemisia tridentata*), fringed sage (*A. frigida*), fourwing saltbush (*Atriplex canescens*), shadscale (*Atriplex confertifolia*), winterfat (*Eurotia lanata*) and black greasewood (*Sarcobatus vermiculatus*) (Jameson, 1952). Many mid grasses, such as Junegrass, plains bluegrass, western wheatgrass, and needle-and-thread, show a strong tendency to increase under moderate grazing during a series of wet years and this may occur to such a degree that the layer of short grasses are more or less obscured. Moreover, it is in ranges only moderately grazed where mid grasses are most plentiful. Conversely, especially in highly erodable soils, heavy grazing and consequent erosion may remove practically all the other vegetation, leaving only the big sage and other shrubs.

TOPOGRAPHY, SOILS, AND GRAZING TYPES

Extensive studies on the Northern Great Plains have been made near the Yellowstone River at Miles City, Montana (Fig. 79). Woolfolk (1949) presents the following data on the topography, soils, and vegetation of the four typical areas (a total of more than 1,600 acres) included in the experimental ranges studied. These are representative of a large part of the Northern Great Plains.

1. Well-drained sandy clay loams on rolling topography, with high water-absorbing capacity and normally moderately moist well into the growing season. Chief grasses were blue grama, western wheatgrass, thread-leaf sedge and needle-and-thread. Other species were scarlet globemallow, prairie clover, biscuitroot, and species of plantain. Big sage was common and fringed sage and cactus were frequently present. The average surface cover was 25 to 35 per cent.

2. Sandy to gravelly loam soils on moderately steep topography with high water-absorbing capacity and low runoff. These soils dry out rather

rapidly. Chief grasses were bluebunch wheatgrass (*Agropyron spicatum*), side-oats grama, needle-and-thread, western wheatgrass, stonyhills muhly (*Muhlenbergia cuspidata*) and blue grama. Chief other species were scarlet globemallow, lupine, licorice, skunkbush sumac (*Rhus trilobata*), and small soapweed. Average surface cover was 20 to 25 per cent.

3. Flood plains of the major streams, with level or gently rolling topography and generally heavy, and frequently alkaline, clay soils. Chief grasses were western wheatgrass (most abundant), buffalo grass, green needlegrass, sandberg bluegrass and blue grama (on drier edges). Forbs were few, silver sage was frequently present. The surface cover was 33 to 50 per cent.

4. Heavy, often alkaline, soils, sometimes rocky locally—gumbo soils with high runoff and slow water absorption on rough topography with precipitous slopes and sharply cut canyons. Vegetation was sparse; the chief grasses were western wheatgrass, bluebunch wheatgrass, blue grama, alkali sacaton (*Sporobolus airoides*). Other species, scarlet globemallow, dwarf phlox, and evening primrose (*Oenothera*), composed a small percentage of the vegetation; big sagebrush, black greasewood, greenplume rabbitbrush (*Chrysothamnus nauseosus*), winterfat (*Eurotia lanata*) and shadscale saltbush (*Atriplex confertifolia*) made up the remainder.

Woolfolk points out that the rolling, grass-covered areas (type 1), which characterize large sections of the Northern Great Plains, have the highest grazing value. This is not only because such areas produce a great amount and variety of forage but also because they are best adapted to summer and fall grazing owing to the abundance of the late-starting blue grama and the variety of herbaceous plants which are green and succulent in summer. Moreover, the perennial grasses cure well on the ground and furnish good fall and winter grazing. The first green forage in spring appears in the hilly areas (type 2). These ranges are most valuable either as early spring or winter range, when sheep may eat the old forage of the previous summer's crop. The flood plains (type 3) are best suited to summer grazing; the vegetation remains green longer than on other areas and water for the grazing animals is often available. Extensive use of the rough lands (type 4) is prevented in summer by scarcity of stock water; the steep topography and sticky gumbo soil make them unsuitable for spring pasture. Hills provide protection against storms in winter, and browse species in winter furnish excellent food of high protein content.

SEASONAL GROWTH AND SEASONAL USE

In this semiarid region, of 10 to 16 inches rainfall with great annual fluctuations, determination of the proper degree of grazing the vegetation is an important but difficult problem. During dry years the range is often too closely grazed but in good years much herbage may be left uneaten. In a seven-year study of this problem in eastern Montana, the distribution of the various species, their season of growth, and season of use were thoroughly examined (Holscher and Woolfolk, 1953). Since this study gives such a valuable insight into the nature of the vegetation, a portion of their work has been abstracted.

Western wheatgrass, the most abundant species, had a wide range of adaptability. It usually occurred less frequently on the rolling uplands and was characteristic of heavy soils. Here it grew with buffalo grass, which occurred much less frequently than wheatgrass elsewhere. Conversely, blue grama was generally distributed throughout the lighter and better drained soil; it rarely grew on the heavy soils. Needle-and-thread, which was closely associated with blue grama, was somewhat more restricted to sandy, well-drained soils. This was true also of thread-leaf sedge. Sandberg bluegrass showed little regard for topography, soil type, or associated species. It was well distributed throughout.

The growing season usually begins late in March or early April. Sandberg bluegrass and thread-leaf sedge begin growth as soon as day temperatures rise well above freezing. They are ready for grazing early in April and by mid-April they produce much highly palatable forage. Western wheatgrass and needle-and-thread require slightly warmer weather. These grasses develop rapidly under maximum day temperatures of 70° F., in late April and early May. The bluegrass and sedge blossom and produce seed early and become dormant when hot weather begins. They are grazed intensively until mid-May when the cattle begin to graze the new growth of wheatgrass.

The warm-season grasses, blue grama and buffalo grass, renew growth much later. Usually not until late May do the short grasses and needle-and-thread begin to furnish considerable amounts of forage. Except where wheatgrass occurs in thick stands, its use is generally reduced by the presence of the short-grasses or needle-and-thread. During May and June, the two months of greatest rainfall, vegetation makes its most rapid development. July and August are usually hot and dry, and there is normally little plant development in August. Growth is usually terminated by summer drought.

In fall, needle-and-thread and wheatgrass both become green if soil moisture is available. They continue to furnish considerable forage into the fall and winter. The cured blue grama furnishes good winter grazing, but it is of such low stature that it is covered with only a few inches of snow. Western wheatgrass is the only grass that consistently provides winter forage. It is during winter that browse plants such as silver sage (*Artemisia cana*), big sage (*A. tridentata*) and others are utilized. "Although the bulk of the forage in the Northern Great Plains is provided by only a few species, mainly grasses, no single species can be designated as the most important because each is a part of the vegetation that composes the range and helps provide forage" (Holscher and Woolfolk, 1953).

About 31 acres per cow per year is recommended as a basis for proper stocking on northern short-grass or mixed-prairie ranges by Hurtt (1951) and by Holscher and Woolfolk (1953).

DROUGHT AND GRASSHOPPERS

Drought often stalks the Northern Great Plains. This is true even when dry years are separated from those of drought. In east-central Montana the average rainfall is only about 13 inches. If the 9.18-inch spring-summer average is reduced to less than 70 per cent (6.4 inches) the effects upon vegetation are usually so serious as to cause a drought. Distribution of the rainfall may, of course, be a deciding factor. These data by Hurtt (1951) were ascertained by a study of rainfall at Miles City for the 62-year period preceding 1940. He states: "The semiarid climate imposes a very delicate balance between favorable and unfavorable growing conditions. A small decline below average annual precipitation may result in reduced growth or even in total failure of all but the most drought-resistant forage plants."

In the great drought of 1934, the summer rainfall was only 3.5 inches. The drought was accompanied by the highest monthly temperatures ever experienced at Miles City, where Ellison and Woolfolk (1937) studied its effects, mostly on moderately grazed land. Herbaceous vegetation reached its maximum development and summer dormancy began about a month earlier than in the preceding and following more normal years. Blue grama and western wheatgrass grew only one-third and three-fifths as tall, respectively, as usual. Decrease in density of various grasses was ascertained from 55 permanent, square-meter quadrats in 1935. It was between 62 and 79 per cent for blue grama, western wheatgrass, buffalo grass and needle-and-thread. Thread-leaf sedge lost 12 per cent. Sandberg bluegrass (*Poa secunda*) actually increased 179 per cent. This bluegrass seemed to profit most from late fall (1934) and early spring (1935) growth. Unfortunately this grass flowers and becomes dormant so quickly that it does not actually compensate for the loss of more stable species. Needle-and-thread produced large numbers of deeply rooted seedlings in 1935. Silver sage (*Artemisia cana*), although found on uplands, was most abundant in coulees and bottoms. In some instances three-fifths of the plants were killed back to the ground, only one per cent of the original volume was replaced the following year. Big sage died when the plants were killed to the ground. Such loss was not infrequent. "The sagebrush [big sage] outposts [in grassland] are the most severely stricken and some whole stands of this drought-resistant species have been practically wiped out, and the result is a shrinking of the frayed edges of the stand toward sites where it is able to maintain itself compactly." These excellent data are from Ellison and Woolfolk (1937).

Frequently drought is accompanied by infestation of grasshoppers, often in almost unbelievable numbers. Allred (1941a) describes the coincidence of a severe drought and a grasshopper plague in 1936 on a 40-mile strip of drainage area of the Little Powder River in northeast Wyoming and part of Montana. Grasshoppers had been abundant in the area during the five preceding years, but there was usually enough grass to feed upon and the less desirable big sage was not eaten. "In 1936 . . . grasshoppers swarmed in such hordes that they devoured all of the edible vegetation, ate the leaves and bark from the twigs of the sagebrush, and completely girdled the more tender stems. . . . The insects occupied this area [during the nymphal stage of development] in numbers from 50 to 100 per square foot." This was the year of greatest drought; the grass made practically no growth, and the grasshoppers were forced to eat sagebrush. On a similar area a few miles southeastward, where the drought was as intense as that on the Little Powder River but where there was only a minor infestation of grasshoppers, only 15 per cent of the sagebrush was killed.

The loss of big sage averaged 50 per cent of the plants. Losses increased as the herbaceous cover was greater (72 per cent of the plant density) and decreased wherever the cover of grass was less (30 per cent). Losses also varied with differences in soil, from 15 per cent on fine sandy loams to 59 per cent on heavy clay soils. "These data indicate that the grasses are better equipped than sagebrush to survive the damaging effects of drought and grasshopper infestation." Grasshoppers roost on sagebrush on warm nights and seek their shade and graze on them during the heat of the day. Where the grasses are thick and the sagebrush sparse, grasshoppers generally concentrate in the grass but also practically destroy the scattered sagebrush when they are roosting or resting on it. Thus, grasshoppers abetted the destruction of the sagebrush during the critical period of drought, whereas the sage would have largely withstood drought alone.

Seldom a series of 5 years goes by in Northern Great Plains without a year of drought or at least a very dry year. This makes the management of the ranges a difficult problem. Extensive studies at Miles City, Montana, have been made on managing ranges to minimize the effects of drought. "As the first of the two most severe drought years of record struck in eastern Montana, range vegetation showed unmistakable signs of impending disaster. Poor color, short growth, and early curing characterized plant development in 1934. By early July scanty vegetation on many ranges threatened livestock with starvation. In 1936 available range forage, largely old vegetation carried over from the 1935 production, rapidly disappeared as hordes of grasshoppers invaded the range. It was necessary to remove experimental cattle from the summer pastures in early August . . . By early summer in 1937 less than 10 per cent of the 1933 plant cover remained on the experimental range pastures" (Hurtt, 1951).

The following data are from the preceding source. Over the period (1934–37), the density of the 6 most important forage species declined to 8.5 per cent of the predrought (1933) stand. Decrease in both summer and winter pastures in three intensities of stocking were very close to the average decline. Density of two of the most important species, blue grama and buffalo grass, declined to less than 5 per cent of predrought density, and a third, western wheatgrass, to 12 per cent. These were the species that furnished the bulk of the summer and winter forage. Although thread-leaf sedge lost about half of its stand, sandberg bluegrass increased in density 75 per cent. This grass is an early species of limited value for late grazing and the increase with lessened competition was from enlargement of established plants. A large percentage of forage plants decreased, many weedy species increased or invaded. Drought effects were cumulative and the forage supply was greatly reduced. Grasshoppers, like the cattle, greatly preferred the new green growth. They often ate the new herbage as rapidly as it appeared.

"As a result of the 1934 drought, the Federal Government purchased 7.2 million cattle and 3.6 million sheep in 16 Western States [2.5 million cattle in the northern Great Plains] in an effort to prevent utter demoralization of the industry" (Hurtt, 1951).

A comparison of original mixed prairie with true prairie, and an account of early grassland philosophy may be helpful here. At the time of settlement of the prairies of Illinois and eastern Kansas, big bluestem made such growth that a rider had to stand in the stirrups to see over the prairie. "Oldtimers" in Montana discussing the original condition before the ranges were overstocked state that "they could ride across the country with their feet dragging in the grass"—probably wheat grasses or Canby bluegrass (Spragg, 1902). Spragg states that "when the pioneer came west he found the ranges covered with vast forage resources. The question was, how can we get stock enough to use this wealth? Now conditions have changed. There is more stock on our ranges than they can support. Each rancher 'knows that if his stock does not eat the grass, that of somebody else will', and naturally he thinks he might as well benefit by it as anyone. In his effort to get his 'share' he contributes to the general destruction instead of trying to avert it."

STUDIES IN WYOMING AND WEST-CENTRAL MONTANA

In eastern Wyoming, Lang (1945) studied types of vegetation in parts of three counties drained by the Cheyenne River and its tributaries in the Missouri Plateau. They occupied, in the main, gently rolling topography, but hilly sites also occurred and breaks or badlands along the streams. Native vegetation in this grazing disclimax was mostly of the short-grass type. Chief grasses were blue grama with varying amounts of buffalo grass, western wheatgrass, needle-and-thread and the annual six-weeks fescue (*Festuca octoflora*). Forbs were mostly Pursh's plantain (*Plantago purshii*), red false mallow (*Sphaeralcea coccinea*) and pepper-

FIG. 86. (Upper) Mixed Prairie disclimax in eastern Wyoming. The most abundant species is blue grama. Mid grasses were found only in small amounts; pricklypear cactus was moderately abundant. (Lower) Range near Lusk, Wyoming. Overgrazing and drought have combined to greatly reduce the crop of forage. Both pricklypear cactus and sage are rather abundant.

grass (*Lepidium apetalum*). Pricklypear (*Opuntia polyacantha*) was common to abundant. Common shrubs and half-shrubs were big sage (*Artemisia tridentata*), fringed sage (*A. frigida*) and, in localized areas, silver sage (*A. cana*). Broom snakeweed (*Gutierrezia sarothrae*) and winterfat (*Eurotia lanata*) were also of considerable importance. (See figure 86).

Blue grama alone composed 74 per cent of the total density or cover afforded by grasses in the short-grass type. The total cover was 62 per cent grasses, 24 per cent forbs and 14 per cent shrubs and half-shrubs. A mixed grass type occupied much of the sandy soil of hilly lands. Here blue grama composed 60 per cent of the grasses, and several species common to sandy lands were present. In the sagebrush-grass type of rough land, forbs and shrubs were more abundant. Grasses composed only 39 per cent of the cover, forbs 22, and shrubs (91 per cent big sage) made up the remaining 39. Thus, many decades of overstocking had greatly modified the original composition of this mixed prairie.

West of the Big Horn Mountains in the Big Horn and Wind River basins a sagebrush-saltbush type of grassland, mostly browse, occurs. Here the average annual precipitation is only about 7 to 12 inches. "The soils are often highly alkaline or saline, and elevations reach upward to 7,500 feet. The principal species are bluestem [western] wheatgrass, needle-and-thread, bluebunch wheatgrass, Indian ricegrass, Sandberg bluegrass, and sand dropseed. Black and big sagebrush, two or more saltbushes, and greasewood are important shrubs . . . This type is grazed mainly by sheep in fall, winter, and spring, when snow supplements the water supply" (Hurtt, 1948).

Near Tensleep, in the eastern side of the Big Horn Basin, studies have been conducted by Cooper (1953) over a period of years. Here the half-century rainfall average is 10.4 inches, 48 per cent of which falls during the growing season. Big sagebrush was the dominant in this disclimax, and its abundance was largely the result of past grazing practices. "Relative amounts of big sagebrush in excess of 10 per cent of total coverage indicated ecological degeneration. Increase in relative amount of bluebunch wheatgrass afforded a measure of secondary succession . . . when conservative grazing and occasional resting . . . of pastures is practiced on this site, climax grasses can largely replace big sagebrush without artificial aid. Under favorable weather and grazing conditions, climax grasses can displace big sagebrush . . . within a decade or less." (See figure 87.)

In central Montana the grasslands of the plains merge into Palouse Prairie. The part of the Palouse Prairie that occurs in southeastern Washington and adjacent Idaho has been studied by Weaver (1917). It was composed of two communities or consociations. The more mesic Idaho

FIG. 87. A typical plant of bluebunch wheatgrass (*Agropyron spicatum*) about 8 inches in basal diameter and 3 feet tall.

fescue (*Festuca idahoensis*) consociation was found at higher elevations or in habitats with a more favorable moisture supply. The bluebunch wheatgrass consociation occurred on lower and more western portions of the region or in the more xeric habitats.

This prairie covered extensive areas in eastern Oregon, southern Idaho, and northern Nevada and Utah. Only through Montana and parts of Idaho and Wyoming does it come in contact with the mixed prairie of the plains.

According to Clements (1920), "the bunch-grass prairie passes so gradually into the mixed prairie in central Montana, that no line can be drawn between them. This is readily understood when it is known that *Stipa comata, Koeleria cristata,* and *Agropyrum glaucum* [*smithii*] occur in both, and that a large number of the societies are identical. The change is marked chiefly by the appearance and increasing importance of *Bouteloua,* and the transfer of the major dominance from *Agropyrum spicatum,* to *Stipa comata* and *Agropyrum glaucum.*"

The Palouse climate is characterized not by more rainfall than that of the Great Plains but by precipitation which largely occurs as snow in winter. This results in relatively deep percolation of the water because of its accumulation in winter and its small loss by evaporation. Rainfall in June and July, if any, is very light. The summer days are warm or hot but nights are cool. The native grasses are almost exclusively northern in origin and in their distribution.

Both consociations of Palouse Prairie occur frequently in valleys and on exposed ridges throughout the western or mountainous and foothill section of Montana as far eastward as Bozeman and Livingston. They are favored by the relatively cool growing season of the intermountain valleys. On the foothills the two communities often alternate, Idaho fescue is found on the less arid north-facing slopes and bluebunch wheatgrass occupies the drier south-facing ones. The bluebunch wheatgrass type extends farthest eastward to meet the mixed prairie.

Heady (1950, 1952) studied the Palouse Prairie near Havre (2,650 ft. altitude), in the Bearpaw Mountains (4,800 ft.) and at several other stations in central Montana. He states that "the environment at an elevation of approximately 5,000 feet in the foothills between the northern Rocky Mountains and the Great Plains presented the optimum for development of the Palouse Prairie in central Montana."

It is believed that the Palouse Prairie formerly extended across Montana and to the Badlands and Black Hills of the Dakotas. This is presumed to have occurred during a glacial period when a climate with winter and spring rainfall like that of the present Palouse country prevailed over part of the northern Great Plains. Typical Palouse species occur in protected plains habitats. Bluebunch wheatgrass persists on north-facing slopes, in burned clay soils (scoria) and in loose talus—all habitats with increased water content—in the western Dakotas. Sandberg bluegrass, a dominant in Palouse Prairie, is widespread over the northern plains, and balsamroot (*Balsamorhiza sagittata*) likewise occurs as a relic.

As a result of close grazing over long periods the native vegetation of Montana has been greatly modified. Its original composition, however, can be ascertained by the examination of numerous areas that have been protected (Clements, 1934). Wright and Wright (1948) located a number of such places in the south-central part of the state and studied the composition of their vegetation.

The Idaho fescue (*Festuca idahoensis*) type, which was most mesic, with a rainfall of 18 inches, occurred in three areas in the foothills of the intermountain region north of Bozeman (Fig. 79). This grass grew in almost pure stands. In drier places such as Virginia City, about 50 miles southwestward, (14 inches rainfall) bluebunch wheatgrass (*Agropyron spictatum*) was the dominant. Both species are chief dominants in the Palouse Prairie (Weaver, 1917). They were favored here by the relatively cool growing season. Many of the legumes and other forbs were also those of Palouse prairie.

About 120 miles east of Bozeman (near Laurel), Square Butte rises abruptly from the floor of the Yellowstone Valley. Because of its steep sides the 3 acres of prairie on its level top were inaccessible to livestock. In the sandy loam soil, thread-leaf sedge, bluebunch wheatgrass, and blue grama were the dominant species. Needle-and-thread, Junegrass and Sandberg bluegrass were of secondary importance. Forbs were nearly all those of mixed prairie. This is a transitional type between the bunch-grass zones (Palouse prairie) of the foothills and the mixed prairie of the plains.

Heavily grazed vegetation near Square Butte, at the same elevation and on similar soil, was dominated by big sage. Bluebunch wheatgrass survived only where the thick stand of sage protected it from grazing. The other dominants were entirely absent, and only scattered, small bunches of Junegrass and Sandberg bluegrass remained where they were protected by the big sage.

A few miles eastward an area exclosed to livestock for 40 years was studied. The soil was clay loam. The dominants were Junegrass, blue grama and needle-and-thread. Hood's phlox (*Phlox hoodii*), pricklypear (*Opuntia polyacantha*), fringed sage and red false mallow were of frequent occurrence. Big sage grew only in disturbed places. In a nearby, severely grazed pasture big sage grew thickly, broom snakeweed was abundant, and only scattered bunches of Sandberg bluegrass, blue grama and Junegrass were present.

In still another relic area near Hardin, 60 miles eastward and on silt loam soil, blue grama, green needlegrass and Junegrass were dominant. Needle-and-thread, western wheatgrass, and Sandberg bluegrass were of secondary importance. This and other relic areas were believed to represent the original mixed prairie of this portion of the Great Plains.

Grasslands in central and northern Montana need further study. They appear to be similar to those to be described in adjacent Canada where extensive studies have been made.

Despite the increasing number of well-managed ranges and a great awakening to the nature and value of grassland, the present condition in the Northern Great Plains is not good. It is well summarized by Hurtt (1950). "Drought, overstocking, uneven distribution, and unwise breaking of native sod are important causes of material deterioration on an estimated 25 million to 40 million acres of range land. Evidence of this subnormal condition is widespread in the form of accelerated soil movement; reduced height growth, or density; change in composition from valuable to less desirable species; and excessive erosion and run-off. Better management, including reseeding in cases of extreme depletion, is needed to restore top productivity. Such a program is also necessary for greater economic stability and to counteract the decline of rural population that has been under way on the plains for a quarter of a century or more."

Properly managed grasslands in the Great Plains represent the most stable part of their economy. Under good management, grassland vegetation returns to the soil fully as much as it removes. Continued overgrazing, however, fails in this respect; therefore, overuse as a practice is bad for soil, grass, livestock and man.

Knowledge of grasslands and their proper use is relatively new and, consequently, inadequate to solve all of the problems of the range. It will require the combined effort of workers in many phases of the study of grasslands to obtain sufficient information for carrying out a program of use so that a maximum yield of high quality forage may be maintained from generation to generation. Of equally great or even greater importance is getting all ranchers and cattlemen to benefit from this knowledge as applied to their ranges. It is currently believed by most experienced investigators that complete application of currently available information on range management could double the present grazing returns.

CLASSIFICATION OF VEGETATION

Before proceeding to a study of the mixed prairie of Canada, which is definitely an area dominated by needle grasses and blue grama, it may be well to summarize the major mixed prairie types. Clements (1936) pointed out the concrete subdivisions of the climax mixed prairie association, that is the faciations. "Each faciation corresponds to a particular regional climate of real but smaller differences in rainfall/evaporation and temperature . . . In general, temperature appears to play the leading part in the differentiation of faciations, since they usually fall into a sequence determined by latitude or altitude, though rainfall/evaporation is naturally concerned also."

The two or more dominants which characterize each faciation and the general area over which each faciation extends are as follows:

1. *Stipa-Bouteloua* (Needle-and-thread–Blue grama) Canada and northern Montana and North Dakota
2. *Bouteloua-Carex-*[*Stipa*] (Blue grama–Thread-leaf sedge–Needle-and-thread) Montana, North Dakota and northern South Dakota
3. *Stipa-Agropyron-Buchloe* (Needle-and-thread–wheatgrass–Buffalo grass) South Dakota and northeastern Wyoming.
4. *Bouteloua-Buchloe* (Blue grama-Buffalo grass) Nebraska, Kansas, northwestern Texas and Oklahoma, Colorado and southern Wyoming.
5. *Hilaria-Bouteloua-Stipa* (Curly mesquite, Tobosa grass, side-oats grama, blue grama, Texas needlegrass, New Mexico feathergrass) Texas and New Mexico.

The review of the numerous descriptions of the plant cover in the several states bears out the preceding classification. Blue grama ranges throughout the mixed prairie and is the most important species of the understory. Side-oats grama is principally central and southern in distribution as is also buffalo grass. Needle-and-thread ranges widely, but is largely replaced by Texas wintergrass (*Stipa leucotricha*) or New Mexico feathergrass (*S. neomexicana*) in central and southern Texas and in New Mexico. In northern Montana and in Canada, short-awn needlegrass (*Stipa spartea curtiseta*) is often intermixed with needle-and-thread.

Curly mesquite, like tobosa grass, (both species of *Hilaria*) is confined to the south and southwestern prairie. Western wheatgrass, so abundant on the hard lands of South Dakota, ranges far northward into Canada and southward into Texas. Bluebunch wheatgrass accompanies it in Wyoming and Montana as do also thickspike and slender wheatgrass and various other species in the northern states and provinces. Needle-leaf sedge, thread-leaf sedge and other sedges of the understory are of little importance south of the Platte River, but their abundance increases northward with the decline and final disappearance of buffalo grass in the understory. As we have seen, numerous bluegrasses have a similar northward range and together furnish considerable forage. Further classification throughout the four more northerly states especially, seems unnecessary here.

CHAPTER 21

Canadian Mixed Prairie

ACROSS THE vast level to rolling Great Plains in Canada, there extends from eastern Saskatchewan to the foothills of western Alberta the northern portion of the mixed prairie. The northward limit is about the latitude of Saskatoon. In this cooler climate with a short growing season, decreased temperature, and light precipitation there are some marked changes in vegetation from that of the Central Great Plains. Buffalo grass reaches its limit south of the Canadian border; side-oats grama and little bluestem are limited almost entirely to the extreme southeastern part; three-awn, squirreltail and tumblegrass are found rarely and only southward. This is a land of needlegrasses, blue grama, wheatgrasses, low-growing sedges, Junegrass and bluegrass, with fewer forbs and a small assortment of half-shrubs. The cover of vegetation is thinner, the plants are of smaller stature, rarely exceeding 12 to 18 inches in height except in very wet years, and forage production is correspondingly decreased. As in adjacent Montana, ranges in the driest area on brown soils (southeastern Alberta and southwestern Saskatchewan) are necessarily large, since experiments have shown that about 30 acres of range land are required to support a cow during the grazing period (April to October, inclusive) and an additional 15 acres must be reserved for winter grazing. Here the warm, westerly, chinook winds often keep the range in southern Alberta free of snow even in midwinter. In the dark-brown soil zone, where grazing and wheat-growing share prominence, range requirements are only about two-thirds as great. Here winter grazing is not dependable (Clarke *et al.*, 1942).

HISTORICAL BACKGROUND

The history of Canada's western ranges is much like that of the plains grassland in the United States. Before the coming of the dryland farmer most of the grazing lands were free, open range. The cover of native grasses provided an abundance of herbage for livestock in summer and, except when the weather was unusually unfavorable, during winter as well. Production of livestock increased rapidly. In the first decade of this century it was the common belief that wheat could be grown in the semi-arid parts of southern Saskatchewan and Alberta. The western invasion of farmers and also an increase in stock raising resulted in fencing or plowing the land. It was the end of the era of free range.

"With further settlement of the country most of the more productive lands were brought under cultivation, mainly for cereal production. Native pastures were confined more and more to areas which, by reason of their climate, soil or topography, were not suitable for the production of cultivated crops. . . . The native sod was broken in many areas which subsequent experience showed to be entirely unfit for cultivation. Several million acres of this submarginal land were later abandoned and allowed to go back to weeds and eventually to grass. In some cases artificial re-seeding with suitable introduced forage species was employed to speed up the normally slow return to a grass cover" (Clarke, Tisdale and Skoglund, 1943). In 1944 the livestock population of the three prairie provinces, Alberta, Saskatchewan, and Manitoba, included over 4.6 million cattle, 1.8 million sheep, and 1.7 million horses (Clarke and Tisdale, 1945).

In 1936 there were about 12 million acres of native range pastures in southern Alberta and Saskatchewan and an estimated 4 million acres of abandoned farm lands. Marginal lands composed several million acres more, the correct utilization of which had not been decided upon. The use continued to fluctuate between ranching and crop production, depending upon climatic cycles and the relative price of livestock and wheat (Clarke and Tisdale, 1936).

The poor condition of many overgrazed range lands, the ravages of drought, and decrease in prices of livestock following the first world war resulted in a realization of the need for studies on the management of the ranges and conservation of grazing resources. In 1927, the Dominion Range Experiment Station was established at Manyberries, Alberta, for scientific studies of native pasture lands. Eighteen thousand acres of native range land (mixed prairie) were thus made available for fundamental plant studies, range improvement, range management, and grazing capacity and production. These studies over a period of years have furnished a rich source of information on the composition of the vegetation in this area, its growth and development, and its maintenance under grazing and related problems.

EXTENT AND ENVIRONMENT OF THE PRAIRIE

The part of the northern portion of the Great Plains occupied by mixed prairie is shown in figure 88. "It occupies all of the brown soils of southwestern Saskatchewan and southeastern Alberta and is also typical of most of the adjacent dark-brown soil zone in Saskatchewan and the drier half of that zone in Alberta" (Coupland, 1952). This prairie borders that in Montana and North Dakota from near the foothills of the Rocky Mountains eastward nearly 500 miles. Its northern edge crosses the eastern Alberta boundary more than 200 miles north of Montana.

The surface of the Great Plains region slopes mostly eastward from its western border in Alberta, at about 4,000 feet altitude, to about 800 feet in the great Central Lowland in Manitoba. The plain is separated into three divisions by two eastward-facing escarpments. The Missouri Coteau, extending northwestward from North Dakota, marks the boundary between the second and third prairie steppes within which the mixed prairie is located. True Prairie occurs east of the southern part of the Manitoba Escarpment on the first prairie steppe (*cf.* Coupland, 1950). The continuity of the plain is also broken by a number of hilly areas. The Cypress Hills, the most prominent elevation, rise from 3,000 to 4,700 feet above sea level. They represent the remnants of an old plateau, now much dissected by many valleys and coulees. Other elevated areas are far less prominent. The Great Sandhills, north of this plateau, illustrate areas, smaller elsewhere, with rough topography. The broad valleys of the North and South Saskatchewan Rivers, the only large rivers that flow through the area, and others are 100 to 500 feet below the general level of the plain. Most of the drainage is northeastward into Hudson Bay. Old glacial drainage channels occur, many with non-perennial streams, as well as glacial lake beds. Badlands are common along the Milk River, which flows through the southwestern part. In 1945, it was estimated that there were nearly 30 million acres of pasture land in the region occupied by Brown and Dark-brown soils (Fig. 88).

Soils have been derived mostly from material deposited by glaciers. In some places the mantle of till is thin and the native rock has greatly influenced formation of soil. Loam soils are most common, but the range in texture is from sand to heavy clay. Organic matter in the soil ranges from 4.6 to 6.2 per cent and nitrogen content of soil varies from 0.14 to 0.40 per cent (Coupland, 1950).

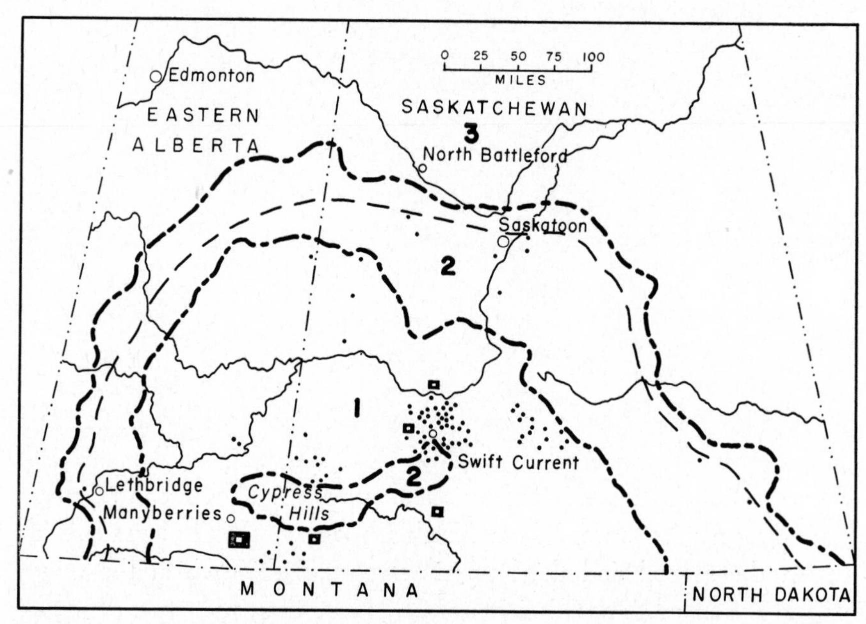

FIG. 88. Outline map showing the relationship between the extent of mixed prairie and the soil zones (1, brown soils, 2, dark-brown soils, and 3, black and gray wooded soils). Heavy broken lines mark boundaries between soil zones. Light broken line marks the approximate zone of tension between mixed prairie on the south and the fescue grassland on the north. Dots indicate the locations of sites studied. Enclosed square areas indicate the locations of Grassland Research Areas (small squares) and the Dominion Range Experiment Station at Manyberries (large square). (After Wyatt *et al.*, 1938–43, Mitchell *et al.*, 1944, Moss & Campbell, 1947). Redrawn from Coupland, 1950. (Courtesy of Ecological Monographs)

Brown soils, with color ranging from light brown to grayish brown and with low amounts of organic matter, have thin A horizons. Accumulations of calcium carbonate usually occur at a depth of 10 to 12 inches. These soils developed under a precipitation of only 11 to 14 inches.

Dark brown soils, developed under somewhat higher rainfall and with presumably denser vegetation, have a greater content of organic matter, mostly 50 per cent greater than that of Brown soils. The zone of calcium carbonate accumulation is deeper, usually occurring at 16 to 18 inches below the soil surface (Fig. 89).

Precipitation over the entire prairie is low in amount and irregular in distribution. It is lowest in the area of the Dominion Range Experiment Station at Manyberries where the average annual rainfall is between 11 and 12 inches. It increases to the west, north, and east but only beyond the brown soil zone does it exceed 14 inches. Further increase in the dark brown soil area may reach 17 to 18 inches. Seventy to 80 per cent of the precipitation occurs from April to October. As elsewhere over the Great Plains, variations from year to year are extreme. Soil moisture, not fertility, is usually the limiting factor for plant growth. Low temperature is also a limiting factor for some species in spring.

FIG. 89. Medium-textured soils developed on rolling undifferentiated glacial till deposits in the moister part of the brown soil zone. The Stipa-Bouteloua community occurs on the intermediate slopes. Tops of knolls are occupied by the Bouteloua-Stipa community and lower slopes support the Stipa-Agropyron type. Mesic vegetation occurs in the depression in the background. Photo by J. B. Campbell.

The level to undulating land, according to Coupland (1950), has the most satisfactory drainage. "Much of the strongly rolling and hilly land is excessively drained due to loss of precipitation through runoff. Low-lying flats and depressions are characterized by varying degrees of restricted drainage. When depressions receive runoff water from adjacent uplands the soil often contains excessive amounts of soluble salts. Alkali sloughs are therefore common throughout the prairie area."

The frost-free growing season scarcely exceeds 100 days in the northern part; this is only half its length in Oklahoma. The season for growth is often further shortened by drought. Hot winds are frequent in summer and strong winds occur in April and May. The southwesterly winds, the Chinooks, are warm and dry. They sometimes affect vegetation adversely in summer, but in winter they are beneficial in removing the snow from the ranges, especially in the western area, and thus permitting grazing even in December and January. Rates of evaporation from a free water surface (May to September, inclusive) are relatively low, varying from 33 inches in the south to 27 inches at Saskatoon.

A fairly close relationship between soil and air temperatures and the renewal of growth in spring was ascertained at Manyberries by Clarke *et al.* (1943). "*Stipa comata* began growth each year when the 6-inch soil temperature approached a daily average of 42° F. Mean daily air temperatures at this time averaged 40° F. *Agropyron, Koeleria* and *Poa* all started at slightly lower temperatures. *Bouteloua* on the other hand, did not begin to grow until the 6-inch soil temperature averaged 52° F., which condition was usually reached about a month later. There was a fairly close association between rising soil temperatures and increased growth rate for the four earlier species from the time that growth began till the end of April. At that time the weekly soil temperature was 52° F. "During most years temperatures remained suitable for growth until some time in October, but due to lack of soil moisture little active growth of the major species occurred after the end of July, and most of the vegetation cured in July or August." Throughout the entire mixed prairie, soil moisture is usually exhausted by late in July. There is little if any renewal of growth in autumn, unless rains are unusually heavy.

KINDS AND COMPOSITION OF PLANT COMMUNITIES

A comprehensive study of mixed prairie in Canada, including the structure of the vegetation, natural classification of the plant communities, and certain ecological characteristics of the chief species composing them, was made by Coupland (1950) over a long period of years. All data in the following discussion, unless otherwise indicated, are from this source. This prairie, entirely within the Great Plains, contacts true prairie on the east at an altitude of about 1,600 feet along the international boundary. Near the mountains on the west it gives way to Fescue grassland as it does also in the moister part of the Dark-Brown soil area northward. In addition to widespread observations, Coupland made detailed studies in nearly 100 carefully selected sites.

"Within the area as a whole, variations in water content of soil caused by differences in climate are revealed in the nature of the vegetation. Each climax grassland type is associated with certain conditions of soil moisture as affected by soil and topography." In any one locality different communities of grassland may occur because of the influence of slope and soil texture on soil moisture. Approximately 40 per cent of the mixed prairie area is covered with soils of medium texture, developed on undifferentiated deposits of till. It will be remembered that types or communities are named after one or more of the dominant species, the most abundant species occurring first in the name. The *Stipa–Bouteloua* (Needle-and-thread–Blue grama), the *Bouteloua–Stipa* (Blue grama–Needle-and-thread), and the *Stipa–Agropyron* (Needle-and-thread–Wheatgrass) communities are characteristic where vegetation has completed its development and become climax on deep glacial deposits. The second community (*Bouteloua–Stipa*) is characteristic of coarse textured soils in the drier districts. The *Agropyron–Muhlenbergia* (Wheatgrass-Plains muhly) community is prominent where considerable erosion has occurred. Two other communities occurring on other types of soil will also be described. Five of these well defined communities are climax, the other is subclimax as a result of erosion.

Needle-and-thread–Blue grama Community

The *Stipa–Bouteloua* type is the most extensive. On hilly land it is typically limited to the lower slopes in the dry part of the brown soil zone and to midslopes in the moister part of this zone (Fig. 90). In the dark-brown soil zone it is limited to the upper slopes and knolls. Thus, it moves upward on the hills with an increase of soil moisture. Undulating areas of medium-textured soil in the moister part of the brown soil zone are also typically occupied by this community.

A second *Stipa* shares dominance with needle-and-thread. This is a variety (*curtiseta*) of the needlegrass (*Stipa spartea*), so common in true prairie. The common name is short-awn needlegrass. Although the awns of *Stipa spartea* are 5 to 8 inches long, those of the variety are only about 3 inches in length. Together they compose 30 per cent of the vegetation and occupy nearly a third of the basal cover; the ratio of *Stipa comata* to *S. spartea curtiseta* increases in the drier districts. Blue grama makes up 25 per cent of the vegetation and furnishes about a fourth of the basal cover. Thus, these are clearly the dominants. Together they constitute 55 per cent of the vegetation.

Two wheatgrasses, thickspike wheatgrass (*Agropyron dasystachyum*) and western wheatgrass (*A. smithii*), Junegrass (*Koeleria cristata*), needle-leaf sedge (*Carex eleocharis*) and thread-leaf sedge (*C. filifolia*) are the principal secondary grasses or grasslike plants. All have high forage value.

Fringed sage (*Artemisia frigida*) and dwarf phlox (*Phlox hoodii*) furnish 89 per cent of the cover composed of forbs. The sage is here considered as a forb since it dies back to the ground each winter. Red false mallow (*Sphaeralcea coccinea*) and pasque flower (*Anemone patens*) are other high-ranking forbs. Roses (*Rosa* spp.) and western snowberry (*Symphoricarpos occidentalis*) are the most abundant shrubs.

Both the upper and lower layers of the vegetation are well developed. The upper layer, including numerous forbs, is 6 to 20 inches high; the lower one is only 1 to 5 inches tall. The average basal cover is about 13 per cent, which is the same as the average in upland True Prairie.

Blue Grama—Needle-and-thread Community

The *Bouteloua gracilis—Stipa comata* type is characteristic of areas of medium- to coarse-textured soils in the drier part of the brown soil zone. It also characterizes areas of coarse-textured soil of exposed locations throughout the prairie. The upper slopes and tops of knolls in the moister part of the brown soil zone are often occupied by this community as preclimax to the *Stipa—Bouteloua* type. Its distribution on dark-brown soils is limited.

Early studies on the blue grama—needle-and-thread range at Manyberries as reported by Clarke (1930) and Clarke, Tisdale and Skogland (1943) are presented here. The most abundant grasses in the experimental range area, near the Montana-Alberta boundary and about 40 miles west of Saskatchewan, were blue grama (*Bouteloua gracilis*) and needle-and-thread (*Stipa comata*), with western wheatgrass (*Agropyron smithii*) and Junegrass (*Koeleria cristata*) ranking somewhat lower. Blue grama composed about 20 per cent of the entire vegetation (forage), needle-and-thread 33 per cent, western wheatgrass 22, and Junegrass 10 per cent. The total density of the vegetation (basal cover) was only 10.8 per cent. Blue grama covered 4.1 per cent of the soil, needle-and-thread

2.2, wheatgrass 1.2 and Junegrass 0.7 per cent. Other species in the shortgrass understory were Sandberg bluegrass (*Poa secunda*) and thread-leaf sedge (*Carex filifolia*). These six species comprised over 80 per cent of the vegetation. Winterfat (*Eurotia lanata*) and Nuttall's sage (*Atriplex nuttallii*) were important browse plants. All of these eight species were not only abundant but also highly palatable to livestock.

The principal forbs were fringed sage (*Artemisia frigida*) and dwarf phlox (*Phlox hoodii*). Other characteristic species were many-spined opuntia (*Opuntia polyacantha*), red false mallow (*Sphaeralcea coccinea*) and broom snakeweed (*Gutierrezia sarothrae*). Dwarf shrubs were winterfat (*Eurotia lanata*) and Nuttall saltbush (*Atriplex nuttallii*) and the somewhat taller silver sage (*Artemisia cana*). Forbs, including fringed sage, composed 14 per cent of the cover, and the three shrubs more than 4 per cent.

Among 475 meter quadrats distributed over the area, about half were dominated mainly by blue grama, 25 per cent by needle-and-thread, and 21 per cent by western wheatgrass. The productivity of areas dominated by each of the three principal species was ascertained over a period of 6 years. Areas of blue grama yielded an average of 160 pounds per acre, those of needle-and-thread 280 pounds, but those of western wheatgrass 340 pounds. These data are from Clarke (1930) and Clarke *et al.* (1943) who listed 21 grasses or grasslike plants, 15 broad-leaved forbs, and 9 shrubs as the principal important species. These constitute almost the entire plant cover. They point out that moderately moist areas are dominated by more mesophytic grasses, such as slender wheatgrass (*Agropyron trachycaulum*), green needlegrass (*Stipa viridula*) and Canby bluegrass (*Poa canbyi*). Even patches of shrubs, especially western snowberry (*Symphoricarpos occidentalis*), occur where moisture penetrates deeply.

The principal subtype produced as a result of differences in soil and topography is the western wheatgrass community. It occurs on alluvial flats where moisture conditions are usually more favorable than those in the general area. The sole dominant is *Agropyron smithii* which often forms pure stands. Blue grama and particularly needle-and-thread are rare or absent, although certain other grasses and various forbs may occur. According to Coupland (1950) this subtype is found on slightly alkaline clay flats and on certain alluviated clay flats elsewhere in Canada's mixed prairie.

Clarke, Tisdale, and Skoglund (1943) state: "The annual growth cycle of the principal plants is well adapted to the seasonal conditions. Most species begin growth early in April and develop rapidly during the relatively favourable period of April, May, and June. Plant development is practically completed in most cases by the first of July, before the regular mid-summer drought has begun. While some species produce a certain amount of seed in all but very dry years, abundant seed production for the majority of plants occurs only in seasons when precipitation is above normal. . . . The principal exception to the common growth cycle occurs in the development of *Bouteloua gracilis*. This species begins growth nearly a month later than do the other dominant grasses and continues to grow slowly for several weeks after the latter have become relatively inactive. . . . Because of its late period of development, seed production in this species is confined mainly to years when precipitation during July and August is above normal.

"A feature of the response of the vegetation to the climatic conditions is the annual drying or curing which occurs, particularly in the case of the grasses. When the available soil moisture becomes exhausted, as usually happens before the end of July, the vegetation becomes cured, and usually remains in that condition for the remainder of the year. This curing of the native grasses is one of the principal factors which make the region so well adapted for range live-stock production. The dried plants remain erect and available for grazing for many months after drying while their nutritive value is generally adequate for the maintenance of range livestock in good condition" (*cf.* Clarke and Tisdale, 1945).

Long overuse of the area by livestock had given it a general appearance similar to the grazing disclimax in Colorado (except for the absence of buffalo grass) which early in the century was designated as short grass. The presence of both mid- and short-grass layers, however, identifies it clearly as a portion of the mixed prairie. This most xeric part of Canadian mixed prairie is now designated as the blue grama–needle-and-thread or the *Bouteloua–Stipa* community (Coupland, 1950).

According to the surveys of Coupland (1950), sampling in many areas of the grama–needle-and-thread community revealed that the two dominants occupied 7.6 and 2.4 per cent of the soil surface, respectively, and composed 52 and 17 per cent of the vegetation. The general appearance of the community is given by the carpet of short grass and sedges interspersed most abundantly with needle-and-thread. Also the same mid grasses that are listed in the preceding community occur here. The same two species of forbs, phlox and sage, are again the principal ones. Silver sage (*Artemisia cana*) is the most widely scattered shrub; it is especially abundant in sandy soil. The usual height is less than 12 to 18 inches. Sedges and forbs, as a group, are less abundant in this drier type than in the preceding one. Grasses and sedges compose 85 per cent of the vegetation. Forbs are less abundant in this type than in the preceding but shrubs are more abundant. Height of both layers of vegetation is greatly reduced in these drier sites.

Needle-and-thread—Wheatgrass Community

In the *Stipa—Agropyron* grouping the dominant mid grasses are needle-and-thread, short-awn needlegrass and thickspike wheatgrass (*Agropyron dasystachyum*). Together their basal area is 5.1 per cent and the percentage composition of vegetation is 43 per cent. Western wheatgrass and Junegrass are other important mid grasses. In the short-grass understory needle-leaf sedge is more than twice as abundant as blue grama. With small amounts of thread-leaf sedge, these three species cover 4 per cent of the soil and compose 35 per cent of the vegetation. Associated forbs and shrubs are similar to those of the *Stipa—Bouteloua* community. Total basal area is about 12 per cent (Fig. 90).

The general appearance of this grassland is more luxuriant than that of the two preceding communities. The mid-grass layer is more conspicuous and obscures the layer of shorter vegetation beneath. This type is characteristic of areas of undulating to gently rolling topography with soil of medium texture in the dark-brown soil zone. Where the land is hilly it occupies only the sheltered and lower slopes below the needle-and-thread—blue grama community in the brown soil zone.

Thus, the soil moisture relationships of the three communities become clear. On a hillside in the dark-brown soil zone the lower slopes are clothed with vegetation of the needle-and-thread—wheatgrass type. The mid slopes bear the needle-and-thread—blue grama community, but the drier upper slopes and hilltops present the more xeric grama grass—needle-and-thread type. In areas of increased rainfall the mid-slope vegetation extends upward and replaces the more xeric hilltop type and may also extend over level land. Meanwhile the more mesic needle-and-thread

—wheatgrass type is no longer confined to the lower slopes but extends its territory upward. Conversely, as one proceeds into an area of decreased rainfall the blue grama—needle-and-thread type extends from upper slopes downward to midslopes and finally to lower slopes or continues over the level or slightly undulating land. Thus, topography through moisture relations largely determines distribution of this vegetation.

FIG. 90. (Upper) View of the needle-and-thread—blue grama community in Canada. The brown loam soil has developed on rolling undifferentiated glacial till deposits. Needle-and-thread is the dominant mid grass. (Lower) View of the *Stipa-Agropyron* community on a nearly level plateau in the eastern extremity of the Cypress Hills ridge south of Swift Current. The principal dominants are *Stipa spartea* var. *curtiseta* and *Agropyron dasystachyum*. Photos by R. T. Coupland. (Reproduced by courtesy of Ecological Monographs)

Wheatgrass—Plains Muhly Community

Modification of the cover afforded by any of the three preceding communities on rolling topography may result from erosion. These eroded places are generally limited in extent. They are marked by an incomplete cover of grass and a lighter color of soil where the topsoil has been removed. Sometimes these eroded spots cover many acres. Chief grasses in such places are thickspike wheatgrass (*Agropyron dasystachyum*) and plains muhly (*Muhlenbergia cuspidata*). Each may compose 16 to 18 per cent of the vegetation. Together they may cover nearly 5 per cent of the soil; total basal cover of vegetation is about 14 per cent. Needle-leaf sedge and blue grama of the understory may make up 28 per cent of the vegetation and cover about 4 per cent of the soil. Numerous other species occur, the population of forbs almost doubling that of the climax types. Fringed-leaf sage, dwarf phlox, and prairie cat's-foot (*Antennaria microphylla*) are often most abundant. Many of the subdominant species are those characteristic of heavy clay soils.

Wheatgrass—Junegrass Community

The *Agropyron—Koeleria* type occurs on soils that have developed on uniform clay deposits in the beds of glacial lakes. The mid-grass layer consists largely of thickspike wheatgrass, Junegrass, western wheatgrass and green needlegrass (*Stipa viridula*). Needle-leaf sedge is the only important species of the understory, but Sandberg bluegrass (*Poa secunda*) and Cusick bluegrass (*P. cusickii*) also occur. Needle-and-thread, short-awn needlegrass and blue grama, although dominant in adjacent soil on glacial till, are absent from this community. Forbs are less abundant than in other types but they are of the same species. Winterfat (*Eurotia lanata*) is conspicuous. The type has the general appearance of uniformity.

Blue grama—Wheatgrass Type

The *Bouteloua—Agropyron* type is similar in general appearance to the blue grama—needle-and-thread community. It occupies clay loam, solonetzic soils in the dry part of the brown-soil zone. The so-called "burn-out" or "blow-out" spots may occupy 5 to 15 per cent of the soil surface. They are especially abundant south and southwest of the Cypress Hills. Because of low permeability of moisture and low precipitation these are droughty soils. The drought-resistant blue grama often becomes prominent and the wheatgrasses are favored by the fine texture of the soil. The short grass alone may compose more than half of the vegetation and western wheatgrass 10 to 15 per cent. Needle-and-thread and Junegrass are usually present. Fringed sage, dwarf phlox and many-spined opuntia (*Opuntia polyacantha*) are other common species.

Other Grasses, Forbs and Shrubs

In addition to the seven species of grass dominants, repeatedly mentioned, twelve other grasses and four sedges are characteristic of upland prairie. Of the sedges, needle-leaf sedge (*Carex eleocharis*) is most abundant, thread-leaf sedge (*C. filifolia*) is second, but sun sedge (*C. heliophila*) and *C. obtusata* are of frequent occurrence. Other grasses are listed:

Green needlegrass
Stipa viridula
Sandberg bluegrass
Poa secunda
Canby bluegrass
Poa canbyi
Cusick bluegrass
Poa cusickii
Plains reedgrass
Calamagrostis montanensis
Sand reed
Calamovilfa longifolia
Sand dropseed
Sporobolus cryptandrus
Spike oat
Avena (Helictotrichon) hookeri
Rough fescue
Festuca scabrella
Aparejo grass
Muhlenbergia squarrosa (utilis)
Tumblegrass
Schedonnardus paniculatus
Squirreltail
Sitanion hystrix

Avena, Festuca and *Muhlenbergia* occur only infrequently in the climax; *Schedonnardus* and *Sitanion* are found rarely and only in the southern part of the area. Grasses and sedges occupy 85 to 95 per cent of the total basal area in the several climax plant communities.

Forbs are components of all of the grassland communities. Shrubs are less abundant but conspicuous in some types. Of the forbs, fringed sage (*Artemisia frigida*) is the most abundant; dwarf phlox (*Phlox hoodii*) ranks second. The phlox is a low, tufted, mat-forming plant, with coarse woody roots. In early spring it produces masses of flowers that vary in color from white through pale blue to purple. A clubmoss (*Selaginella densa*) is the only non-flowering plant of any abundance; although the plant rarely exceeds an inch in height, it occurs widely and often covers 6 to 10 per cent of the soil. It has no grazing value and its role in vegetation is poorly understood. It seems to have little effect on other vegetation. Therefore it was not included in any of the grassland studies.

Other forbs most common throughout the area (with current names in parentheses) are *Malvastrum coccineum* (*Sphaeralcea coccinea*), *Pulsatilla ludoviciana* (*Anemone patens*), *Gutierrezia diversifolia* (*G. sarothrae*), *Solidago glaberrima* (*S. missouriensis*), *S. dumetorum*, *Sideranthus* (*Haplopappus*) *spinulosus*, *Chrysopsis villosa*, species of *Potentilla*, *Artemisia gnaphalodes* (*A. ludoviciana*) and *A. pabularis*. Species of *Rosa* and *Artemisia cana* are the most important shrubs in the climax communities.

Other common forbs are silver-leaf psoralea, lance-leaved psoralea, milfoil or yarrow, many-flowered aster, ball cactus, rush-like lygodesmia, blazing star, scarlet gaura, puccoon, prairie clover, several species of *Astragalus*, and wild onion.

Students of grassland everywhere are deeply indebted to Coupland for his excellent analysis and description of Canada's wonderful prairies. He has informed the writer that during recent, unusually wet years the cover of vegetation has increased at least 50 per cent and that there has been a definite increase in relative abundance of mid grasses as compared with short grasses.

FESCUE PRAIRIE

Mixed prairie does not extend through the entire area of Dark Brown soils (Fig. 91). It is bounded on the west and north by the fescue grassland, which is associated with the parkland ecotone lying between grassland and forest. Clarke *et al.* (1942) described grassland areas in the foothills of southwestern Alberta where blue grama was not present and needle-and-thread occurred only occasionally. These grasslands were dominated by rough fescue (*Festuca scabrella*), a bunch grass with foliage 8 to 15 inches high and clumps 5 to 20 inches in diameter. Extensive studies by Moss (1944) and Moss and Campbell (1947) showed that this Fescue association borders mixed prairie in a wide zone westward to the Rocky Mountains and northward through Alberta to the Boreal Forest. Coupland and Brayshaw (1953) have shown that mixed prairie gives way to the *Festuca scabrella* association in Saskatchewan. "It is more fully developed in Alberta, waning in western Saskatchewan where it occupies only the more northerly grassland area. . . . Throughout much of its range the

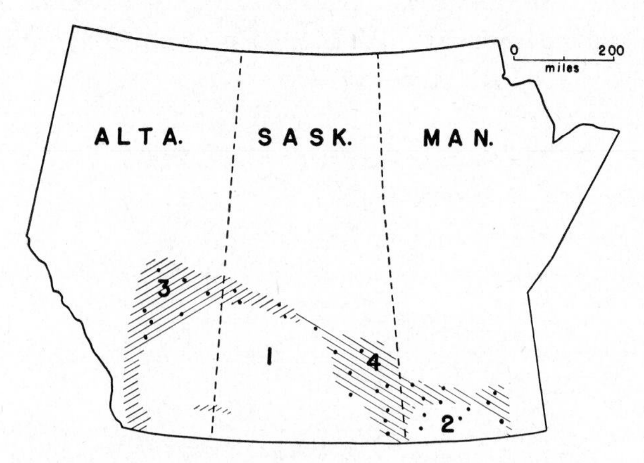

FIG. 91. Grasslands in western Canada. (1) Mixed Prairie, (2) True Prairie, (3) Fescue Prairie interspersed with aspen groves (dots), and (4) transitional area of grassland composed of various species from each of the preceding associations. Map prepared by R. T. Coupland.

fescue grassland is associated with the aspen-grove section" (Coupland, 1952). It occurs continuously in the drier parts adjacent to mixed prairie but finally, northward, only as small openings within the almost continuous forest cover. Patches of Fescue Prairie occur in eastern Saskatchewan, but here fescue is often intermixed with species from both true and mixed prairie. Representative areas of rough fescue occur on the Cypress Hills. Higher altitudes and northern latitudes, more rainfall, lower mean temperatures, and less evaporation than that of mixed prairie all favor the best growth of this dominant.

CHAPTER 22

Non-Grasses of Mixed Prairie

PLANTS OTHER than grasses constitute an important part of mixed prairie. Considerable attention has been given to them in preceding pages but not so much as they deserve. In the first quarter of the present century non-grasslike herbs were designated weeds, even by range examiners. Then they were differentiated by Clements from herbs with the grass life-form. Thus, mixed prairie consists of grasses and forbs, and in places shrubs and half-shrubs are intermixed. Forb does not replace the word weed, since forbs include all non-grasslike herbs, native or introduced, some of which are weeds.

SEASONAL ASPECTS

Most forbs of prairie, probably 85 to 90 per cent, are perennials, and some have a life span of many years. They live with the grasses and seem to accommodate themselves to the environment created by the grasses, which are the dominants. Many species renew growth early in spring, blossom and produce seed in nearly full sunlight before they are much shaded by the grasses. Examples are biscuitroot (*Lomatium* spp.), pasque flower (*Anemone patens*), prairie violet (*Viola pedatifida*), onions (*Allium drummondi* and *A. textile*), stemless Townsendia (*Townsendia exscapa*), star lily (*Leucocrinum montanum*), decumbent pearlwort (*Sagina decumbens*) and dwarf phlox (*Phlox hoodii*).

Forbs with this early habit of flowering are designated prevernal (early spring) or vernal (spring) bloomers. Later they may disappear above ground or become more or less hidden in the shade of the grasses. Prevernal species compose not more than 2 to 4 per cent of the total. All carry out their life processes near the soil surface.

The vernal aspect presents four or five times as many important species as the preceding. In the central plains, the plants blossom mostly late in April or in May. Vernal bloomers are low in stature and by midsummer nearly all are overtopped by sand dropseed, little bluestem, needle-and-thread or other mid grasses. The following are representative examples:

Ground plum
Astragalus crassicarpus
Woolly loco
Astragalus mollissimus
Crazyweed
Oxytropis lambertii
Ragwort
Senecio plattensis
Puccoon
Lithospermum spp.
Prairie cat's-foot
Antennaria neglecta
Sheep sorrel
Oxalis stricta
Spiderwort
Tradescantia spp.
Silky sophora
Sophora sericea
Low poppymallow
Callirrhoe involucrata
Dwarf phlox
Phlox hoodii
Vetch
Vicia americana

During the vernal period species that blossom in summer or autumn also make a vigorous growth. Many keep pace with the grasses in their development and reach a similar height or later overtop them.

Plants which blossom in summer (late May to late July) form the largest group of all. They are nearly as numerous as the vernal and autumnal bloomers combined. Myriads of flowers contribute to the great wealth of midsummer beauty. Among these are the purple and white flowers of prairie clovers. The red or salmon-colored blossoms of red false mallow are plentiful. Pricklypear adorns the landscape with large yellow blossoms which may become pink or red. The white to pink flowers of wild rose are common and the bluish-indigo tops of the lead plant stand out just above the grasses. Tooth-leaved primrose, certain species of flax, and cut-leaved goldenweed furnish tinges of yellow, as do also prairie coneflower and sunflower. Large white flowers are conspicuous on small soapweed and prickly poppy (*Argemone platyceras*), and purple ones on bush morning-glory and poppymallow (*Callirrhoe involucrata*). Other species are few-flowered psoralea, prairie turnip, silver-leaf psoralea, purple coneflower, fleabane, milkwort, milkweeds, lupines, and many species of milk vetch, larkspurs, thistles, four-o'clocks, sensitive brier, gumweed, beardtongues, gilias, Indian paintbrushes and many others. When moisture is plentiful blossoming is profuse and the landscape is beautifully decorated.

Plants of the summer aspect are strikingly of greater stature than those of early or later spring. Only a few are overtopped by the mid grasses. The rest either reach the general level of the grass upperstory or extend still farther upward into full sunshine. Thus, certain plants secure good lighting by blossoming early near the ground before the grasses shade them; others develop a naked stem a few to several inches high before they branch and produce leaves. Few-flowered and silver-leaf psoraleas are examples, as are also stenosiphon and slender parosela. They extend well into the light above the grasses; often the spreading crowns of the psoraleas produce only a little shade. Quite different are other forbs, such as false boneset, smooth goldenrod and broom snakeweed. Their stems are often numerous and very leafy, and some lean outward over the new growth of grasses, the spreading top covering several times the area of the base of the plant (Fig. 13).

The autumnal aspect normally begins late in July and is ushered in by the blossoming of blazing stars, goldenrods, asters and sunflowers. On dry years earlier blooming occurs. Characteristic autumnal species are *Liatris punctata*, *L. squarrosa* (both blazing stars), stiff goldenrod (*Solidago rigida*), smooth goldenrod (*S. missouriensis*), velvety goldenrod (*S. mollis*) and gray goldenrod (*S. nemoralis*). Many-flowered aster (*Aster ericoides*), aromatic aster (*A. oblongifolius*) and tansy aster (*A. tanacetifolius*) are representative of this group. Chief native sunflowers are prairie sunflower (*Helianthus petiolaris*), willow-leaved sunflower (*H. salicifolius*) and common sunflower (*H. annuus*). Rabbitbrush (*Chrysothamnus* spp.) and broom snakeweed (*Gutierrezia sarothrae*) are conspicuous, yellow-flowered composites. In fact the family compositae furnishes a very large percentage of all autumnal bloomers. Sages of many species occur, such as fringed sage (*Artemisia frigida*), silver sage (*A. cana*), sand sage (*A. filifolia*), cudweed sage (*A. ludoviciana*) and linear-leaved sage (*A. dracunculus*). Umbrella plant (*Eriogonum*), false boneset (*Kuhnia eupatorioides*), fetid marigold (*Dyssodia papposa*) and ironweeds (*Vernonia baldwini* and *V. marginata*) are further examples of autumnal bloomers. Numerous others contribute to the autumnal aspect, which about equals the vernal aspect in number of important species.

Almost all of the autumnal species are plants of considerable stature. Their plan of life is to exceed the grasses in height and to blossom and produce seed at the end of a long growing season.

RELATION OF FORBS TO SOIL MOISTURE

In mixed prairie the relation of forbs to soil moisture is nearly always more critical than their relation to light. A few native forbs are rooted shallowly, extending their absorbing organs only 1 to 2 feet into the prairie soil. These are indeed few. The general depth of root extent of most grasses of uplands is 4 to 5 feet. The writers have found this to be true not only in hard lands and sandy soils of mixed prairie but also in true prairie eastward and in Palouse prairie of the far Northwest. Much less than half of the forb population absorbs only at this level. Indeed most forbs extend their roots far below the grasses.

A method of root study has been devised by which the exact depth and spread of roots may be ascertained and the relation of forb to grass underground may be shown (Weaver and Darland, 1949). The sample in figure 92 is from a little bluestem pasture in good range condition.[1] The *Psoralea* is a young plant; mature plants have thick taproots which reach depths of 7 to 10 feet. Other forbs in this pasture, such as lead plant (*Amorpha*), prairie boneset (*Khunia*), many-flowered aster (*Aster*), ground plum (*Astragalus*) and blazing star (*Liatris*), were rooted at depths of 8 to 18 feet. This illustrates an important fact; forbs may live largely on the water that penetrates beyond the depth of the grass roots. This was clearly demonstrated in the early years of drought. When the grasses were dried and bleached by drought, the wild rose, psoralea, and blazing star were unwilted, blooming and absorbing water far below the reach of the grasses (Weaver *et al.*, 1935). Indeed, the upper 3 or 4 feet of the strong taproots of several species of plants were permanently separated from the soil surrounding them, but the taproots were not cut. They grew 2 years during drought without visible harm to the tops (Nedrow, 1937).

After several years of study, it was found that in true prairie 65 per cent of the 43 species selected as representative of the flora had roots which extended over 5 feet in depth (some to 12 or even 22 feet). Moreover, of these deeply rooted plants only about one-fifth rely to any marked degree upon the shallow soils for their water and solutes. Many carried on but little absorption in the upper 2 feet of soil.

Deep rooting in the sand hills and sandy soils of mixed prairie has been shown to be marked. The surface-absorbing habit is far more pronounced in hard lands. Even here about 11 per cent of the species had little or no provision for absorbing in the upper few feet of soil, and 61 per cent were fairly deeply rooted.

Most forbs farm deeply. Root tubercles occur abundantly both in the

---

[1] This and the following figure are from Weaver "Effects of different intensities of grazing on depth and quantity of roots of grasses" 1950. (Courtesy of Journal of Range Management)

soil (solum) and in parent materials far below the soil. Prairie clovers, lead plant, and various psoraleas are examples. The free nitrogen, by the action of nitrogen-fixing bacteria which grow on the roots in tubercles, is made available to all other plants. Lime and various other nutrients are absorbed far below the soil surface; some are transferred to the parts above ground, which upon their death leave them on the surface soil. When coarse taproots and their branches die they add humus and leave open channels into which water infiltrates both vertically downward and laterally. Roots of smaller size enormously increase the number of these passageways. The authors are among the few who have spent many days studying this phenomenon in deep, trench walls. When one has seen the water filter through these root-made passageways and darken the color of the dry soil quite beyond the general depth of water penetration, no doubt is left about root channels promoting water infiltration. Other roots follow these enriched, moist and well-aerated passageways. Along these routes some roots of grasses penetrate several to many inches beyond the general root level. Thus, roots of forbs utilize, enrich, and make the deeper soils more porous. Forbs are also soil builders. Disappearance of the best forbs from a range is a serious loss.

When a prairie is grazed so long or so heavily that most native forbs have disappeared and have been replaced by weeds, serious changes have occurred in the soil-plant relationships. By this time the roots of the best grasses are dying. They are fewer and shallower since the ends are dying or dead. Root relations in a part of the same little bluestem range from which the soil monolith (Fig. 92) was taken but where forbs were scarce and grazing pressure was becoming too great are shown in figure 93. A vigorous bunch of little bluestem remains on the right; a bunch much weakened by frequent grazing is on the left; the space between has become occupied by invading Kentucky bluegrass. The general effect is a decrease in the depth of absorption.

RELATION OF FORBS TO GRAZING

Most forbs are valuable as food for livestock. Mostly in overused ranges, where the species with good grazing preference have disappeared, does one find the remaining forbs of little or no value as forage. The most-liked species belong to the group called decreasers, since they become fewer and fewer in areas that are overgrazed. The following list is representative of

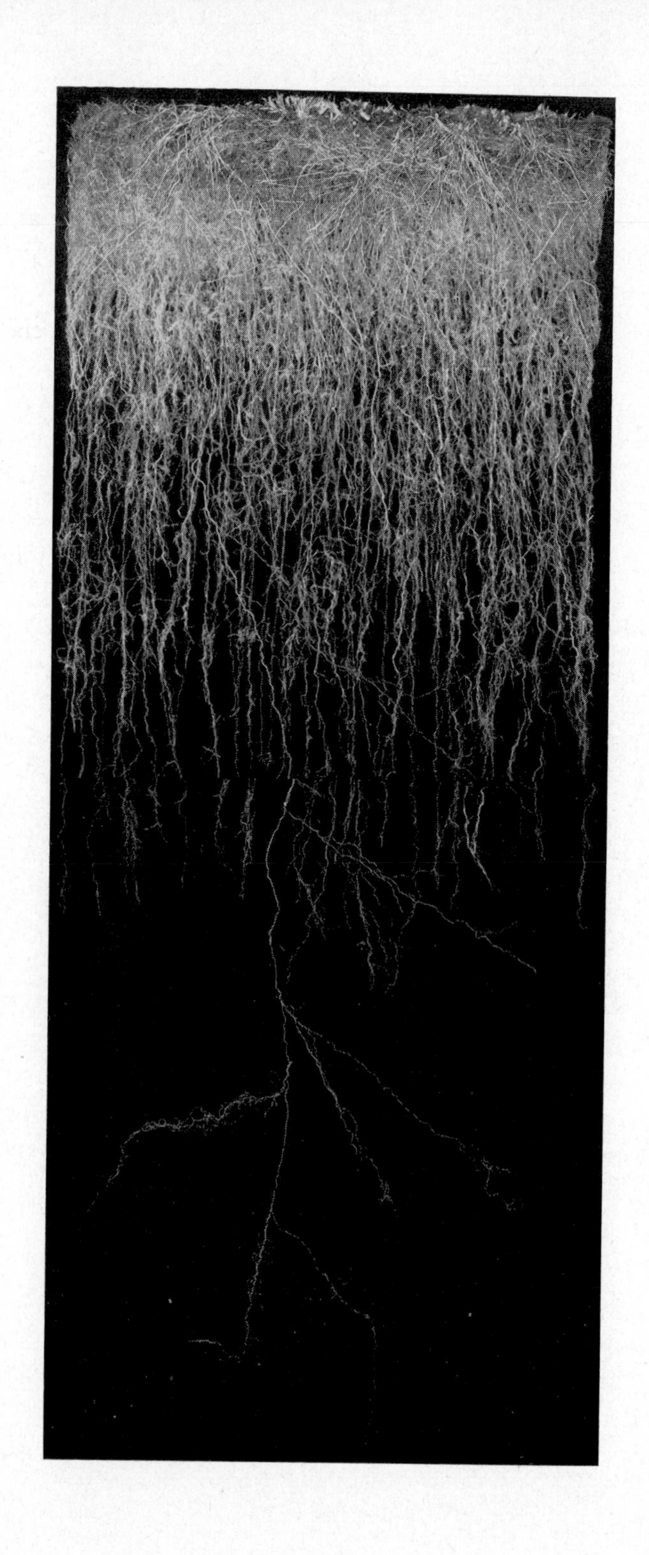

FIG. 92. Roots from a monolith of soil 2.5 feet wide, 3 inches thick and 6 feet deep. It was taken in two three-foot sections. The deepest grass roots were about 4 feet long. Roots of a prairie legume (*Psoralea tenuiflora*) extended even deeper.

FIG. 93. Typical root distribution in a mid-grade pasture. The soil monolith is 2.5 feet wide, 3 inches thick and 6 feet deep. From left to right are shown a non-vigorous bunch of little bluestem, bluegrass, and a vigorous (lightly grazed) bunch of little bluestem. The 2-foot depth of roots is about normal in this soil for bluegrass. Differences in root habit of the bluestem may be attributed to differences in vigor resulting from grazing.

forbs with good palatability and high food value. They are regularly eaten with the grasses and are liked by livestock and prairie wildlife not only because of their protein and other nutrient content, which are high, but also because they usually remain green and succulent in drought after the grasses have become dry. The following are representative decreasers:

Lead plant
Amorpha canescens
Ground plum
Astragalus crassicarpus
Drummond milk vetch
Astragalus drummondi
Licorice
Glycyrrhiza lepidota
Prairie clovers
Petalostemum spp.
Silver-leaf psoralea
Psoralea argophylla
Silver lupine
Lupinus argenteus
Purple coneflower
Echinacea angustifolia
Beardtongue
Pentstemon spp.
Purple vetch
Vicia americana
Prairie rose
Rosa suffulta
Wild onions
Allium spp.
False boneset
Kuhnia eupatorioides
Blazing star
Liatris punctata

Some plants, such as biscuitroot (principally species of *Lomatium,* which are plants of the carrot family with large, much-divided and mostly prostrate leaves), pasque flower (*Anemone patens*) and sego or star lily (*Calochortus nuttallii*), are sought out and eaten in early spring when green forage is scarce.

In areas where lead plant was abundant the forage was clipped 4 times during the growing season. This species alone furnished 150 to 200 pounds of air-dry forage per acre. This, however, is often the total air-dry weight of edible forbs per acre on many prairies. Sensitive brier contains as much as 20 per cent protein. Despite its prickles this forb is closely grazed when young by cattle and horses. Red false mallow is also high in protein. It is eaten by all classes of stock throughout mixed prairie.

It has been shown that since the drought the edible forbs are coming back much more slowly than the grasses. Repeated removal of the tops of forbs always produces decrease in vigor and often results in their death. A good intermixture of forbs gives needed variety in many excellent ranges. They add to the amount and especially to the quality of food for livestock. Animals get more nutrients from a smaller volume of forage when grasses and forbs are intermixed.

Cattle have a preference for certain species and this preference is seasonal. In the Northern Great Plains where the growing season is short and where a great variety of cool-season and warm-season grasses and forbs are intermixed, it is especially necessary to understand the distribution of the various elements of the forage on different sites, their season of growth and their season of use by livestock (Holscher and Woolfolk, 1953).

A considerable number of native forbs either are entirely uneaten by livestock or are grazed so sparingly that they are not much handicapped. They profit by release from vigorous competition of the decreasers and often by the opening of the plant cover. They usually increase greatly in numbers and often in stature. The following list is representative but includes only a small number of species (increasers) whose presence in abundance indicates a downward trend in grazing (Weaver and Hansen, 1941; Dyksterhuis, 1948, 1949; Voigt and Weaver, 1951).

Yarrow
Achillea lanulosa
Cudweed sage
Artemisia ludoviciana
Many-flowered aster
Aster ericoides
Cut-leaved goldenweed
Haplopappus spinulosus
Rush-like lygodesmia
Lygodesmia juncea
Hood's or dwarf phlox
Phlox hoodii
Western ragweed
Ambrosia psilostachya
Gumweed
Grindelia squarrosa
Crazyweed
Oxytropis lambertii
Indian paintbrush
Castilleja spp.
Stiff goldenrod
Solidago rigida
Ironweed
Vernonia baldwini
Wooly vervain
Verbena stricta
Scarlet gaura
Gaura coccinea

Some species, such as gumweed, have no grazing value; others, such as broom snakeweed, are of low forage value even to sheep and goats.

Certain increasers are of such wide distribution and occur so abundantly that they are generally considered as indicators of overuse of mixed prairie. These are fringed sage (*Artemisia frigida*), especially northward, broom snakeweed (*Gutierrezia sarothrae*) in the central plains, and sand sage (*Artemisia filifolia*) in sand. Even pricklypear cactus is of good forage value if the spines are removed. It may be eaten by sheep to a limited extent in early summer before the spines of the new branches become rigid. In drought areas in the southwest, ranges may become almost devoid of grass, and pricklypear (*Opuntia*) burning may develop into a daily occupation. The original method was to cut the cactus and hold it, with a pitchfork, over a flame. The spines singe off rather readily. Now the flames from mobile gasoline torches ("pear burners") are employed. As the operators of the pear burners work, hungry cattle on the grassless ranges follow closely at their heels, devouring the green and succulent food as fast as it is burned (Cunningham, 1952).

As long as prairie maintains a complete cover, only decreasers and increasers grow among the grasses, at least in any abundance. When grazing and trampling result in the death of many native species and thus opens the cover, a host of unwanted plants, weeds, invade. Many of these are inedible forbs, such as buffalo bur (*Solanum rostratum*), fetid marigold (*Dyssodia papposa*), and knotweed (*Polygonum aviculare*). Others, such as lamb's quarters (*Chenopodium album*), peppergrass (*Lepidium densiflorum*) and various plantains (*Plantago*), are of low forage value. They are mostly shallowly rooted, absorbing only in the first two or three feet of soil, and their taproot systems do not hold the soil well against erosion. They are a low-grade lot, using the space (light), water and nutrients that were formerly used by far more productive and nutritious plants. They are neither decreasers nor increasers but are best classified as invaders, since none occurs generally in mixed prairie in good condition.

The quality of the forage may also be much reduced in disclimax mixed prairie. "Native grass ranges and pastures [in southwestern North Dakota] which have been reduced to a predominately short-grass type by heavy grazing have a definitely lower quality from the standpoint of season-long nutritive value than ranges and pastures which have been maintained in the mixed-grass condition" (Whitman *et al.*, 1951). They found that the maximum levels of carotene, protein and phosphorus were higher in cool-season grasses than in warm-season grasses. The maximum levels of these constituents were reached about two months later in warm-season than in cool-season species.

The rancher was quite right in his answer to the question about the kind of grass his cattle liked best. Green grass was his reply. The grazing of patches of sand dropseed to the neglect of the supposedly more palatable short grasses is of interest and quite common in occurrence. It results from the fact that sand dropseed had been grazed the previous year (or very early in spring) while the short grasses had been neglected. Thus, what may seem to be a poorer quality of green forage is often selected by cattle in preference to a better one intermixed with dry leaves.

Grazing animals not only prefer green feed but also seldom graze one species to the exclusion of others, because they prefer a mixed diet. In one experiment cattle were observed to leave a good pasture of bluestem, bluegrass, and western wheatgrass to graze summer cypress (*Kochia scoparia*) which grew on an adjacent lowland. They removed 1.55 tons per acre of this "weed" in June and somewhat more in July, grazing it almost daily (Darland and Weaver, 1945). The leaves and stems were green and succulent and were greatly relished. Similar attraction for young Russian thistles and various other species has long been noted by cattlemen. Livestock will often leave a good stand of short grasses to graze succulent weeds, such as lamb's quarters and pigweeds.

Many stockmen have wondered whether this craving for variety is of any practical significance. It has been shown that gains in weight of cattle are strongly influenced by weeds and shrubs as well as by grasses. Grazing experiments at Nunn in northeastern Colorado have been conducted in a series of 12 pastures of 320 acres each. Here as in most eastern Colorado short-grass ranges, blue grama and buffalo grass furnish 80 per cent and often much more of the forage. Costello (1942) states that the grazing experiments have shown consistent differences of 35 to 60 pounds in the seasonal gains of yearling Herefords. "These differences in gains between pastures are not explainable on the basis of grazing intensity, location of forage, or effect of feeding during the winter. Instead, they seem to be related to the composition of the forage as determined by the percentage of certain grasses, weeds, and shrubs in the pastures." The secondary grasses were mostly western wheatgrass (*Agropyron smithii*), red three-awn (*Aristida purpurea*), and desert saltgrass (*Distichlis stricta*). Most abundant forbs were Russian thistle (*Salsola kali*), red false mallow (*Sphaeralcea coccinea*), tansy aster (*Aster tanacetifolius*), lamb's quarters (*Chenopodium album*) and peppergrass (*Lepidium*). The preceding, with fourwing saltbush (*Atriplex canescens*), made up 10 to 20 per cent of the total forage. "Apparently, the relatively small amount of forage provided by the secondary species balances possible nutrient deficiencies that may occur when the diet is almost exclusively grama and buffalo grass." The tendencies have been observed over a period of years.

Many ranges of mixed prairie, as we have seen, contain various shrubs and half-shrubs which furnish browse for livestock. Chief among these species are the following:

Sand sage *Artemisia filifolia*	Fringed sage *Artemisia frigida*
Big sage *Artemisia tridentata*	Skunkbush sumac *Rhus trilobata*
Saltbush shadscale *Atriplex confertifolia*	Fendler rose *Rosa woodsii*
Fourwinged saltbush *Atriplex canescens*	Winterfat *Eurotia lanata*
Black greasewood *Sarcobatus vermiculatus*	Small soapweed *Yucca glauca*
Silver sage *Artemisia cana*	Greenplume rabbitbrush *Chrysothamnus nauseosus*

Nearly all browse species are most useful for winter forage when the grasses and forbs no longer furnish green feed, although the leaves and twigs (or fruits and seeds) of some are eaten in summer and fall. Many have a very high protein and carotene content and therefore furnish excellent supplementary feed in winter when the cured grasses are low in these essentials; moreover, the grasses may be covered with snow. Cattle prefer to use browse in winter, and in severe winters they utilize it extensively. In the sandy lands of southern Kansas and in Oklahoma the ranges are used year-long. In summer the layer of short and mid grass and even some tall grasses grow mostly below the sand sage and furnish good summer grazing. In winter the cattle utilize the remaining grasses in part and the semipalatable sand sage, which is often grazed by choice in winter. In most areas ranges with considerable browse are reserved for winter grazing; most species would not be utilized in summer. As pointed out by Holscher and Woolfolk (1953), "forage species should be grazed, insofar as possible, when they are most useful and most attractive to cattle: early maturing species early; summer growing species during the summer months; tall species, which cure well, during the winter." To do this, of course, the range manager must know the growth habits, season of greatest palatability, and grazing values of the 15 to 25 most important plants on his range. In addition he must thoroughly understand range management.

Palatable perennial forbs and desirable shrubs should and can be maintained by conservative grazing. Experienced range managers have found that "forage of good or excellent quality is the outcome of conservative grazing which permits the establishment and maintenance of a variety of forage species, including grasses, perennial weeds [forbs], and shrubs that contribute to a well-balanced animal diet. Grazing management contributes more to this variety of plants on the range than the occasional year of heavy precipitation" (Costello, 1944).

Under sound range management plant communities of the mixed prairie are allowed to produce their best density in relation to climate, their greatest volume of forage, and their maximum expression of a varied composition (*cf.* Allred, 1940).

MIXED VEGETATION IS BEST

It is well known by range managers that the better the range condition the greater will be the variety of grasses and other plants. There are many disadvantages in a range composed of only one or a few species instead of the 15 to 25 important grasses and forbs which often occur. When the upper story of vegetation has been destroyed and it is safe to remove only half of the remaining forage produced by blue grama and buffalo grass, average annual yield in the central plains is often limited to 350 to 500 pounds per acre. Yields are nearly always less than when the vegetation grows at various heights and numerous grasses and forbs contribute a part. They utilize the light to better advantage and absorb water and nutrients at several soil levels, thus decreasing the dwarfing effects of severe competition. Some species of cool-season grasses and forbs furnish valuable green feed weeks before the short grasses renew growth. In drought, when short grasses dry many other species remain green somewhat longer, and deeply rooted forbs are often succulent during extended drought. Forbs as well as shrubs often remain green later in the fall than do most grasses. Moreover, available data indicate that many possess a higher nutritive value than the drying or cured grasses.

Mid grasses mature early in the Northern Great Plains, mostly before infestations of grasshoppers occur. Hence, these insects eat the grasses which are tender and growing in summer, native forbs and weeds. Thus, the mid grasses are left as forage for livestock in late summer and winter. In major grasshopper plagues, of course, all green plants, including mid grasses and shrubs, may be consumed. "However, in chronically but mildly infested regions common to areas in the northern plains the major livestock forage is produced by the mid grasses because the incessant crop of grasshoppers make away with the summer-growing short grasses" Allred (1941).

In southwestern North Dakota two mid grasses, western wheatgrass and needle-and-thread, and a short grass and a short sedge, blue grama and thread-leaf sedge, compose the great bulk of the vegetation. An 8-year clipping experiment has revealed that per unit of vegetational area each of the mid grasses yields about twice as much forage as thread-leaf sedge and about eight times as much as blue grama. Under heavy use by cattle the mid grasses, which are 15 to 30 inches high when in bloom, decrease; but blue grama which is 4 to 12 inches high, may increase greatly. This results in a general decrease in the quantity of forage (Whitman *et al.*, 1953).

Common Names Used Without Accompanying Scientific Names

GRASSES AND SEDGES

Alkali sacaton	*Sporobolus airoides*
Big bluestem	*Andropogon gerardi*
Black grama	*Bouteloua eriopoda*
Bluebunch wheatgrass	*Agropyron spicatum*
Blue grama	*Bouteloua gracilis*
Blowout grass	*Redfieldia flexuosa*
Bromegrass	*Bromus*
Buffalo grass	*Buchloe dactyloides*
Canada bluegrass	*Poa compressa*
Canada wild-rye	*Elymus canadensis*
Canby bluegrass	*Poa canbyi*
Cane bluestem	*Andropogon barbinodis*
Curly mesquite	*Hilaria belangeri*
Desert saltgrass	*Distichlis stricta*
False buffalo grass	*Munroa squarrosa*
Galleta	*Hilaria jamesii*
Green needlegrass	*Stipa viridula*
Hairy chess	*Bromus commutatus*
Hairy grama	*Bouteloua hirsuta*
Idaho fescue	*Festuca idahoensis*
Indian grass	*Sorghastrum nutans*
Indian ricegrass	*Oryzopsis hymenoides*
June grass	*Koeleria cristata*
Kentucky bluegrass	*Poa pratensis*
Little barley	*Hordeum pusillum*
Little bluestem	*Andropogon scoparius*
Needle-and-thread	*Stipa comata*
Needlegrass	*Stipa spartea*
Needle-leaf sedge	*Carex eleocharis*
New Mexico feathergrass	*Stipa neomexicana*
Nuttall alkaligrass	*Puccinellia airoides*

Penn sedge	*Carex pennsylvanica*
Plains bluegrass	*Poa arida*
Plains muhly	*Muhlenbergia cuspidata*
Prairie Junegrass	*Koeleria cristata*
Purple three-awn	*Aristida purpurea*
Red three-awn	*Aristida longiseta*
Ringgrass	*Muhlenbergia torreyi*
Sandberg bluegrass	*Poa secunda*
Sand bluestem	*Andropogon hallii*
Sand dropseed	*Sporobolus cryptandrus*
Sandhill muhly	*Muhlenbergia pungens*
Sand lovegrass	*Eragrostis trichodes*
Sand reed	*Calamovilfa longifolia*
Scribner panic grass	*Panicum scribnerianum*
Side-oats grama	*Bouteloua curtipendula*
Silver beardgrass	*Andropogon saccharoides*
Six-weeks fescue	*Festuca octoflora hirtella*
Sloughgrass	*Spartina pectinata*
Squirreltail	*Sitanion hystrix*
Stinkgrass	*Eragrostis cilianensis*
Stonyhills muhly	*Muhlenbergia cuspidata*
Sun sedge	*Carex heliophila*
Switchgrass	*Panicum virgatum*
Tall dropseed	*Sporobolus asper*
Tobosa grass	*Hilaria mutica*
Thickspike wheatgrass	*Agropyron dasystachyum*
Thread-leaf sedge	*Carex filifolia*
Three-awn grass	*Aristida*
Tumblegrass	*Schedonnardus paniculatus*
Virginia wild-rye	*Elymus virginicus*
Western wheatgrass	*Agropyron smithii*
Windmill grass	*Chloris verticillata*
Wire grass	*Aristida*
Witchgrass	*Panicum capillare*

OTHER SPECIES

Ball cactus	*Neomammillaria vivipara*
Big sage	*Artemisia tridentata*
Biscuitroot	*Lomatium*
Blazing star	*Liatris punctata*
Broom snakeweed	*Gutierrezia sarothrae*

Buffalo bur	*Solanum rostratum*
Bush morning-glory	*Ipomoea leptophylla*
Common sunflower	*Helianthus annuus*
Cut-leaf goldenweed	*Haplopappus spinulosus*
Dwarf phlox	*Phlox hoodii*
False boneset	*Kuhnia eupatorioides*
Few-flowered psoralea	*Psoralea tenuiflora*
Flax	*Linum*
Fleabane	*Erigeron*
Fringed sage	*Artemisia frigida*
Hairy golden aster	*Chrysopsis villosa*
Hood's phlox	*Phlox hoodii*
Horseweed	*Conyza canadensis*
Lamb's quarters	*Chenopodium album*
Lance-leaved psoralea	*Psoralea lanceolata*
Lead plant	*Amorpha canescens*
Licorice	*Glycyrrhiza*
Linear-leaved sage	*Artemisia dracunculus*
Many-flowered aster	*Aster ericoides*
Mesquite	*Prosopis*
Milfoil	*Achillea*
Milkwort	*Polygala*
Missouri goldenrod	*Solidago missouriensis*
Narrow-leaved four-o'clock	*Mirabilis linearis*
Narrow-leaved goosefoot	*Chenopodium leptophyllum*
Peppergrass	*Lepidium densiflorum*
Pigweed	*Amaranthus*
Plantain	*Plantago*
Prairie clover	*Petalostemum*
Prairie coneflower	*Ratibida columnifera*
Prairie rose	*Rosa suffulta*
Prairie sunflower	*Helianthius petiolaris*
Prairie turnip	*Psoralea esculenta*
Prickleypear	*Opuntia*
Puccoon	*Lithospermum*
Red false mallow	*Sphaeralcea coccinea*
Rush-like lygodesmia	*Lygodesmia juncea*
Russian thistle	*Salsola kali*

Sand sage	*Artemisia filifolia*
Scarlet gaura	*Gaura coccinea*
Scarlet globemallow	*Sphaeralcea coccinea*
Silver-leaf psoralea	*Psoralea argophylla*
Silver sage	*Artemisia cana*
Smooth goldenrod	*Solidago missouriensis*
Small soapweed	*Yucca glauca*
Stickseed	*Lappula*
Stiff sunflower	*Helianthus laetiflorus (rigidus)*
Tooth-leaved primrose	*Oenothera serrulata*
Wavy-leaved thistle	*Cirsium undulatum*
Western ragweed	*Ambrosia psilostachya*
Wild onion	*Allium*

LITERATURE CITED

Albertson, F. W. 1937. Ecology of mixed prairie in west central Kansas. Ecol. Monog. 7:481–547.

———. 1949. Man's disorder of nature's design in the Great Plains. Trans. Kans. Acad. Sci. 52:117–131.

———, A. Riegel and J. L. Launchbaugh, Jr. 1953. Effects of different intensities of clipping on short grasses in west-central Kansas. Ecology 34:1–20.

——— and J. E. Weaver. 1942. History of the native vegetation of western Kansas during seven years of continuous drought. Ecol. Monog. 12: 23–51.

——— and J. E. Weaver. 1944. Effects of drought, dust, and intensity of grazing on cover and yield of shortgrass pastures. Ecol. Monog. 14:1–29.

——— and J. E. Weaver. 1945. Injury and death or recovery of trees in prairie climate. Ecol. Monog. 15:393–433.

Allred, B. W. 1940. Range conservation practices for the Great Plains. U.S. Dept. Agr. Misc. Pub. 410.

———. 1941. The significance of grassland ecology to the northern Great Plains. Northern Great Plains grassland conference, Mandan, N. Dak. (Soil Conserv. Serv., Mimeo.)

———. 1941a. Grasshoppers and their effect on sagebrush on the Little Powder River in Wyoming and Montana. Ecology 22:387–392.

———. 1945. Some conditions and influences pertaining to the native forage crop of the northern mixed prairie. Journ. Amer. Soc. Agron. 37:876–887.

———. 1946. Articles on range vegetation and range management. Sheep and Goat Raiser. Jan. 1946 to Nov. 1955. San Angelo, Texas.

———. 1950. Practical Grassland Management. Sheep and Goat Raiser, San Angelo, Texas.

——— and H. C. Mitchell. 1954. Major plant types of Arkansas, Louisiana, Oklahoma and Texas. U.S. Dept. Agr. Soil Conserv. Serv.

——— and H. C. Mitchell. 1955. Major plant types of Arkansas, Louisiana, Oklahoma and Texas and their relation to climate and soils. Texas Journ. Sci. 7(1):7–19.

——— and W. W. Nixon. 1955. Grass conservation in the southern Great Plains. U.S. Dept. Agr., Farmers' Bull. 2093.

Atwood, W. W. 1940. The Physiographic Provinces of North America. Ginn and Co., Chicago.

Beetle, A. A. 1950. Buffalograss—Native of the shortgrass plains. Univ. Wyo. Agr. Expt. Sta. Bull. 293.

Bennett, H. H. 1939. Soil Conservation. McGraw-Hill Book Co., Inc. New York.

Bentley, H. L. 1898. Cattle ranges of the southwest: a history of the exhaustion of the pasturage and suggestions for its restoration. U.S. Dept. Agr., Farmers' Bull. 72.

Black, W. H. *et al.* 1937. Effect of different methods of grazing on native vegetation and gains of steers in the northern Great Plains. U.S. Dept. Agr. Tech. Bull. 547.

——— and O. R. Mathews. 1930. Wintering steers in the northern Great Plains section. U.S. Dept. Agr. Tech. Bull. 192.

Booth, W. E. 1941. Revegetation of abandoned fields in Kansas and Oklahoma. Amer. Journ. Bot. 28:415–422.

Borchert, J. R. 1950. The climate of the central North American grassland. Ann. Assoc. Amer. Geographers 40:1–39.

Brandon, J. F. and A. Kezer. 1936. Soil blowing and its control in Colorado. Colo. Agr. Expt. Sta. Bull. 419.

Branson, F. A. 1952. Native pastures of the dissected Loess Plains of central Nebraska. Doctorate thesis, Dept. Botany, Univ. Nebr.

——— and J. E. Weaver. 1953. Quantitative study of degeneration of mixed prairie. Bot. Gaz. 114:397–416.

Bray, W. L. 1906. Distribution and adaptation of the vegetation of Texas. Univ. Texas Bull. 82.

Brinegar, T. E. and F. D. Keim. 1942. The relations of vegetative composition and cattle grazing on Nebraska range land. Nebr. Agr. Expt. Sta. Res. Bull. 123.

Bruner, W. E. 1931. The vegetation of Oklahoma. Ecol. Monog. 1:99–188.

——— and J. E. Weaver. 1923. Size and structure of leaves of cereals in relation to climate. Univ. Nebr. Studies 23:163–200.

Bugbee, R. E. and A. Riegel. 1945. The cactus moth, *Melitara dentata* (Grote), and its effect on *Opuntia macrorhiza* in western Kansas. Amer. Midl. Nat. 33:117–127.

Campbell, R. S. 1936. Climatic fluctuations on western ranges and corresponding fluctuations in vegetative growth. In The Western Range, pp. 135–150. Senate Document 199.

———, L. Ellison and F. G. Renner, 1948. Management that restores the range. U.S. Dept. Agr. Yearbook, Grass.

Carpenter, J. R. 1940. The grassland biome. Ecol. Monog. 10:617–683.

Chapline, W. R. 1936. Excessive stocking. In The Western Range, pp. 151–171. Senate Document 190.

Chilcott, E. C. 1927. The relation between crop yields and precipitation in the Great Plains area. U.S. Dept. Agr. Misc. Circ. 81, p. 94.

Clarke, S. E. 1930. Pasture investigations on the short grass plains of Saskatchewan and Alberta. Sci. Agr. 10:732–749.

———, J. A. Campbell and J. B. Campbell. 1942. An ecological and grazing capacity study of the native grass pastures in southern Alberta, Saskatchewan and Manitoba. Dom. Can., Dept. Agr. Tech. Bull. 44.

——— and E. W. Tisdale. 1936. Pasture studies in southern Alberta and Saskatchewan. Herbage Rev. 4:51–64.

——— and E. W. Tisdale. 1945. The chemical composition of native forage plants of southern Alberta and Saskatchewan in relation to grazing practices. Dom. Can., Dept. Agr. Tech. Bull. 54.

———, E. W. Tisdale and N. A. Skoglund. 1943. The effects of climate and grazing practices on short-grass prairie vegetation. Dom. Can., Dept. Agr. Tech. Bull. 46.

Clements, F. E. 1916. Plant Succession. Carnegie Inst. Wash., Pub. 242.

———. 1920. Plant Indicators. Carnegie Inst. Wash., Pub. 290.

———. 1934. The relict method in dynamic ecology. Journ. Ecol. 22:39–68.

———. 1936. Origin of the desert climax and climate. Reprint from Essays in Geobotany. Univ. Calif. Press.

———. 1936a. Nature and structure of the climax. Journ. Ecology 24:252–284.

———. 1938. Climatic cycles and human populations in the Great Plains. Sci. Monthly 47:193–210.

———. 1949. Dynamics of Vegetation. H. W. Wilson Co., New York.

——— and R. W. Chaney. 1936. Environment and life in the Great Plains. Carnegie Inst. Wash., Supplementary Pub. 24.

——— and E. S. Clements. 1939. The

sagebrush disclimax. Carnegie Inst. Wash., Yearbook 38:139–140.
——— and V. E. Shelford. 1939. Bio-ecology. John Wiley and Sons, New York.
——— and J. E. Weaver. 1924. Experimental Vegetation. Carnegie Inst. Wash., Pub. 355.
Condra, G. E. 1920. The soil resources of Nebraska. Univ. Nebr. Conserv. and Soil Surv. Bull. 15.
———. 1939. An outline of the principal natural resources of Nebraska and their conservation. Univ. Nebr. Conserv. and Surv. Div. Bull. 20.
———, E. C. Reed and E. D. Gordon. 1950. Correlation of the Pleistocene deposits of Nebraska. Univ. Nebr. Conserv. and Surv. Div. Geol. Surv. Bull. 15A.
Cook, C. W. 1942. Insects and weather as they influence growth of cactus on the central Great Plains. Ecology 23:209–214.
Cooper, H. W. 1953. Amounts of big sagebrush in plant communities near Tensleep, Wyoming, as affected by grazing treatment. Ecology 34:186–189.
Cornelius, D. R. 1947. The effect of source of little bluestem grass seed on growth, adaptation, and use in revegetation seedings. Journ. Agr. Res. 74:133–143.
———. 1950. Seed production of native grasses under cultivation in eastern Kansas. Ecol. Monog. 20:1–29.
Costello, D. F. 1941. Pricklypear control on the shortgrass range in the central Great Plains. U.S. Dept. Agr. Leaflet 210.
———. 1942. Weight gains of cattle strongly influenced by weeds and shrubs as well as by grasses. Colo. Farm Bull. 4:14–15.
———. 1944. Efficient cattle production on Colorado ranges. Extension serv., Colo. State College Bull. 383-A.
———. 1944a. Natural revegetation of abandoned plowed land in the mixed prairie association of northeastern Colorado. Ecology 25:312–326.
———. 1944b. Important species of the major forage types in Colorado and Wyoming. Ecol. Monog. 14:107–134.
——— and G. T. Turner. 1944. Judging condition and utilization of short-grass ranges on the central Great Plains. U.S. Dept. Agr., Farmers' Bull. 1949.
Coupland, R. T. 1950. Ecology of mixed prairie in Canada. Ecol. Monog. 20:271–315.
———. 1952. Grassland communities of the western Canadian prairies—climax and subclimax. Proc. Sixth International Grassland Congress.
——— and T. C. Brayshaw. 1953. The fescue grassland in Saskatchewan. Ecology 34:386–405.
Cunningham, J. 1952. Prickly pear. The Cattlemen 39:82–84. Fort Worth, Texas.
Darland, R. W. and J. E. Weaver. 1945. Yields and consumption of forage in three pasture-types: an ecological analysis. Univ. Nebr. Conserv. and Surv. Div. Bull. 27.
Dyksterhuis, E. J. 1948. The vegetation of the Western Cross Timbers. Ecol. Monog. 18:325–376.
———. 1949. Condition and management of range land based on quantitative ecology. Journ. Range Mgt. 2:104–115.
Edwards, E. E. 1948. The settlement of grasslands, U.S. Dept. Agr. Yearbook, Grass.
Elias, M. K. 1932. Grasses and other plants from the Tertiary rocks of Kansas and Colorado. Univ. Kans. Bull. 33:333–367.
———. 1935. Tertiary grasses and other prairie vegetation from the High Plains of North America. Amer. Journ. Sci. 5th Ser. 29:24–33.
———. 1942. Tertiary prairie grasses and other herbs from the High Plains. Geol. Soc. Amer. Special papers. No. 41.

Ellison, L. and E. J. Woolfolk. 1937. Effects of drought on vegetation near Miles City, Montana. Ecology 18: 329–336.

Ellison, W. D. 1944. Studies of raindrop erosion. Agricultural Eng. 25: 131–136.

Fenneman, N. M. 1931. Physiography of Western United States. McGraw-Hill Book Co., Inc., New York.

Finnell, H. H. 1948. The dust storms of 1948. Scientific American 179 (2):7–11.

Flory, E. L. and D. F. Trussell. 1938. Observation of plant competition, plant succession, plant-soil relationships, overgrazing and erosion on sagebrush areas. U.S. Dept. Agr., Soil Conserv. Service, Region 8. Regional Bull. 24 (Mimeo.).

Franzke, C. J. and A. N. Hume. 1942. Regrassing areas in South Dakota. S. Dak. Agr. Expt. Sta. Bull. 361.

Frolik, A. L. and W. O. Shepherd. 1940. Vegetative composition and grazing capacity of a typical area of Nebraska sandhill range land. Univ. Nebr. Agr. Expt. Sta. Res. Bull. 117.

Gleason, H. A. 1952. The New Britton and Brown Illustrated Flora of the Northeastern United States and Adjacent Canada. The New York Botanical Garden.

Great Plains Committee. 1937. The Future of the Great Plains. U.S. Govt. Printing Office. Wash., D.C.

Hanson, H. C. 1955. Characteristics of the *Stipa comata—Bouteloua gracilis—Bouteloua curtipendula* association in northern Colorado. Ecol. Monog. 36:269–280.

———, L. D. Love and M. S. Morris. 1931. Effects of different systems of grazing by cattle upon a western wheat-grass type of range. Colo. Expt. Sta. Bull. 377.

——— and W. Whitman. 1937. Plant succession on solenetz soils in western North Dakota. Ecology 18: 516–522.

——— and W. Whitman. 1938. Characteristics of major grassland types in western North Dakota. Ecol. Monog. 8:57–114.

Harrington, H. D. 1954. Manual of the Plants of Colorado. Sage Books, Denver, Colo.

Harvey, A. D. 1936. Rootsprouts as a means of vegetative reproduction in *Opuntia polyacantha.* Journ. Amer. Soc. Agron. 28:767–768.

Hayward, H. E. 1928. Studies of plants in the Black Hills of South Dakota. Bot. Gaz. 85:353–412.

Heady, H. F. 1950. Studies on bluebunch wheatgrass in Montana and height-weight relationships of certain range grasses. Ecol. Monog. 20:55–81.

———. 1952. Reseeding, fertilizing, and renovating in an ungrazed mixed prairie. Journ. Range Mgt. 5:144–149.

Hitchcock, A. S. and A. Chase. 1950. Manual of the Grasses of the United States. U.S. Dept. Agr. Misc. Pub. No. 200.

Holscher, C. E. and E. J. Woolfolk. 1953. Forage utilization by cattle on northern Great Plains ranges. U.S. Dept. Agr. Circ. 918.

Hopkins, H. H. 1941. Variations in the growth of side-oats grama grass at Hays, Kansas, from seed produced in various parts of the Great Plains region. Trans. Kans. Acad. Sci. 44: 86–95.

———. 1951. Ecology of the native vegetation of the loess hills in central Nebraska. Ecol. Monog. 21:125–147.

Hubbard, W. A. 1950. The climate, soils, and soil-plant relationships of an area in southwestern Saskatchewan. Sci. Agr. 30:327–342.

Hull, A. C., Jr., N. A. Kissinger, Jr. and W. T. Vaughn. 1952. Chemical control of big sagebrush in Wyoming. Journ. Range Mgt. 5:398–402.

Hurtt, L. C. 1948. The types of plains vegetation, pp. 484–486. In Yearbook of Agriculture, Grass.

———. 1950. Northern Great Plains

range problems. Northwestern Science 24:126–131.
———. 1951. Managing northern Great Plains cattle ranges to minimize effects of drought. U.S. Dept. Agr. Circ. 865.
Jameson, D. A. 1952. Nutritive value of browse on Montana winter ranges. Journ. Range Mgt. 5:306–310.
Johnson, L. E. *et al.* 1951. Cows, calves and grass. Effects of grazing intensities on beef cow and calf production and on mixed prairie vegetation on western South Dakota Ranges. S. Dak. Agr. Expt. Sta. Bull. 412.
Johnson, W. D. 1899–1900. The high plains and their utilization. Ann. Rept. U.S. Geol. Surv. 21^4:612.
———. 1900–1901. Ann. Rept. U.S. Geol. Surv. 22^4:637–638.
Judd, B. I. 1940. Natural succession of vegetation on abandoned farm lands in Teton County, Montana. Journ. Amer. Soc. Agronomy 32:330–336.
——— and M. L. Jackson. 1939. Natural succession of vegetation on abandoned farm lands in the Rosebud soil area of western Nebraska. Journ. Amer. Soc. Agron. 31:541–557.
Keim, F. D., A. L. Frolik and G. W. Beadle. 1932. Studies of prairie hay in north central Nebraska. Nebr. Agr. Expt. Sta. Res. Bull. 60.
Kincer, J. B. 1923. The climate of the Great Plains as a factor in their utilization. Ann. Assoc. Amer. Geographers 13:67–80.
Lang, R. 1945. Density changes of native vegetation in relation to precipitation. Wyo. Agr. Expt. Sta. Bull. 272.
——— and O. K. Barnes. 1942. Range forage production in relation to time and frequency of harvesting. Wyo. Agri. Expt. Sta. Bull. 253.
Larson, F. and W. Whitman. 1942. A comparison of used and unused grassland mesas in the Badlands of South Dakota. Ecology 23: 438–445.
Livingston, R. B. 1952. Relict true prairie communities in central Colorado. Ecology 33:72–86.
Lugn, A. L. 1939. Nebraska in relation to the problems of Pleistocene stratigraphy. Amer. Journ. Sci. 237:877.
McArdle, R. E. and D. F. Costello. 1936. The virgin range, pp. 71–80. In the Western Range. Senate Document 199.
——— *et al.* 1936. The white man's toll, pp. 81–116. In The Western Range. Senate Document 199.
McCorkle, J. S. and A. Heerwagen. 1951. Effects of range condition on livestock production. Jour. Range Mgt. 4:242–248.
McDonald, A. 1938. Erosion and its control in Oklahoma Territory. U.S. Dept. Agr. Misc. Pub. 301.
McIlvain, E. H., A. L. Baker and W. R. Kneebone. 1954. Eighteen-year summary of range improvement studies at the U.S. Southern Great Plains Field Station, Woodward, Oklahoma.
——— *et al.* 1955. Nineteen-year summary of range improvement studies at the U.S. Southern Great Plains Field Station, Woodward, Oklahoma.
——— and D. A. Savage. 1950. Fourteen-year summary of range improvement studies at the U.S. Southern Great Plains Field Station, Woodward, Oklahoma.
——— and D. A. Savage. 1954. Progress in range improvement. In Advances in Agronomy 6:1–65. Academic Press, Inc., New York.
Moorefield, J. G. and H. H. Hopkins. 1951. Grazing habits of cattle in a mixed-prairie pasture. Journ. Range Mgt. 4:151–157.
Morris, H. E. *et al.* 1950. Important grasses on Montana ranges. Mont. State Col. Agr. Expt. Sta. Bull. 470.
Moss, E. H. 1944. The prairie and associated vegetation of southwestern Alberta. Canadian Journ. Res. C 22:11–31.
Moss, E. H. 1955. The vegetation of Alberta. Bot. Rev. 21:493–567.
——— and J. A. Campbell. 1947. The

fescue grassland of Alberta. Canadian Journ. Res. C 25:209–227.

Moxon, A. L. *et al.* 1951. Grass hay at its best. S. Dak. Agr. Expt. Sta. Bull. 405.

Mueller, I. M. and J. E. Weaver. 1942. Relative drought resistance of seedlings of dominant prairie grasses. Ecology 23:387–398.

Nedrow, W. W. 1937. Studies on the ecology of roots. Ecology 18:27–52.

Newport, F. C. 1937. A corduroy coat protects High Plains from drought. Soil Conserv. 2(7):139.

Osborn, B. 1950. Some effects of the 1946–48 drought on ranges in southwest Texas. Journ. Range Mgt. 3:1–15.

Parker, K. W. 1954. Application of ecology in the determination of range condition and trend. Journ. Range Mgt. 7:14–23.

Peterson, R. A. and E. J. Woolfolk. 1955. Behavior of Hereford cows and calves on short grass range. Jour. Range Mgt. 8:51–57.

Phillips, P. 1935. Rodent distribution in overgrazed and normal grasslands. Thesis. Univ. Okla.

Pool, R. J. 1912. Glimpses of the Great American Desert. Popular Sci. Monthly 80:209–235.

———. 1914. A study of the vegetation of the sandhills of Nebraska. Minn. Bot. Studies 4:189–312.

Pound, R. and F. E. Clements. 1900. The Phytogeography of Nebraska. 2nd ed. Jacob North and Company, Lincoln.

Ramaley, F. 1939. Sand-hill vegetation of northeastern Colorado. Ecol. Monog. 9:1–51.

Rechenthin, C. A. 1949. Articles on range grasses of Texas. The Cattleman. Dec. 1949 to Aug. 1951. Fort Worth, Texas.

Reitz, L. P. and H. E. Morris. 1939. Important grasses and other common plants on Montana Ranges. Mont. State Col. Agr. Expt. Sta. Bull. 375.

Riegel, D. A. 1940. A study in the variations in the growth of blue grama grass from seed produced in various sections of the Great Plains region. Trans. Kans. Acad. Sci. 43:155–171.

———. 1941. Life history and habits of blue grama. Trans. Kans. Acad. Sci. 44:76–83.

———. 1947. Forage yields (1945) of various native pasture grasses established artificially at Hays, Kansas, in 1941. Trans. Kans. Acad. Sci. 50: 174–190.

Rydberg, P. A. 1895. Flora of the sandhills of Nebraska. Contrib. U.S. Natl. Herb. 3., No. 3.

Sampson, A. W. 1939. Plant indicators—concept and status. Bot. Review 3:155–206.

Sampson, H. S. 1921. An ecological survey of the prairie vegetation of Illinois. Ill. Nat. Hist. Surv. 13:523–577.

Sarvis, J. T. 1920. Composition and density of the native vegetation in the vicinity of the Northern Great Plains Field Station. Journ. Agr. Res. 19:63–72.

———. 1923. Effects of different systems and intensities of grazing upon the native vegetation at the Northern Great Plains Field Station. U.S. Dept. Agr. Bull. 1170.

———. 1941. Grazing investigations on the northern Great Plains. N. Dak. Agr. Expt. Sta. Bull. 308.

Sauer, C. O. 1950. Grassland climax, fire, and man. Jour. Range Mgt. 3: 16–21.

Saunderson, M. H. 1950. Western Stock Ranching. Univ. Minn. Press, Minneapolis.

Savage, D. A. 1937. Drought survival of native grass species in the central and southern Great Plains, 1935. U.S. Dept. Agr. Tech. Bull. 549.

———. 1939. Grass culture and range improvement in the central and southern Great Plains. U.S. Dept. Agr. Circ. 491.

——— and D. F. Costello, 1948. Range

management, pp. 522–537. In Yearbook of Agriculture, Grass.
——— and H. E. Runyon. 1937. Natural revegetation of abandoned farm land in the central and southern Great Plains. Rept., Fourth Intern. Grassland Congress, Aberystwyth, Gt. Britain. Sec. 1. Grassland Ecology, 178–182.
Schuchert, C. and C. O. Dunbar. 1941. Textbook of Geology: pt. 2, Historical Geology (pp. 443–444). John Wiley and Sons. New York.
Shantz, H. L. 1906. A study of the vegetation of the mesa region east of Pike's Peak: the Bouteloua Formation. Bot. Gaz. 42:16–47.
———. 1911. Natural vegetation as an indicator of the capabilities of land for crop production in the Great Plains area. U.S. Dept. Agr., Bureau Plant Industry, Bull. 201.
———. 1917. Plant succession on abandoned roads in eastern Colorado. Journ. Ecol. 5:19–42.
———. 1923. The natural vegetation of the Great Plains. Ann. Assoc. Amer. Geographers 13:81–107.
———. 1924. Grassland vegetation. Atlas of Amer. Agr. Pt. 1, Sec. E. U.S. Dept. Agr.
———. 1950. The ecological approach to land management. Journ. Forestry 48:673–675.
Shively, S. B. and J. E. Weaver. 1939. Amount of underground plant materials in different grassland climates. Univ. Nebr. Conserv. and Surv. Div. Bull. 21.
Smith, C. C. 1940. The effect of overgrazing and erosion upon the biota of the mixed-grass prairie of Oklahoma. Ecology 21:381–397.
———. 1940a. Biotic and physiographic succession on abandoned eroded farmland. Ecol. Monog. 10:421–484.
Smith, J. G. 1899. Grazing problems in the southwest and how to meet them. U.S. Dept. Agr. Div. Agrost., Bull. 16.
Smith, R. C. 1932. Upsetting the balance of nature, with special reference to Kansas and the Great Plains. Science 75:649–654.
Spang, E. F. 1954. Utilization of fringed sagewort on a winter sheep range. Journ. Range Mgt. 7:73–74.
Spragg, F. A. 1902. Forage conditions of central Montana. Mont. Agr. Expt. Sta. Bull. 36.
Stewart, G. 1936. History of range use, pp. 119–133. In The Western Range. Senate Document 199.
Stewart, O. C. 1953. Why the Great Plains are treeless. The Colorado Quarterly 2(1):40–50.
Stoddart, L. A. 1941. The Palouse grassland association in northern Utah. Ecology 22:158–163.
Tharp, B. C. Texas Range Grasses. 1952. Univ. Texas Press, Austin.
Timmons, F. L. and L. E. Wenger. 1940. Jackrabbits and cactus team up; present serious problem in 30 counties. Kansas Farmer 77(8):5, 22.
Tolstead, W. L. 1941. Plant communities and secondary succession in south-central South Dakota. Ecology 22:322–328.
———. 1942. Vegetation of the northern part of Cherry County, Nebraska. Ecol. Monog. 12:255–292.
Tomanek, G. W., F. W. Albertson, and A. Riegel. 1955. Natural revegetation on a field abandoned for thirty-three years in central Kansas. Ecology 36:407–412.
Turner, G. T. and D. F. Costello. 1942. Ecological aspects of the pricklypear problem in eastern Colorado and Wyoming. Ecology 23:419–426.
Turner, G. T. and G. E. Klipple. 1952. Growth characteristics of blue grama in northeastern Colorado. Journ. Range Mgt. 5:22–28.
Vass, A. F. and H. Pearson. 1933. Cattle production on Wyoming's mountain valley ranches. Wyo. Agr. Expt. Sta. Bull. 197.
Vestal, A. G. 1914. Prairie vegetation of a mountain-front area in Colorado. Bot. Gaz. 58:377–400.

Voigt, J. W. 1951. Vegetational changes on a 25 year subsere in the Loess Hill Region of central Nebraska. Journ. Range Mgt. 4:254–263.

——— and J. E. Weaver. 1951. Range condition classes of native midwestern pasture: an ecological analysis. Ecol. Monog. 21:39–60.

Weaver, J. E. 1917. A study of the vegetation of southeastern Washington and adjacent Idaho. Univ. Nebr. Studies 17:1–133.

———. 1919. The Ecological Relations of Roots. Carnegie Inst. Wash., Publ. 286.

———. 1920. Root Development in the Grassland Formation. Carnegie Inst. Wash., Pub. 292.

———. 1924. Plant production as a measure of environment: a study in crop ecology. Journ. Ecol. 12:205–237.

———. 1926. Root Development of Field Crops. McGraw-Hill Book Co., Inc., New York.

———. 1942. Competition of western wheat grass with relict vegetation of prairie. Amer. Journ. Bot. 29:366–372.

———. 1943. Replacement of True Prairie by Mixed Prairie in eastern Nebraska and Kansas. Ecology 24: 421–434.

———. 1950. Effects of different intensities of grazing on depth and quantity of roots of grasses. Journ. Range Mgt. 3:100–113.

———. 1954. North American Prairie. Johnsen Pub. Co., Lincoln, Nebr.

———. 1954a. A seventeen-year study of plant succession in prairie. Amer. Journ. Bot. 41:31–38.

——— and F. W. Albertson. 1936. Effects of the great drought on the prairies of Iowa, Nebraska, and Kansas. Ecology 17:567–639.

——— and F. W. Albertson. 1940. Deterioration of grassland from stability to denudation with decrease in soil moisture. Bot. Gaz. 101:598–624.

——— and F. W. Albertson. 1940a. Deterioration of midwestern ranges. Ecology 21:216–236.

——— and F. W. Albertson. 1943. Resurvey of grasses, forbs, and underground plant parts at the end of the great drought. Ecol. Monog. 13:63–117.

——— and F. W. Albertson. 1944. Nature and degree of recovery of grassland from the great drought of 1933 to 1940. Ecol. Monog. 14:393–479.

——— and W. E. Bruner. 1948. Prairies and pastures of the dissected loess plains of central Nebraska. Ecol. Monog. 18: 507–549.

——— and W. E. Bruner. 1954. Nature and place of transition from True Prairie to Mixed Prairie. Ecology 35: 117–126.

——— and F. E. Clements. 1938. Plant Ecology, 2nd ed. McGraw-Hill Book Co., Inc. New York.

——— and J. W. Crist. 1924. Direct measurement of water loss from vegetation without disturbing the normal structure of the soil. Ecology 5:153–170.

——— and R. W. Darland. 1947. A method of measuring vigor of range grasses. Ecology 28:146–162.

——— and R. W. Darland. 1949. Soil-root relationships of certain native grasses in various soil types. Ecol. Monog. 19:303–338.

——— and T. J. Fitzpatrick. 1932. Ecology and relative importance of the dominants of tall-grass prairie. Bot. Gaz. 93:113–150.

——— and T. J. Fitzpatrick. 1934. The prairie. Ecol. Monog. 4:109–295.

——— and E. L. Flory. 1934. Stability of climax prairie and some environmental changes resulting from breaking. Ecology 15:333–347.

——— and W. W. Hansen. 1941. Native midwestern pastures; their origin, composition, and degeneration. Univ. Nebr. Conserv. and Surv. Div. Bull. 22.

——— and G. W. Harmon. 1935. Quantity of living plant materials in prairie

soils in relation to runoff and soil erosion. Univ. Nebr. Conserv. and Surv. Div. Bull. 8.
——— and I. M. Mueller. 1942. Role of seedlings in recovery of midwestern ranges from drought. Ecology 23: 275–294.
———, L. A. Stoddart and W. Noll. 1935. Response of the prairie to the great drought of 1934. Ecology 16: 612–629.
——— and G. W. Tomanek. 1951. Ecological studies in a midwestern range: the vegetation and effects of cattle on its composition and distribution. Univ. Nebr. Conserv. and Surv. Div. Bull. 31.
Webb, J. J., Jr. 1941. The life history of buffalo grass. Trans. Kans. Acad. Sci. 44:58–75.
Wenger, L. E. 1943. Buffalo grass. Kans. Agr. Expt. Sta. Bull. 321.
Whitfield, C. J. and J. H. Jones. 1951. Production of feeder yearling steers at the Amarillo Station, 1950–51. Progress Rept. 1478. Texas Agr. Expt. Sta., College Station, Texas.
Whitman, W. *et al.* 1941. Grass. N. Dak. Agr. Expt. Sta. Bull. 300.
——— *et al.* 1943. Relation of drought and grazing to North Dakota range lands. N. Dak. Agr. Expt. Sta. Bull. 320.
——— *et al.* 1951. Carotene, protein, and phosphorus in range and tame grasses of western North Dakota. N. Dak. Agr. Expt. Sta. Bull. 370.
——— *et al.* 1953. Utilization of native grass in western North Dakota. N. Dak. Agr. Exp. Sta. Bi-monthly Bull. 15, No. 3.
——— and H. C. Hanson. 1939. Vegetation on scoria and clay buttes in western North Dakota. Ecology 20: 455–457.
———, H. T. Hanson, and G. Loder. 1943. Natural revegetation of abandoned fields in western North Dakota. N. Dak. Agr. Expt. Sta. Bull. 321.
———, H. C. Hanson and R. Petersen. 1943. Relation of drought and grazing to North Dakota Range Lands. N. Dak. Agr. Expt. Sta. Bull. 320.
——— and E. A. Helgeson. 1946. Range vegetation studies. N. Dak. Agr. Expt. Sta. Bull. 340.
Willard, D. E. 1903. The Story of the Prairies or the Landscape Geology of North Dakota.
Woolfolk, E. J. 1945. Important range plants of eastern Montana. The Montana Stockgrower; monthly Nov. 1944 through March 1945; May, June 1945.
———. 1949. Stocking northern Great Plains sheep range for sustained high production. U.S. Dept. Agr. Circ. 804.
——— and B. Knapp, Jr. 1949. Weight and gain of range calves as affected by rate of grazing. Mont. Agri. Expt. Sta. Bull. 463.
Wooton, E. O. and P. C. Standley. 1915. Flora of New Mexico. U.S. Natl. Mus., Contrib. U.S. Natl. Herbarium 19.
Wright, J. C. and E. A. Wright. 1948. Grassland types of south central Montana. Ecology 29:449–460.
Young, V. A. 1953. The effect of the 1950–1952 drought on range vegetation of certain areas in Texas. Texas Journ. Sci. 5(3):273–279.

INDEX

Boldface type indicates pages on which illustrations appear